The Complete Course for AQA

Contents

How to use this book

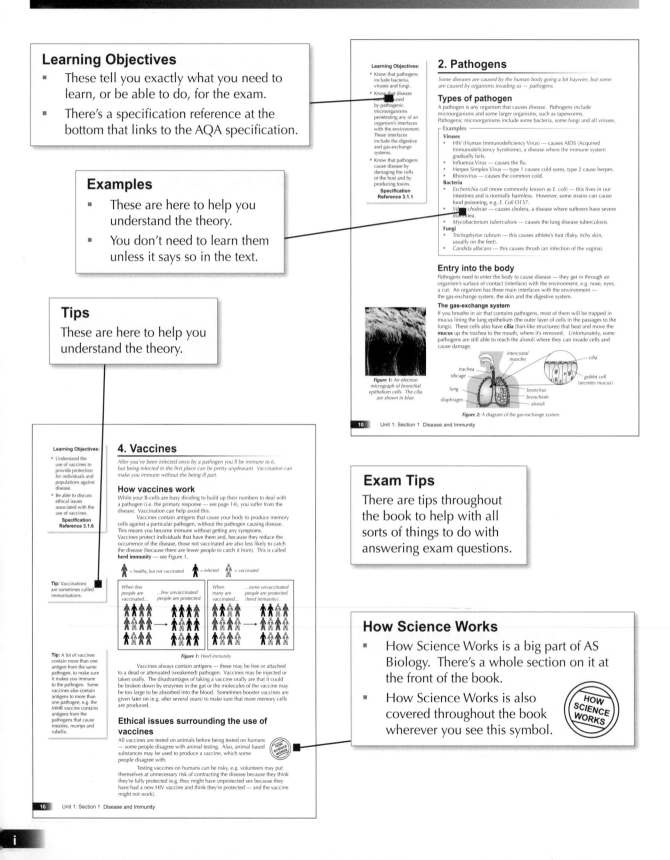

Learning Objectives

- These tell you exactly what you need to learn, or be able to do, for the exam.
- There's a specification reference at the bottom that links to the AQA specification.

Examples

- These are here to help you understand the theory.
- You don't need to learn them unless it says so in the text.

Tips

These are here to help you understand the theory.

Exam Tips

There are tips throughout the book to help with all sorts of things to do with answering exam questions.

How Science Works

- How Science Works is a big part of AS Biology. There's a whole section on it at the front of the book.
- How Science Works is also covered throughout the book wherever you see this symbol.

Learning Objectives:

- Know that pathogens include bacteria, viruses and fungi.
- Know that disease can be caused by pathogenic microorganisms penetrating any of an organism's interfaces with the environment. These interfaces include the digestive and gas-exchange systems.
- Know that pathogens cause disease by damaging the cells of the host and by producing toxins.

Specification Reference 3.1.1

2. Pathogens

Some diseases are caused by the human body going a bit haywire, but some are caused by organisms invading us — pathogens.

Types of pathogen

A pathogen is any organism that causes disease. Pathogens include microorganisms and some larger organisms, such as tapeworms. Pathogenic microorganisms include some bacteria, some fungi and all viruses.

Examples

Viruses
- HIV (Human Immunodeficiency Virus) — causes AIDS (Acquired Immunodeficiency Syndrome), a disease where the immune system gradually fails.
- Influenza Virus — causes the flu.
- Herpes Simplex Virus — type 1 causes cold sores, type 2 cause herpes.
- Rhinovirus — causes the common cold.

Bacteria
- *Escherichia coli* (more commonly known as *E. coli*) — this lives in our intestines and is normally harmless. However, some strains can cause food poisoning, e.g. *E. Coli* O157.
- *Vibrio cholerae* — causes cholera, a disease where sufferers have severe diarrhoea.
- *Mycobacterium tuberculosis* — causes the lung disease tuberculosis.

Fungi
- *Trichophyton rubrum* — this causes athlete's foot (flaky, itchy skin, usually on the feet).
- *Candida albicans* — this causes thrush (an infection of the vagina).

Entry into the body

Pathogens need to enter the body to cause disease — they get in through an organism's surface of contact (interface) with the environment, e.g. nose, eyes, a cut. An organism has three main interfaces with the environment — the gas-exchange system, the skin and the digestive system.

The gas-exchange system

If you breathe in air that contains pathogens, most of them will be trapped in mucus lining the lung epithelium (the outer layer of cells in the passages to the lungs). These cells also have **cilia** (hair-like structures) that beat and move the **mucus** up the trachea to the mouth, where it's removed. Unfortunately, some pathogens are still able to reach the alveoli where they can invade cells and cause damage.

Figure 1: An electron micrograph of bronchial epithelium cells. The cilia are shown in blue.

Figure 2: A diagram of the gas-exchange system.

Learning Objectives:

- Understand the use of vaccines to provide protection for individuals and populations against disease.
- Be able to discuss ethical issues associated with the use of vaccines.

Specification Reference 3.1.6

Tip: Vaccinations are sometimes called immunisations.

Tip: A lot of vaccines contain more than one antigen from the same pathogen, to make sure it makes you immune to the pathogen. Some vaccines also contain antigens to more than one pathogen, e.g. the MMR vaccine contains antigens from the pathogens that cause measles, mumps and rubella.

4. Vaccines

After you've been infected once by a pathogen you'll be immune to it, but being infected in the first place can be pretty unpleasant. Vaccination can make you immune without the being ill part.

How vaccines work

While your B-cells are busy dividing to build up their numbers to deal with a pathogen (i.e. the primary response — see page 14), you suffer from the disease. Vaccination can help avoid this.

Vaccines contain antigens that cause your body to produce memory cells against a particular pathogen, without the pathogen causing disease. This means you become immune without getting any symptoms. Vaccines protect individuals that have them and, because they reduce the occurrence of the disease, those not vaccinated are also less likely to catch the disease (because there are fewer people to catch it from). This is called **herd immunity** — see Figure 1.

Figure 1: Herd immunity

Vaccines always contain antigens — these may be free or attached to a dead or attenuated (weakened) pathogen. Vaccines may be injected or taken orally. The disadvantages of taking a vaccine orally are that it could be broken down by enzymes in the gut or the molecules of the vaccine may be too large to be absorbed into the blood. Sometimes booster vaccines are given later on (e.g. after several years) to make sure that more memory cells are produced.

Ethical issues surrounding the use of vaccines

All vaccines are tested on animals before being tested on humans — some people disagree with animal testing. Also, animal based substances may be used to produce a vaccine, which some people disagree with.

Testing vaccines on humans can be risky, e.g. volunteers may put themselves at unnecessary risk of contracting the disease because they think they're fully protected (e.g. they might have unprotected sex because they have had a new HIV vaccine and think they're protected — and the vaccine might not work).

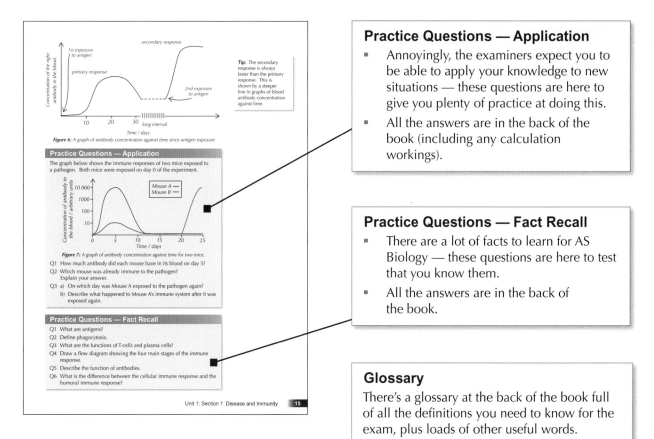

Practice Questions — Application

- Annoyingly, the examiners expect you to be able to apply your knowledge to new situations — these questions are here to give you plenty of practice at doing this.

- All the answers are in the back of the book (including any calculation workings).

Practice Questions — Fact Recall

- There are a lot of facts to learn for AS Biology — these questions are here to test that you know them.

- All the answers are in the back of the book.

Glossary

There's a glossary at the back of the book full of all the definitions you need to know for the exam, plus loads of other useful words.

Exam-style Questions

- Practising exam-style questions is really important — you'll find some at the end of each section.

- They're the same style as the ones you'll get in the real exams — some will test your knowledge and understanding, some will test that you can apply your knowledge and some will test How Science Works.

- All the answers are in the back of the book, along with a mark scheme to show you how you get the marks.

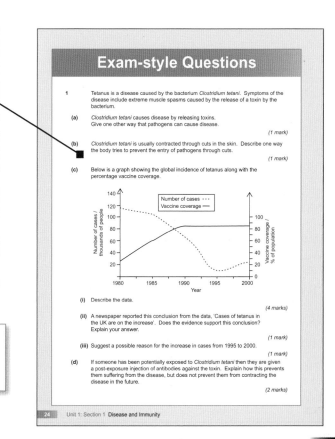

Exam Help

There's a section at the back of the book stuffed full of things to help with your exams.

Published by CGP

Editors:
Ellen Bowness, Charlotte Burrows, Katherine Craig, Emma Elder, Rosie McCurrie,
Rachael Rogers, Hayley Thompson, Jane Towle, Megan Tyler.

Contributors:
Gloria Barnett, Jessica Egan, Barbara Green, Brigitte Hurwitt, Liz Masters,
Stephen Phillips, Claire Ruthven, Adrian Schmit, Anna Fe Williamson.

ISBN: 978 1 84762 787 2

With thanks to Janet Cruse-Sawyer, Rosie McCurrie, Philip Rushworth and Karen Wells for the proofreading.
With thanks to Laura Jakubowski for the copyright research.

Groovy website: www.cgpbooks.co.uk

Printed by Elanders Ltd, Newcastle upon Tyne.
Jolly bits of clipart from CorelDRAW®

1. The Scientific Process

Science tries to explain how and why things happen. It's all about seeking and gaining knowledge about the world around us. Scientists do this by observing things, developing theories and then testing them to see if they're correct — this is the scientific process. There are five main stages...

1. Developing theories

A **theory** is a possible explanation for something. Theories usually come about when scientists observe something and wonder why or how it happens. (Scientists also sometimes form a **model** too — a simplified picture of what's physically going on.)

Tip: A theory is only scientific if it can be tested.

Examples

- Darwin came up with his theory of evolution by natural selection after observing wildlife (e.g. finches) and fossils during a trip around South America and the Galapagos Islands.

- The theory that smoking causes lung cancer was developed after it was observed that many people who contracted lung cancer also smoked.

- John Snow came up with the theory that cholera is transmitted in water, rather than air, after observing lots of cases of cholera clustered around a water pump.

- Edward Jenner came up with the idea that being infected with cowpox protected you from getting smallpox after observing that milkmaids didn't get smallpox.

Figure 1: *Drawings of finches that Darwin made in the Galapagos Islands.*

Tip: Sometimes data from one experiment can be the starting point for developing a new theory.

2. Testing the theories

The next step is to make a **prediction** or **hypothesis** — a specific testable statement, based on the theory, about what will happen in a test situation. Then an experiment or study is carried out to provide evidence that will support the prediction (or help to disprove it). If it's disproved it's back to the drawing board — the theory is modified or a completely new one is developed.

Tip: The results of one experiment can't prove that a theory is true — they can only suggest that it's true. They can however disprove a theory — show that it's wrong.

Examples

- Louis Pasteur designed an experiment to test his idea that 'germs' in the air caused disease and decomposition. He boiled two flasks of broth, both of which were left open to the air. One of the flasks had a curved neck (see Figure 2) to trap any airborne bacteria so they couldn't get into the broth. The broth in the flask with the curved neck stayed fresh, whereas the other broth went off. This provided evidence to support his theory. (After more evidence like this modern microbiology was born.)

- Edward Jenner tested his idea that getting cowpox protected people from getting smallpox by infecting a boy with cowpox, then exposing him to smallpox. The boy didn't get smallpox, which provided evidence to support his theory. (Eventually this lead to the development of a smallpox vaccine.)

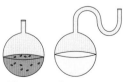

Figure 2: *Pasteur's experiment — the flask with the curved neck stayed fresh.*

3. Communicating the results

The results are then published — scientists need to let others know about their work. Scientists publish their results in **scientific journals**. These are just like normal magazines, only they contain scientific reports (called papers) instead of the latest celebrity gossip.

Tip: Some well known biological journals are Nature, The Lancet and the British Medical Journal.

Scientific reports are similar to the lab write-ups you do in school. And just as a lab write-up is reviewed (marked) by your teacher, reports in scientific journals undergo **peer review** before they're published. The report is sent out to peers — other scientists who are experts in the same area. They examine the data and results, and if they think that the conclusion is reasonable it's published. This makes sure that work published in scientific journals is of a good standard.

Tip: Scientific findings are also communicated at conferences around the world.

But peer review can't guarantee the science is correct — other scientists still need to reproduce it. Sometimes mistakes are made and flawed work is published. Peer review isn't perfect but it's probably the best way for scientists to self-regulate their work and to publish quality reports.

Tip: Other scientists need to reproduce results to make sure they're reliable — see the next page for more.

4. Validating the theory by more testing

Other scientists read the published theories and results, and try to test the theory themselves in order to validate it (back it up). This involves:

- Repeating the exact same experiments.
- Using the theory to make new predictions and then testing them with new experiments.

Tip: Even negative results are communicated — knowing that something is wrong improves scientific knowledge.

Examples

- In 1998 a study was published that linked the MMR vaccine to autism (a developmental disorder). Other scientists then conducted different studies to try to find the same link, but their results didn't back up (validate) the theory. See page 21 for more.
- In the 1940s a study was published linking smoking and lung cancer. After this many more studies were conducted all over the world that validated the conclusion of the first study.

Tip: Once an experimental method is found that gives good evidence it becomes a <u>protocol</u> — an accepted method to test that particular thing that all scientists can use.

5. The theory is rejected, or accepted

If multiple experiments show a theory to be incorrect then scientists either have to modify the theory or develop a new one, and start the testing again. If all the experiments in all the world provide good evidence to back a theory up, the theory is thought of as scientific 'fact' (for now) — see Figure 3. But it will never become totally indisputable fact. Scientific breakthroughs or advances could provide new ways to question and test the theory, which could lead to new evidence that conflicts with the current evidence. Then the testing starts all over again... And this, my friend, is the tentative nature of scientific knowledge — it's always changing and evolving.

Tip: 'Good evidence' means reliable evidence — see the next page.

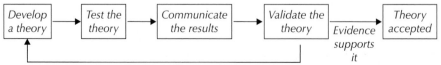

Figure 3: Flow diagram summarising the scientific process.

2. Scientific Evidence

So scientists need good evidence to back up their theories. A lot of scientific evidence comes from laboratory experiments, but there are things you can't investigate in a lab (e.g. whether stress causes heart attacks) — so you have to do a study instead. Good evidence basically means reliable evidence...

Reliable evidence

Scientific evidence needs to be **reliable**. This means that it can be consistently reproduced in independent experiments.

┌─ Example ───

Experiment 1 result = 15 ⎫ Reliable Experiment 1 result = 15 ⎫ Unreliable
Experiment 2 result = 16 ⎬ evidence Experiment 2 result = 200 ⎬ evidence
Experiment 3 result = 15 ⎭   Experiment 3 result = 79 ⎭

└──

If the results are reproducible they're more likely to be true. If the data isn't reliable for whatever reason you can't draw a valid conclusion.

The results of an experiment also need to be as **accurate** and **precise** as possible. Accurate results are those that are really close to the true answer. Precise results are those taken using sensitive instruments that measure in small increments, e.g. using a ruler with a millimetre scale gives more precise data than using a ruler with a scale in centimetres.

Getting reliable evidence

To get reliable evidence you need to do the following things:

1. Control the variables

A **variable** is a quantity that has the potential to change, e.g. weight, temperature, concentration. In an experiment you usually change one variable and measure its effect on another variable:

- The variable you change is called the **independent variable**.

- The variable that you measure is called the **dependent variable**.

Every other variable that could affect the results has to be kept the same (controlled) throughout the experiment. These variables are called **control variables**. If all the variables that could possibly affect the result are controlled then the investigation is said to be a **fair test**.

┌─ Example ───

For an investigation into how temperature affects the rate of an enzyme-controlled reaction:

- The independent variable is temperature (as it's the one you change).

- The dependent variable is the rate of reaction (the thing you measure).

- The control variables are the pH of the solution, the concentration of the solution, the volume of the solution etc. (as these could all affect the result if they aren't kept the same throughout).

└──

It's usually straightforward to control all the variables in a lab experiment, but it can be quite tricky when doing studies. You often can't control all the variables, but the more you do control the more reliable the results will be.

2. Use control experiments and control groups

Even if you do manage to keep all the control variables the same, it's still possible that something else you're doing could affect the results. Scientists use control experiments and control groups to eliminate this possibility.

Tip: Evidence is the same thing as data or results.

Exam Tip
Make sure you really understand what reliable means — it crops up in loads of exam questions.

Tip: It's possible to be precise without being accurate. E.g. you could use a pH meter to measure pH of a solution to five decimal places (which would be very precise) — but if you hadn't calibrated the pH meter properly, it wouldn't be an accurate measurement.

Tip: Control variables are also sometimes called confounding variables.

Tip: In a study with human participants, you should try to keep the variables of all the participants the same, e.g. they should all be the same age, sex, etc.

Figure 1: *Well-designed lab experiments where all the variables are controlled give reliable results.*

In lab experiments, controls or **control experiments** are used.

Example

You investigate antibiotic resistance in bacteria by growing cultures of bacteria on agar plates, then adding paper discs soaked in antibiotic.

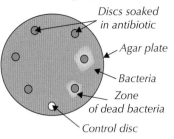

Discs soaked in antibiotic

Agar plate

Bacteria

Zone of dead bacteria

Control disc

If the bacteria are resistant to the antibiotic they will continue to grow. If they aren't resistant a clear patch will appear around the disc where they have died.

A disc that isn't soaked in antibiotic is included to act as a **negative control**. This makes sure any result is down to the antibiotic, not the presence of a paper disc.

In studies, **control groups** are used. The subjects in the study are split into two groups — the experimental group and the control group. The control group is treated in exactly the same way as the experimental group, except for the factor you're investigating.

Example

Say you're investigating the effect of margarine containing omega-3 fish oils on heart disease. You'd have two groups — an experimental group that would be given margarine containing omega-3 fish oils, and a control group that would be given margarine without fish oils. This is done so that you can tell any reduction in heart disease is due to the fish oil, not some other substance in the margarine.

When testing new drugs to see if they work, control groups should always be used. The control group is treated in exactly the same way as the experimental group, except they're given a thing called a **placebo** instead of the drug. A placebo is a dummy pill or injection that looks exactly like the real drug, but doesn't contain the drug. It's used to make sure that people don't improve just because they think they're being treated.

Drug trials also should be **double-blind trials**. This means that the doctor involved doesn't know whether the patient is getting the drug or the placebo, and neither does the patient. This is done to remove **bias**, e.g. doctors who expect the patients on the drugs to get better might report a greater improvement than there was.

3. Use a large sample size

Sample size is the number of samples in the investigation, e.g. the number of people in a drug trial. The general rule is the larger the sample size, the more reliable the data is. This is because it reduces the chance of getting a freak result (e.g. if you get the same result twice it might be because of chance, but if you get it 100 times it's much more likely that it's not due to chance).

Annoyingly, there are no rules about how big the sample size has to be to be for the investigation to be considered as 'reliable' — all you need to know is that bigger is always better.

4. Collect data carefully

The method used to collect the data can affect how reliable it is. For example, people aren't always truthful when answering questionnaires, which reduces the reliability of the data. Also, if you're using control groups, it's important that subjects are split into the two groups at **random**. This helps to avoid bias, and so makes the data more reliable.

Tip: A negative control is not expected to have any effect on the experiment.

Exam Tip
If you get an exam question asking why a control group is important in a particular experiment make sure your answer is specific to that experiment (not just generally about why control groups are good).

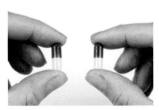

Figure 2: *The placebo (left) should look identical to the real drug (right).*

Tip: A large data set is the same thing as a large sample size.

Tip: Scientists can use statistical tests to figure out if a result is likely to be due to chance or not.

Tip: Bias is when someone intentionally, or unintentionally, favours a particular result.

5. Repeat the measurements

The reliability of a single experiment can be improved by repeating the measurements and calculating the mean. Also, the larger the number of repeats the easier it is to spot **anomalous data** (measurements that fall outside the range of values you'd expect or any pattern you already have).

Drawing conclusions from data

Conclusions need to be **valid**. A conclusion can only be considered as valid if it answers the original question and uses reliable data. It's quite tricky to draw conclusions from data — so scientists need to look out for a couple of things:

Correlations and causal relationships

The results of investigations often show a relationship between two variables, e.g. between smoking and lung cancer. A relationship between two variables is called a **correlation**. There are two types of correlation — **positive correlations** and **negative correlations**.

Positive	*Negative*	*No correlation*
As one variable increases the other increases.	*As one variable increases the other decreases.*	*There is no relationship between the variables.*

Scientists have to be very careful when drawing conclusions from data like this because a correlation between two variables doesn't always mean that a change in one variable causes a change in the other.

> **Example**
>
> There's a correlation between hours spent playing frisbee and skin cancer — the more you play frisbee the higher your risk of getting skin cancer. Playing frisbee doesn't cause skin cancer though — the reason for the correlation is that frisbee is usually played outside in the sun, and excessive exposure to sunlight does cause cancer.

If there's a relationship between two variables and a change in one variable does cause a change in the other (e.g. increased exposure to sunlight does cause an increase in skin cancer) it's called a **causal relationship**. It can be concluded that a correlation is a causal relationship if every other variable that could possibly affect the result is controlled. In reality this is very hard to do — correlations are generally accepted to be causal relationships if lots of studies have found the same thing, and scientists have figured out exactly how one factor causes the other.

Drawing specific conclusions

Scientists can't make broad generalisations from data — they have to be very specific. They can only conclude what the results show and no more.

> **Example**
>
> The graph shows the results from a study into the effect of penicillin dosage on the duration of fever in men. The only conclusion you can draw is that as the dosage of penicillin increases, the duration of fever in men decreases. You can't conclude that this is true for any other antibiotic, any other symptom or even for female patients — the results could be completely different.

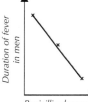

Penicillin dosage

Tip: Repeating measurements in an experiment improves reliability in the same way as a large sample size — it reduces the likelihood that the results are due to chance.

Tip: All data will vary a bit, but anomalous results vary a lot from what you'd expect.

Tip: A causal relationship is sometimes called a causal link.

Tip: What conclusion is drawn might be affected by bias, e.g. if someone works for a chemical company they might be more likely to ignore data that showed their product causing environmental problems.

3. Science and Decision Making

Lots of scientific work eventually leads to important discoveries or breakthroughs that could benefit humankind. These results are used by society to make decisions.

How society uses science to make decisions

Scientific knowledge is used by society (that's you, me and everyone else) to make decisions — about the way we live, what we eat, what we drive, etc. All sections of society use scientific evidence to make decisions, e.g. politicians use it to devise policies and individuals use science to make decisions about their own lives.

Tip: Don't get mixed up — it's not the scientists who make the decisions, it's society. Scientists just produce evidence to help society make the decisions.

Examples

- The maximum amount of salt people are advised to eat per day was reduced in government guidelines in 2004, due to the results of a study which showed that reducing salt intake could significantly reduce heart disease.

- Leaded petrol in cars was phased out in many countries after it was found to cause air pollution that damaged the brain.

Factors affecting decision making

Other factors can influence decisions about science or the way science is used:

Economic factors

Society has to consider the cost of implementing changes based on scientific conclusions. Sometimes it decides the cost doesn't outweigh the benefits.

Tip: Economic factors just mean anything to do with money, and social factors just mean anything to do with people.

Example

The NHS can't afford the most expensive drugs without sacrificing something else. Sometimes they decide to use a less effective, but less expensive drug, despite evidence showing there's a more effective one.

Social factors

Decisions affect people's lives — sometimes people don't want to follow advice, or are strongly against some recommendations.

Examples

- Scientists may suggest banning smoking and alcohol to prevent health problems, but shouldn't we be able to choose whether we want to smoke and drink or not?

- Scientists may be able to cure many diseases using stem cells, but some people are strongly against the idea of embryonic stem cell research.

Environmental factors

Some scientific research and breakthroughs might affect the environment. Not everyone thinks the benefits are worth the possible environmental damage.

Tip: The people making the decisions can be affected by lots of other things too, e.g. public opinion, the media and whether they might benefit from a particular decision.

Examples

- Scientists believe unexplored regions like remote parts of rainforests might contain untapped drug resources. But some people think we shouldn't exploit these regions because any interesting finds may lead to deforestation and reduced biodiversity in these areas.

- Scientists have developed genetically modified (GM) crops (e.g. with frost resistance, or high nutrient content), but some people think the possible environmental harm they could do outweighs their benefits.

1. Disease

Disease is when part of the body doesn't function properly. To make life more difficult for you, different diseases have different causes...

Causes of disease

All diseases can be classed as either **infectious** or **non-infectious**. Infectious diseases are caused by infection with pathogens, e.g. bacteria and viruses. They include things like the common cold, food poisoning and chest infections. Non-infectious diseases are caused by the body malfunctioning (e.g. cancer, heart disease, genetic disorders and diabetes) or lifestyle or the environment (e.g. malnutrition).

Diseases affected by lifestyle

The chance of getting some diseases can be affected by your lifestyle (how you live, e.g. what you eat, how much exercise you get, etc.). Anything that increases the chance of getting a disease is called a **risk factor**. Two diseases that are affected by lifestyle are coronary heart disease and cancer:

Coronary Heart Disease

Coronary heart disease (CHD) is a disease that affects your heart (see p.99 for more). There are plenty of lifestyle factors that increase your risk of developing CHD:

- Poor diet — a diet high in saturated fat or salt increases the risk.
- Smoking, lack of exercise and excessive alcohol intake — these can all lead to high blood pressure, which can damage the heart and the blood vessels, increasing the risk of CHD.

Cancer

Cancer is the result of uncontrolled cell division (see p. 149). Factors that increase the risk of developing cancer include:

- Smoking — the main cause of mouth, throat and lung cancer is smoking.
- Excessive exposure to sunlight — excessive exposure can cause skin cancer. Using sunbeds and sunbathing without sunscreen increases the risk.
- Excessive alcohol intake — this can increase the risk of many types of cancer, especially liver cancer.

Reducing the risk

Changing your lifestyle for the better (e.g. reducing your alcohol intake, doing more exercise, eating healthily etc.) doesn't mean you'll never develop these diseases, but it can reduce the risk. So it's never too late to change.

Example

Studies have shown that the risk to a smoker of developing lung cancer is reduced if they stop smoking.

Learning Objectives:

- Know that lifestyle can affect human health.
- Know that specific risk factors are associated with cancer and coronary heart disease.
- Know that changes in lifestyle are also associated with a reduced risk of contracting cancer and coronary heart disease.
- Be able to analyse and interpret data associated with specific risk factors and the incidence of disease.
- Be able to recognise correlations and causal relationships.

Specification Reference 3.1.1

Tip: A risk factor is just something that <u>increases</u> the chance of getting a disease. Having a risk factor doesn't mean you'll definitely get the disease though, it just makes it more likely.

Interpreting data about risk factors and disease

In the exam you could be asked to interpret data about lifestyle and the risk of disease. This data often shows a **correlation** between the **incidence** of the disease (how many people suffer from it) and the risk factor. But, you've got to be very careful when drawing conclusions from data like this because a correlation between two variables doesn't always mean that one variable causes the other to happen (see page 5).

Here's an example of the kind of data you might come across in the exam, and how to go about interpreting it:

create

Tip: Remember, a correlation is where there's a relationship between two variables. Data can show two types of correlation:

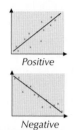

Positive

Negative

Positive — as one variable increases the other increases.

Negative — as one variable increases the other decreases.

If there's no relationship between the variables, it'll look a bit like this:

None

Example

A study looked at the link between body mass index (BMI) and the relative risk of developing cancer. BMI is a measure of obesity.

At the start of the study the BMI of 1.2 million women aged 50-64 was taken, and after five years the number of these women with cancer was recorded. The relative risk of developing cancer was then worked out by taking into account other factors about the women, including daily alcohol intake, smoking status and physical activity. Figure 1 shows the results.

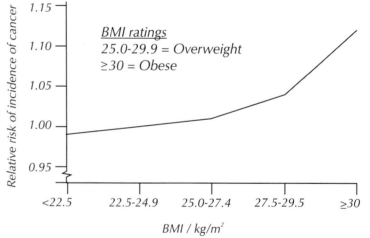

Figure 1: *A graph of BMI versus the relative risk of incidence of cancer.*

You might be asked to describe the data...

The graph shows a positive correlation between BMI and the relative risk of cancer in women. The higher the BMI, the higher the risk of developing cancer. It's not a linear (straight-line) relationship though — the risk increases much more quickly for women with a BMI over 27.5.

...or draw conclusions...

The relative risk of developing cancer is greatly increased for women who are overweight or obese. Be careful — you can't conclude that obesity causes cancer, only that they're linked. Another factor could be involved. For example, obese people are more likely to have diets high in saturated fat — it may be the saturated fat that causes the higher risk of cancer, not the actual increase in body mass.

You can't conclude that the risk of developing a specific form of cancer (e.g. throat cancer) increases with increasing BMI. The data doesn't deal with specific forms of cancer separately. So you can only conclude that the risk of developing cancer in general increases with increasing BMI.

Tip: Relative risk is often used instead of incidence of disease — it's a handy way to compare different groups of people. Relative risk is just the chance of one group getting the disease compared to another group — it's calculated using the incidence of disease.

Tip: See page 5 for more about drawing conclusions.

...or evaluate the methodology

The sample size is large — 1.2 million women. This makes the results more reliable. The study took into account other lifestyle factors (e.g. alcohol intake, smoking) that can affect the risk of developing cancer too. This also makes the results more reliable.

> **Tip:** Sample size is the number of samples in the study (e.g. the number of people) — see page 4 for more.

Practice Questions — Application

In 2000, scientists analysed the results of multiple studies into the effects of alcohol on disease. Figure 2 shows the results of their study for alcohol consumption and coronary heart disease. The relative risk is the risk of getting CHD over a non-drinker. Non-drinkers have a relative risk of 1.0.

> **Tip:** Some studies are done that collect together and analyse the results of lots of studies. They do this to try and increase the reliability of the data. These giant studies are called meta-analyses.

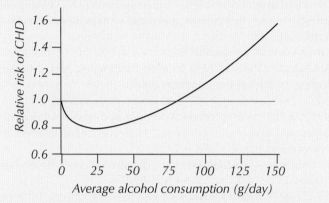

Figure 2: *A graph of average alcohol consumption versus the relative risk of CHD.*

Q1 What is the relative risk of CHD for someone who consumes an average of 25 g of alcohol per day?

Q2 A standard alcoholic drink (one unit) contains around 8 g of alcohol. Does someone who drinks an average of four units per day have a higher or lower risk of CHD than a non-drinker?

Q3 Describe the trend shown by the data.

Q4 Draw conclusions from the data.

Practice Questions — Fact Recall

Q1 Give three factors that increase the risk of developing coronary heart disease.

Q2 Give three factors that increase the risk of developing cancer. For each one, state which type of cancer it increases the risk of.

- Know that pathogens include bacteria, viruses and fungi.

- Know that disease can be caused by pathogenic microorganisms penetrating any of an organism's interfaces with the environment. These interfaces include the digestive and gas-exchange systems.

- Know that pathogens cause disease by damaging the cells of the host and by producing toxins.

Specification Reference 3.1.1

2. Pathogens

Some diseases are caused by the human body going a bit haywire, but some are caused by organisms invading us — pathogens.

Types of pathogen

A pathogen is any organism that causes disease. Pathogens include microorganisms and some larger organisms, such as tapeworms. Pathogenic microorganisms include some bacteria, some fungi and all viruses.

Examples

Viruses
- HIV (Human Immunodeficiency Virus) — causes AIDS (Acquired Immunodeficiency Syndrome), a disease where the immune system gradually fails.
- Influenza Virus — causes the flu.
- Herpes Simplex Virus — type 1 causes cold sores, type 2 cause herpes.
- Rhinovirus — causes the common cold.

Bacteria
- *Escherichia coli* (more commonly known as *E. coli*) — this lives in our intestines and is normally harmless. However, some strains can cause food poisoning, e.g. *E. Coli* O157.
- *Vibrio cholerae* — causes cholera, a disease where sufferers have severe diarrhoea.
- *Mycobacterium tuberculosis* — causes the lung disease tuberculosis.

Fungi
- *Trichophyton rubrum* — this causes athlete's foot (flaky, itchy skin, usually on the feet).
- *Candida albicans* — this causes thrush (an infection of the vagina).

Entry into the body

Pathogens need to enter the body to cause disease — they get in through an organism's surface of contact (interface) with the environment, e.g. nose, eyes, a cut. An organism has three main interfaces with the environment — the gas-exchange system, the skin and the digestive system.

The gas-exchange system

If you breathe in air that contains pathogens, most of them will be trapped in mucus lining the lung epithelium (the outer layer of cells in the passages to the lungs). These cells also have **cilia** (hair-like structures) that beat and move the **mucus** up the trachea to the mouth, where it's removed. Unfortunately, some pathogens are still able to reach the alveoli where they can invade cells and cause damage.

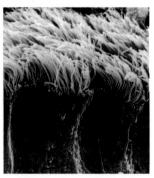

Figure 1: An electron micrograph of bronchial epithelium cells. The cilia are shown in blue.

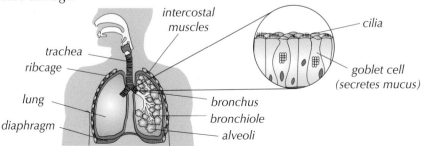

Figure 2: A diagram of the gas-exchange system.

The skin

If you damage your skin, pathogens on the surface can enter your bloodstream. The blood clots and dries to form a scab at the area of damage to prevent pathogens from entering, but some may get in before the scab forms.

The digestive system

If you eat or drink food that contains pathogens, most of them will be killed by the acidic conditions of the stomach. However, some may survive and pass into the intestines where they can invade cells of the gut wall and cause disease.

How pathogens cause disease

Despite our protective mechanisms, pathogens can still successfully enter our bodies. Once inside, they cause disease in two main ways:

1. Production of toxins

Many bacteria release toxins (harmful molecules) into the body.

> **Example**
>
> The bacterium *Clostridium botulinum* causes a disease called botulism. The main symptom of botulism is paralysis. Paralysis is caused by a very potent toxin produced by the bacteria, called botulinum toxin. The toxin stops nerve impulses being transmitted along neurones and so causes paralysis of muscles.

2. Cell damage

Pathogens can physically damage host cells by:

- Rupturing them to release nutrients (proteins etc.) inside them.
- Breaking down nutrients inside the cell for their own use. This starves and eventually kills the cell.
- Replicating inside the cells and bursting them when they're released, e.g. some viruses do this.

> **Example**
>
> HIV infects cells of the immune system. After it has entered the cells it replicates, producing many copies of itself. As the HIV particles emerge the cell ruptures and dies, releasing the virus. This causes a big drop in the number of immune system cells in the body.

Tip: The organism the pathogen has invaded is called the <u>host</u>.

Tip: Another bacterium that produces toxins is *Vibrio cholerae* — it causes cholera (severe diarrhoea). There's loads more on how the cholera toxin works on pages 70-71.

Figure 3: *An electron micrograph of a cell (blue sphere) infected by HIV (yellow dots).*

Practice Questions — Fact Recall

Q1 What is a pathogen?

Q2 Describe how the gas-exchange system prevents the entry of pathogens into the body.

Q3 Describe two other ways that pathogens enter the body.

Q4 Give two ways that pathogens cause disease.

- Know the process of phagocytosis, including the role of lysosomes and lysosomal enzymes in the destruction of pathogens.
- Know the definition of antigen and antibody.
- Know the structure of an antibody and the formation of an antigen-antibody complex.
- Know the difference between humoral and cellular responses as shown by B-cells and T-cells.
- Know the role of plasma cells and memory cells in producing a secondary response.

Specification Reference 3.1.6

3. The Immune Response

If a pathogen gets past your first line of defences, the immune system kicks in.

Activating the immune response

When a pathogen invades the body, the molecules on its cell surface are identified as foreign, which activates cells in the immune system. The molecules found on the surface of cells are called **antigens**. They're usually proteins or polysaccharides.

The four main stages of the immune response

1. Phagocytosis

A **phagocyte** (e.g. a macrophage) is a type of white blood cell that carries out phagocytosis (engulfment of pathogens). They're found in the blood and in tissues and are the first cells to respond to a pathogen inside the body. Here's how they work:

- A phagocyte recognises the antigens on a pathogen.
- The cytoplasm of the phagocyte moves round the pathogen, engulfing it.
- The pathogen is now contained in a **phagocytic vacuole** (a bubble) in the cytoplasm of the phagocyte.
- A **lysosome** (an organelle that contains lysosomal enzymes) fuses with the phagocytic vacuole. The lysosomal enzymes break down the pathogen.
- The phagocyte then presents the pathogen's antigens — it sticks the antigens on its surface to activate other immune system cells.

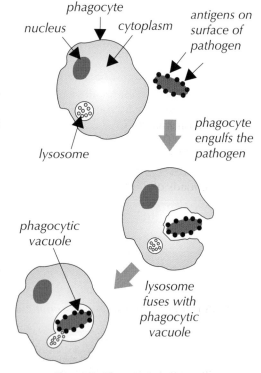

phagocyte

nucleus *cytoplasm* *antigens on surface of pathogen*

lysosome

phagocyte engulfs the pathogen

phagocytic vacuole

lysosome fuses with phagocytic vacuole

Figure 1: *Phagocytosis*

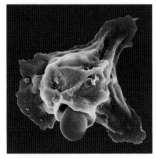

Figure 2: *An electron micrograph of a phagocyte (blue) engulfing a pathogen (red).*

2. T-cell activation

A T-cell is another type of white blood cell. It has proteins on its surface that bind to the antigens presented to it by phagocytes. This activates the T-cell. Different types of T-cells respond in different ways. Some release substances to activate B-cells. Some attach to antigens on a pathogen and kill the cell.

3. B-cell activation and plasma cell production

B-cells are also a type of white blood cell. They're covered with **antibodies** — proteins that bind antigens to form an **antigen-antibody complex**. Each B-cell has a different shaped antibody on its membrane, so different ones bind to different shaped antigens — see Figure 3.

Tip: Antibodies bind to antigens because they have a complementary shape — like a lock fits a key.

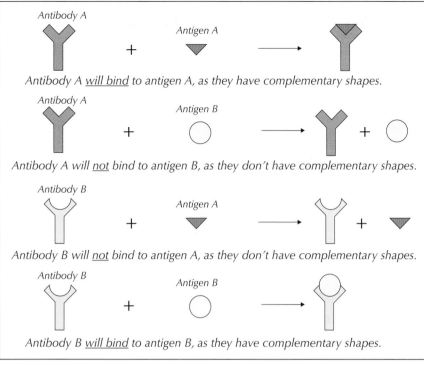

Antibody A will bind to antigen A, as they have complementary shapes.

Antibody A will not bind to antigen B, as they don't have complementary shapes.

Antibody B will not bind to antigen A, as they don't have complementary shapes.

Antibody B will bind to antigen B, as they have complementary shapes.

Figure 3: *Complementary binding between antibodies and antigens.*

When the antibody on the surface of a B-cell meets a complementary shaped antigen, it binds to it. This, together with substances released from T-cells, activates the B-cell. The activated B-cell then divides to produce many more B-cells called plasma cells.

4. Antibody production

The plasma cells are identical to the original B-cell (they're clones). They secrete loads of the antibody specific to the antigen. Antibody functions include:

- Coating the pathogen to make it easier for a phagocyte to engulf it.
- Coating the pathogen to prevent it from entering host cells.
- Binding to and neutralising (inactivating) toxins produced by the pathogen.

Practice Questions — Application

Q1 AIDS is an immune system disorder caused by the Human Immunodeficiency Virus. The virus infects and destroys T-cells, so the number that work properly gradually falls. AIDS patients often suffer from opportunistic infections — infections that wouldn't normally cause too much of a problem in a healthy person. Common ones are tuberculosis, pneumonia and an infection of the brain called toxoplasmosis. Explain why AIDS patients suffer from opportunistic infections.

Q2 Rheumatic fever is a disease where the immune system attacks cells in the heart. It's often triggered by an infection with the bacterium *Streptococcus pyogenes*. Antigens on the surface of *S. pyogenes* have a very similar shape to antigens on the surface of heart cells. Suggest why *S. pyogenes* infection can lead to rheumatic fever.

Exam Tip
Never say that antigens and antibodies have the 'same shape' or a 'matching shape' — you need to use the phrase 'complementary shape'.

Tip: The B-cell divides by mitosis, so that all the cells produced are genetically identical. This means that they all produce identical antibodies specific to the pathogen.

Tip: T-cells and B-cells are sometimes called T-lymphocytes and B-lymphocytes.

Exam Tip
Don't get antigens and antibodies mixed up in the exam. Here's an easy way to remember which is which — anti**bodies** are in the **body** (so anti**gens** are the ones on the patho**gens**).

Antibody structure

Antibodies are proteins — they're made up of chains of amino acid monomers linked by peptide bonds (see p. 30 for more on proteins). The specificity of an antibody depends on its **variable regions**. Each antibody has a different shaped variable region (due to different amino acid sequences) that's complementary to one specific antigen. The **constant regions** are the same in all antibodies.

Figure 4: A molecular model of an antibody.

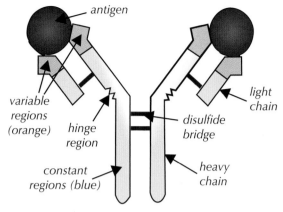

Figure 5: Antibody structure

Cellular and humoral responses

Just to add to your fun, the immune response is often split into two — the cellular response and the humoral response.

- Cellular — The T-cells form the cellular response.
- Humoral — B-cells and the production of antibodies form the humoral response.

Both types of response are needed to remove a pathogen from the body and the responses interact with each other, e.g. T-cells help to activate B-cells.

Primary and secondary immune responses

The primary response

When an antigen enters the body for the first time it activates the immune system. This is called the primary response. The primary response is slow because there aren't many B-cells that can make the antibody needed to bind to it. Eventually the body will produce enough of the right antibody to overcome the infection. Meanwhile the infected person will show symptoms of the disease.

After being exposed to an antigen, both T- and B-cells produce **memory cells**. These memory cells remain in the body for a long time. Memory T-cells and memory B-cells remember the specific antigen and will bind it a second time round. The person is now **immune** — their immune system has the ability to respond quickly to a second infection.

The secondary response

If the same pathogen enters the body again, the immune system will produce a quicker, stronger immune response — the secondary response (see Figure 6). Memory B-cells divide into plasma cells that produce the right antibody to the antigen. Memory T-cells divide into the correct type of T-cells to kill the cell carrying the antigen. The secondary response often gets rid of the pathogen before you begin to show any symptoms.

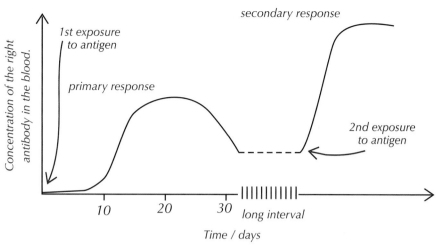

Figure 6: A graph of antibody concentration against time since antigen exposure

Tip: The secondary response is always faster than the primary response. This is shown by a steeper line in graphs of blood antibody concentration against time.

Practice Questions — Application

The graph below shows the immune responses of two mice exposed to a pathogen. Both mice were exposed on day 0 of the experiment.

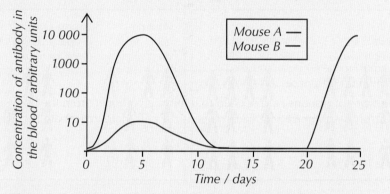

Figure 7: A graph of antibody concentration against time for two mice.

Q1 How much antibody did each mouse have in its blood on day 5?

Q2 Which mouse was already immune to the pathogen?
Explain your answer.

Q3 a) On which day was Mouse A exposed to the pathogen again?

   b) Describe what happened to Mouse A's immune system after it was exposed again.

Practice Questions — Fact Recall

Q1 What are antigens?

Q2 Define phagocytosis.

Q3 What are the functions of T-cells and plasma cells?

Q4 Draw a flow diagram showing the four main stages of the immune response.

Q5 Describe the function of antibodies.

Q6 What is the difference between the cellular immune response and the humoral immune response?

- Understand the use of vaccines to provide protection for individuals and populations against disease.

- Be able to discuss ethical issues associated with the use of vaccines.

Specification Reference 3.1.6

4. Vaccines

After you've been infected once by a pathogen you'll be immune to it, but being infected in the first place can be pretty unpleasant. Vaccination can make you immune without the being ill part.

How vaccines work

While your B-cells are busy dividing to build up their numbers to deal with a pathogen (i.e. the primary response — see page 14), you suffer from the disease. Vaccination can help avoid this.

Vaccines contain antigens that cause your body to produce memory cells against a particular pathogen, without the pathogen causing disease. This means you become immune without getting any symptoms. Vaccines protect individuals that have them and, because they reduce the occurrence of the disease, those not vaccinated are also less likely to catch the disease (because there are fewer people to catch it from). This is called **herd immunity** — see Figure 1.

Tip: Vaccinations are sometimes called immunisations.

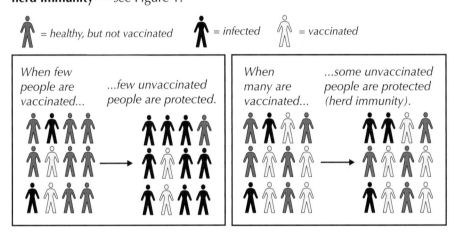

Figure 1: *Herd immunity*

Tip: A lot of vaccines contain more than one antigen from the same pathogen, to make sure it makes you immune to the pathogen. Some vaccines also contain antigens to more than one pathogen, e.g. the MMR vaccine contains antigens from the pathogens that cause measles, mumps and rubella.

Vaccines always contain antigens — these may be free or attached to a dead or attenuated (weakened) pathogen. Vaccines may be injected or taken orally. The disadvantages of taking a vaccine orally are that it could be broken down by enzymes in the gut or the molecules of the vaccine may be too large to be absorbed into the blood. Sometimes booster vaccines are given later on (e.g. after several years) to make sure that more memory cells are produced.

Ethical issues surrounding the use of vaccines

All vaccines are tested on animals before being tested on humans — some people disagree with animal testing. Also, animal based substances may be used to produce a vaccine, which some people disagree with.

Testing vaccines on humans can be risky, e.g. volunteers may put themselves at unnecessary risk of contracting the disease because they think they're fully protected (e.g. they might have unprotected sex because they have had a new HIV vaccine and think they're protected — and the vaccine might not work).

Some people don't want to take the vaccine due to the risk of side effects, but they are still protected because of herd immunity (see p. 16) — other people think this is unfair.

If there was an epidemic of a new disease (e.g. a new influenza virus) there would be a rush to receive a vaccine and difficult decisions would have to be made about who would be the first to receive it.

Practice Questions — Application

Whooping cough is an infection of the respiratory system. The graph below shows the number of cases of whooping cough in Scotland between 1960 and 1999, and the vaccine uptake from the 1970s to 1999.

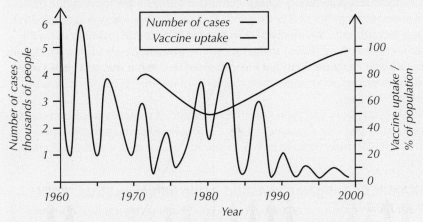

Exam Tip
Always pay attention to the units on the axes — on the graph on the left, the y-axis is number of cases in thousands of people, so in 1963 there weren't 6 cases, there were 6000.

Q1 What percentage of the population were vaccinated in 1990?

Q2 How many cases of whooping cough were there in 1965?

Q3 The whooping cough vaccine was introduced in Scotland in the 1950s. Describe and explain the overall trend in the number of cases of whooping cough after the vaccine was introduced.

Q4 In the 1970s some people were concerned that the vaccine caused neurological problems, such as seizures.

   a) What happened to the uptake of the vaccine in the 1970s?

   b) Explain how this change affected the number of cases between the mid 1970s and the mid-1980s.

Exam Tip
When reading off graphs with multiple scales, double check you've got the right one. If you're struggling to read off the answer, draw lines on the graph to help you.

Practice Questions — Fact Recall

Q1 How do vaccines give people immunity?

Q2 What is herd immunity?

Q3 Describe two issues surrounding the use of vaccinations.

■ Know the effects of antigenic variability in the influenza virus and other pathogens on immunity.

Specification Reference 3.1.6

5. Antigenic Variation

Just to complicate things, pathogens can change their antigens to trick the immune system.

What is antigenic variation?

Antigens on the surface of pathogens activate the primary response. When you're infected a second time with the same pathogen (which has the same antigens on its surface) they activate the secondary response and you don't get ill.

However, some sneaky pathogens can change their surface antigens. This is called antigenic variation. (Different antigens are formed due to changes in the genes of a pathogen.) This means that when you're infected for a second time, the memory cells produced from the first infection will not recognise the different antigens. So the immune system has to start from scratch and carry out a primary response against these new antigens. This primary response takes time to get rid of the infection, which is why you get ill again.

Antigenic variation also makes it difficult to develop vaccines against some pathogens for the same reason. Examples of pathogens that show antigenic variation include HIV, *S. pneumoniae* bacteria and the influenza virus.

Tip: Pathogens of the same type that show antigenic variation are often referred to as strains.

EXAMPLE: Antigenic variation in the influenza virus

The influenza virus causes influenza (flu). Proteins (neuraminidase and haemagglutinin) on the surface of the influenza virus act as antigens, triggering the immune system. These antigens can change regularly, forming new strains of the virus.

Memory cells produced from infection with one strain of flu will not recognise other strains with different antigens. This means your immune system produces a primary response every time you're infected with a new strain (carrying different antigens). So this means you can suffer from flu more than once — each time you're infected with a new strain.

Exam Tip
You need to learn this example for the exam.

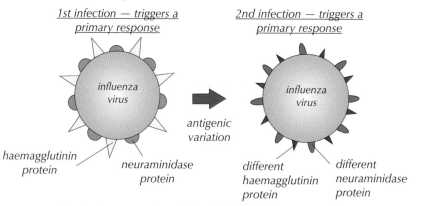

Figure 1: Antigenic variation in the influenza virus.

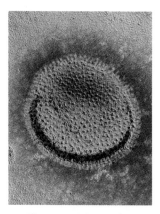

Figure 2: *A TEM of an influenza virus.*

Practice Questions — Fact Recall

Q1 What is antigenic variation?

Q2 Explain why you can suffer from flu more than once.

6. Monoclonal Antibodies

Learning Objectives:

- Understand the use of monoclonal antibodies in enabling the targeting of specific substances and cells.
- Be able to discuss ethical issues associated with the use of monoclonal antibodies.

Specification Reference 3.1.6

Scientists can manufacture antibodies in the lab and use them for all sorts of diagnostic tests... clever stuff.

The use of monoclonal antibodies

Monoclonal antibodies are antibodies produced from a single group of genetically identical B-cells (plasma cells). This means that they're all identical in structure. As you know, antibodies are very specific because their binding sites have a unique structure that only one particular antigen will fit into (one with a complementary shape). You can make monoclonal antibodies that bind to anything you want, e.g. a cell antigen or other substance, and they will only bind to (target) this molecule.

Tip: The unique 3D structure of the antibody binding sites is due to the unique order of the amino acids in the protein — see p. 31 for more on protein structure.

Example of targeting substances — Pregnancy tests

Pregnancy tests detect the hormone human chorionic gonadotropin (hCG) that's found in the urine of pregnant women:

- The application area contains antibodies for hCG bound to a coloured bead (blue).
- When urine is applied to the application area any hCG will bind to the antibody on the beads, forming an antigen-antibody complex.
- The urine moves up the stick to the test strip, carrying any beads with it.
- The test strip contains antibodies to hCG that are stuck in place (immobilised).
- If there is hCG present the test strip turns blue because the immobilised antibody binds to any hCG — concentrating the hCG-antibody complex with the blue beads attached. If no hCG is present, the beads will pass through the test area without binding to anything, and so it won't go blue.

Figure 2: A lab technician testing a urine sample for hCG.

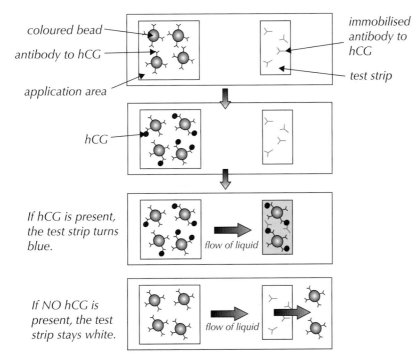

Figure 1: How a pregnancy test works.

Example of targeting cells — Anti-cancer drugs

Different cells in the body have different surface antigens.
Cancer cells have antigens called tumour markers that are not found on normal body cells. Monoclonal antibodies can be made that will bind to the tumour markers. You can also attach anti-cancer drugs to the antibodies. When the antibodies come into contact with the cancer cells they will bind to the tumour markers. This means the drug will only accumulate in the body where there are cancer cells. So, the side effects of an antibody-based drug are lower than other drugs because they accumulate near specific cells.

Tip: Anti-cancer drugs are basically toxic chemicals that kill cells — they cause side effects because they also kill cells that aren't cancerous. Targeting the drugs using antibodies helps reduce this problem.

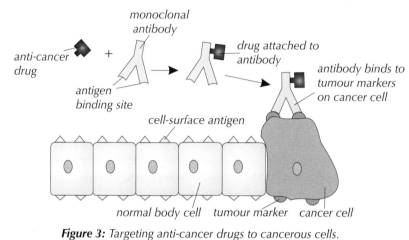

Figure 3: Targeting anti-cancer drugs to cancerous cells.

Ethical issues surrounding the use of antibodies

(HOW SCIENCE WORKS)

Ethical issues surrounding monoclonal antibody therapy often involve animal rights issues. Animals are used to produce the cells from which the monoclonal antibodies are produced. Some people disagree with the use of animals in this way.

Practice Questions — Application

Donated blood is tested to see which type it is. There are four main blood types — A (containing antigen A), B (containing antigen B), AB (containing antigens A and B) and type O (containing neither). The blood type test can be done using monoclonal antibodies produced against these antigens. The table below shows the results for four people.

Tip: Antibody names can get a bit confusing — usually, whatever comes after 'anti-' will be what the antibody will bind to.

Person	Result with anti-antigen A	Result with anti-antigen B
1	Positive — binding occurs	Negative — no binding
2	Positive — binding occurs	Positive — binding occurs
3	Negative — no binding	Negative — no binding
4	Negative — no binding	Positive — binding occurs

Q1 What blood type is:

a) Person 1? b) Person 3?

Q2 People with blood type B carry anti-antigen A antibodies in their blood. If these antibodies meet antigen A the blood clots, which can kill the patient. Could they accept blood from:

a) Person 2? b) Person 4?

7. Validating New Knowledge About Vaccines and Antibodies

Learning Objectives:

- Be able to evaluate methodology, evidence and data relating to the use of vaccines and monoclonal antibodies.

- Be able to explain the role of the scientific community in validating new knowledge about vaccines and monoclonal antibodies, thus ensuring integrity.

- Be able to discuss the ways in which society uses scientific knowledge relating to vaccines and monoclonal antibodies to inform decision-making.

Specification Reference 3.1.6

When a study presents evidence for a new theory (e.g. that a vaccine has a dangerous side effect) it's important that other scientists come up with more evidence in order to validate (confirm) the theory. To validate the theory other scientists may repeat the study and try to reproduce the results, or conduct other studies to try to prove the same theory (see p. 2).

Example 1: The MMR Vaccine

In 1998, a study was published about the safety of the measles, mumps and rubella (MMR) vaccine. The study was based on 12 children with autism (a life-long developmental disability) and concluded that there may be a link between the MMR vaccine and autism.

Not everyone was convinced by this study because it had a very small sample size of 12 children, which increased the likelihood of the results being due to chance. The study may have been biased because one of the scientists was helping to gain evidence for a lawsuit against the MMR vaccine manufacturer. Also, studies carried out by different scientists found no link between autism and the MMR vaccine.

There have been further scientific studies to sort out the conflicting evidence. In 2005, a Japanese study was published about the incidence of autism in Yokohama (an area of Japan). They looked at the medical records of 30 000 children born between 1988 and 1996 and counted the number of children that developed autism before the age of seven. The MMR jab was first introduced in Japan in 1989 and was stopped in 1993. During this time the MMR vaccine was administered to children at 12 months old. Figure 1 shows the results of the study.

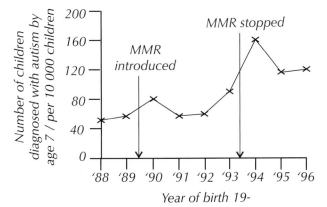

Figure 1: *A graph to show the number of children diagnosed with autism by age 7.*

In the exam you could be asked to evaluate evidence like this.

You might be asked to explain the data...

The graph shows that the number of children diagnosed with autism continued to rise after the MMR vaccine was stopped. For example, from all the children born in 1992, who did receive the MMR jab, about 60 out of 10 000 were diagnosed with autism before the age of seven. However, from all the children born in 1994, who did not receive the MMR jab, about 160 out of 10 000 of them were diagnosed with autism before the age of seven.

Exam Tip
Be specific when describing data in the exam — quote numbers to illustrate your points.

Tip: Sample size is really important in scientific studies — the bigger the better. See page 4 for more on sample size and evaluating studies.

...or draw conclusions

There is no link between the MMR vaccine and autism.

...or evaluate the methodology

You can be much more confident in this study, compared to the 1998 study, because the sample size was so large — 30 000 children were studied. A larger sample size means that the results are less likely to be due to chance.

Example 2: Herceptin — Monoclonal antibodies

About 20% of women with breast cancer have tumours that produce more than the usual amount of a receptor called HER2. Herceptin is a drug used to treat this type of breast cancer — it contains monoclonal antibodies that bind the HER2 receptor on a tumour cell and prevent the cells from growing and dividing.

In 2005, a study tested Herceptin on women who had already undergone chemotherapy for HER2-type breast cancer. 1694 women took the drug for a year after chemotherapy and another 1694 women were observed for the same time (the control group). The results are shown in Figure 2.

Describe the data: Almost twice as many women in the control group developed breast cancer again or died compared to the group taking Herceptin.

Draw conclusions: A one-year treatment with Herceptin, after chemotherapy, increases the disease-free survival rate for women with HER2-type breast cancer.

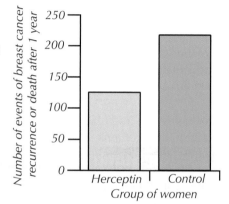

Figure 2: A graph to show the recurrence of breast cancer with and without Herceptin treatment.

Practice Questions — Application

A vaccination programme was conducted in China in 2009 to protect against influenza type A. A study analysed the side effects of 86.9 million vaccines given between September 2009 and March 2010. Figure 3 shows the results of the study.

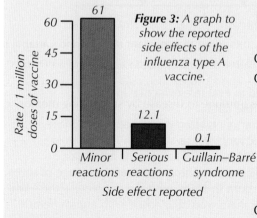

Figure 3: A graph to show the reported side effects of the influenza type A vaccine.

Q1 If 12 million people had the vaccine, how many minor reactions would you expect to see?

Q2 Describe the data.

Q3 The background rate of Guillain-Barré syndrome is 1 per 100 000 people. Does this study support the idea that influenza A vaccination increases the risk of this disease? Explain your answer.

Q4 Evaluate the methodology.

Tip: A background rate is the incidence of something in the general population.

Using scientific knowledge to make decisions

When new scientific information about vaccines and monoclonal antibodies has been validated by scientists, society (organisations and the public) can use this information to make informed decisions. Two examples are given below:

Example 1: The MMR Vaccine

Scientific knowledge:
The validity of the 1998 study that linked MMR and autism is in doubt. New studies have shown no link between the vaccine and autism.

Decision:
Scientists and doctors still recommended that parents immunise their children with the MMR vaccine.

> **Tip:** It's not the scientists who make the decisions — they just provide the information for other people to make the decisions, e.g. people in the government. See page 6 for more.

Example 2: Herceptin — Monoclonal antibodies

Scientific knowledge:
Early studies about Herceptin showed severe heart problems could be a side effect of the drug.

Decision:
All patients receiving Herceptin must be monitored for heart problems, e.g. by having heart tests done.

Section Summary

Make sure you know...

- How the risk of developing coronary heart disease (CHD) is affected by diet, smoking, amount of exercise and alcohol intake.
- How the risk of getting cancer is affected by smoking, sunlight exposure and alcohol intake.
- How to interpret and analyse data on risk factors and the incidence of disease.
- That a pathogen is an organism that causes disease, and how pathogens get into the body — via the gas-exchange system, the skin and the digestive system.
- How pathogens cause disease — by toxin production and cell damage.
- That antigens are molecules found on the surface of cells and antibodies are proteins that bind to antigens.
- That the immune system is activated by foreign antigens on pathogens.
- The four main stages of the immune response — phagocytosis, T-cell activation, B-cell activation and plasma cell production, and antibody production.
- The structure of antibodies, including the constant regions and variable regions.
- What the cellular immune response (T-cells) and the humoral immune response (B-cells) are.
- What the primary and secondary immune responses are and how they work.
- How vaccines make people immune to disease by stimulating memory cell production.
- How vaccines protect people by herd immunity and the ethical issues surrounding vaccine use.
- That antigenic variation is when pathogens change their surface antigens, and the effect it has on immunity.
- What monoclonal antibodies are, how they're used and the ethical issues surrounding their use.
- How new knowledge about vaccines and monoclonal antibodies is validated by scientists and used by society to make decisions.

1   Tetanus is a disease caused by the bacterium *Clostridium tetani*. Symptoms of the disease include extreme muscle spasms caused by the release of a toxin by the bacterium.

  (a)   *Clostridium tetani* causes disease by releasing toxins.
Give one other way that pathogens can cause disease.

(1 mark)

  (b)   *Clostridium tetani* is usually contracted through cuts in the skin.

    (i)   Describe one way the body tries to prevent the entry of pathogens through cuts.

(1 mark)

    (ii)   Give two other ways in which pathogens may enter the body,
and explain how the body tries to prevent their entry.

(4 marks)

  (c)   Below is a graph showing the global incidence of tetanus along with the percentage vaccine coverage.

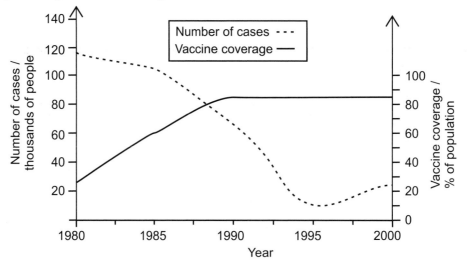

    (i)   Describe the data.

(4 marks)

    (ii)   In 2011 a newspaper used this data to conclude that, 'Cases of tetanus in the UK are on the increase'. Does the evidence support this conclusion? Explain your answer.

(2 marks)

    (iii)   Suggest a possible reason for the increase in cases from 1995 to 2000.

(1 mark)

  (d)   If someone has been potentially exposed to *Clostridium tetani* then they are given a post-exposure injection of antibodies against the toxin. Explain how this prevents them suffering from the disease, but does not prevent them from contracting the disease in the future.

(2 marks)

2   The illegal drug amphetamine can be tested for using monoclonal antibodies. Antibodies that bind to amphetamine are created in the laboratory and used to test urine samples.

(a)   Describe what monoclonal antibodies are and explain why they are specific to one substance.

(3 marks)

(b)   Describe the structure of an antibody.

(5 marks)

(c)   The diagram below shows the structures of amphetamine and the prescription drug bupropion.

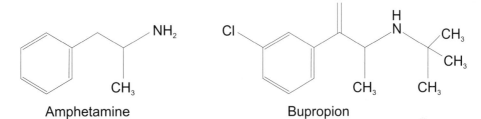

Amphetamine   Bupropion

Taking bupropion can cause a positive result on an amphetamine drug test. Suggest why this happens.

(2 marks)

(d)   Describe one ethical issue surrounding the use of monoclonal antibodies.

(1 mark)

3   In 1918 there was a worldwide outbreak of influenza called 'Spanish flu'. It killed approximately 50-100 million people. The virus responsible was the H1N1 strain of influenza — it had type 1 haemagglutinin and type 1 neuraminidase antigens on its surface.

(a)   When someone is infected with Spanish flu their immune system is activated.

(i)   Describe the process of phagocytosis in detail.

(4 marks)

(ii)   Outline the main stages of the immune response after phagocytosis.

(5 marks)

(iii)   Is antibody production part of the cellular immune response or the humoral immune response?

(1 mark)

(b)   Spanish flu circulated the globe for over a year. Explain why survivors of the Spanish flu did not contract it when exposed for a second time.

(2 marks)

(c)   In 1957 there was another outbreak of influenza called 'Asian flu'. It was caused by the H2N2 strain of influenza. Explain why survivors of the Spanish flu may have contracted Asian flu.

(3 marks)

(d)   Every year new flu vaccines are developed. These contain antigens to multiple strains of influenza. Suggest why this is the case.

(1 mark)

Learning Objectives:
- Understand that biological molecules such as carbohydrates and proteins are often polymers and are based on a small number of chemical elements.
- Know that monosaccharides are the basic molecular units (monomers) of which carbohydrates are composed.
- Understand that digestion is the process in which large molecules are hydrolysed by enzymes to produce smaller molecules that can be absorbed and assimilated.
- Know the gross structure of the human digestive system limited to the oesophagus, stomach, small and large intestines, and rectum.
- Know the glands associated with this system, limited to the salivary glands and the pancreas.

Specification Reference 3.1.2

Tip: Don't get mixed up between absorption and assimilation — absorption is when molecules move from the digestive system into the blood, and assimilation is where absorbed molecules are incorporated into body tissues.

1. Digestion

Digestion is the process of breaking down food into substances that can be used by the body.

The chemical composition of food

Many of the molecules in our food are **polymers**. These are large, complex molecules composed of long chains of **monomers** — small basic molecular units (see Figure 1). Proteins and some carbohydrates are polymers.

In carbohydrates, the monomers are called monosaccharides. They contain the elements carbon, hydrogen and oxygen. In proteins the monomers are called amino acids. They contain carbon, hydrogen, oxygen and nitrogen — see Figure 2.

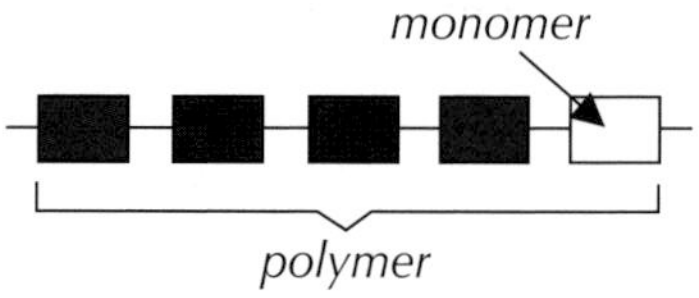

Figure 1: A polymer.

	Monomers	Elements
Carbohydrates	monosaccharides	carbon, hydrogen, oxygen
Proteins	amino acids	carbon, hydrogen, oxygen, nitrogen

Figure 2: Summary table of the composition of carbohydrates and proteins.

The two types of digestion

The food we eat can't be used immediately by the body. It needs to be broken down into molecules that can be absorbed into the bloodstream. There are two types of digestion that make this happen:

Physical digestion

Food is broken down into smaller pieces by the teeth in the mouth. It then moves into the stomach where it's broken down further by the churning movement of the stomach muscles. Breaking food down into smaller pieces gives it a larger surface area, which makes chemical digestion faster.

Chemical digestion

The polymers in our food are insoluble — they can't be directly absorbed into our bloodstream and assimilated (made) into new products. The polymers have to be hydrolysed (broken down) into smaller, more soluble molecules by adding water — see Figure 3. This process happens during chemical digestion. **Hydrolysis** is catalysed by digestive enzymes.

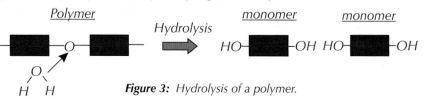

Figure 3: Hydrolysis of a polymer.

Parts of the digestive system

All the organs in the digestive system have a role in breaking down food and/or absorbing nutrients:

Mouth

The mouth starts the digestive process. Teeth are used to break down food and the tongue is used to push food down into the oesophagus. Saliva is secreted to make the food easier to swallow and it contains enzymes, which start the chemical digestion process.

Oesophagus

The tube that takes food from the mouth to the stomach using waves of muscle contractions called **peristalsis**. Mucus is secreted from tissues in the walls, to lubricate the food's passage downwards.

The stomach

The stomach is a small sac. It has lots of folds, allowing the stomach to expand — it can hold up to 4 litres of food and liquid. The entrance and exit of the stomach are controlled by sphincter muscles. The stomach walls produce gastric juice, which helps break down food. Gastric juice consists of hydrochloric acid (HCl), pepsin (an enzyme) and mucus. Pepsin hydrolyses proteins, into smaller polypeptide chains. It only works in acidic conditions (provided by the HCl). Peristalsis of the stomach turns food into an acidic fluid called chyme.

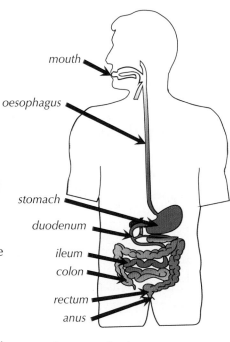

mouth

oesophagus

stomach

duodenum

ileum

colon

rectum

anus

Figure 4: *The digestive system.*

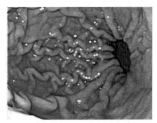

Figure 5: *Folds in the stomach.*

The small intestine

The small intestine has two main parts — the **duodenum** and the **ileum**. Chyme is moved along the small intestine by peristalsis. In the duodenum, bile (which is alkaline) and pancreatic juice neutralise the acidity of the chyme and break it down into smaller molecules. In the ileum, the small, soluble molecules (e.g. glucose and amino acids) are absorbed through structures called **villi** that line the gut wall. Villi are finger-like projections that increase the surface area for absorption (see Figure 6). Molecules are absorbed by diffusion, facilitated diffusion and active transport (see pages 62-66 for more).

Large intestine

The large intestine (also called the colon) absorbs water, salts and minerals. Like other parts of the digestive system, it has a folded wall — this provides a large surface area for absorption. Bacteria that decompose some of the undigested nutrients are found in the large intestine.

Rectum

Faeces are stored in the rectum and then pass through sphincter muscles at the anus during defecation. Nice.

Figure 6: *Villi in the small intestine.*

Glands involved with digestion

Glands along the digestive system release enzymes to help break down food. You need to know about two of these glands — the salivary glands and the pancreas.

The salivary glands

Tip: See page 37 for more on starch and disaccharides.

There are three main pairs of salivary glands in the mouth. They secrete saliva that consists of mucus, mineral salts and salivary amylase (an enzyme). Salivary amylase breaks down starch into maltose, a disaccharide. Saliva has other roles in digestion — e.g. it helps to lubricate food, making it easier to swallow.

The pancreas

Tip: The acidity has to be neutralised so that the digestive enzymes in the small intestine work properly.

The pancreas releases pancreatic juice into the duodenum (see previous page) through the pancreatic duct. Pancreatic juice contains amylase, trypsin, chymotrypsin and lipase (the functions of these enzymes are listed below). It also contains sodium hydrogencarbonate, which neutralises the acidity of hydrochloric acid from the stomach.

Types of digestive enzyme

Digestive enzymes can be divided into three classes:

1. **Carbohydrases** catalyse the hydrolysis of carbohydrates.
2. **Proteases** catalyse the hydrolysis of proteins.
3. **Lipases** catalyse the hydrolysis of lipids.

The table below shows some specific enzyme reactions.

Tip: The names of most digestive enzymes end with '<u>ase</u>'. And you can usually figure out what the enzyme breaks down by looking at what comes before that, e.g. <u>malt</u>ase breaks down <u>malt</u>ose, <u>peptid</u>ase breaks down <u>peptid</u>es.

Location	Enzyme	Class	Hydrolyses	Into
Salivary glands	amylase	carbohydrase	starch	maltose
Stomach	pepsin	protease	protein	peptides
Pancreas	amylase	carbohydrase	starch	maltose
	trypsin	protease	protein	peptides
	chymotrypsin	protease	protein	peptides
	carboxypeptidase	protease	peptides	amino acids
	lipase	lipase	lipids	fatty acids + glycerol
Ileum	maltase	carbohydrase	maltose	glucose
	sucrase	carbohydrase	sucrose	glucose + fructose
	lactase	carbohydrase	lactose	glucose + galactose
	peptidase	protease	peptides	amino acids

Practice Questions — Application

Q1 Sufferers of bowel cancer sometimes have to have part of their intestines surgically removed to prevent the cancer from spreading.

   a) Suggest one symptom that someone who has had part of their ileum removed might have. Give a reason for your answer.

   b) Suggest one symptom that someone who has had part of their large intestine removed might have. Give a reason for your answer.

Q2 Antacids can be taken to treat heartburn. Antacids work by neutralising stomach acidity. Suggest how taking antacids might affect digestion.

Q1   What is a polymer?

Q2   What are the monomers of carbohydrates called?

Q3   What elements are proteins made from?

Q4   Describe what happens during physical digestion and state what the purpose of physical digestion is.

Q5   Why does food have to be broken down into smaller molecules during digestion?

Q6   What happens during hydrolysis reactions?

Q7   Label the diagram:

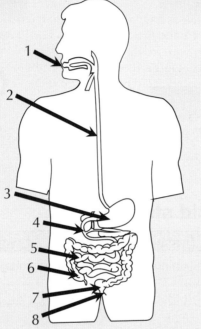

Exam Tip
Make sure you know which bit comes first in the small intestine — the duodenum or the ileum.

Q8   How does food move from the mouth to the stomach?

Q9   Describe the structure of the stomach.

Q10 Describe the structure and function of the small intestine.

Q11 What substances are absorbed by the large intestine?

Q12 What class of digestive enzyme catalyses the hydrolysis of carbohydrates?

Q13 Complete the following equations:

a)   ___?___ $\xrightarrow{\text{proteases}}$ amino acids

b) lipids $\xrightarrow{\text{?}}$ fatty acids

Exam Tip
It's essential that you learn the three main classes of enzymes, but it's also a good idea to be familiar with specific types, e.g. trypsin.

Learning Objectives:

- Know the general structure of an amino acid as:

R
|
$H_2N-C-COOH$
|
H

- Understand condensation and the formation of peptide bonds linking together amino acids to form polypeptides.

- Understand the relationship between primary, secondary, tertiary and quaternary structure, and protein function.

- Know that proteins have a variety of functions within all living organisms.

- Recall the biuret test for proteins.

Specification Reference 3.1.2

2. Proteins

Proteins are an essential part of a healthy diet. They're made of amino acids, which the body uses to make new proteins for a huge variety of functions.

What are proteins made from?

The monomers of proteins are amino acids. A **dipeptide** is formed when two amino acids join together. A **polypeptide** is formed when more than two amino acids join together. Proteins are made up of one or more polypeptides.

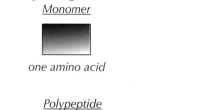

Monomer

one amino acid

Dipeptide

two amino acids

Polypeptide

more than two amino acids

Proteins

one or more polypeptides

Figure 1: *Amino acids join together to form peptides and proteins.*

Amino acid structure

All amino acids have the same general structure — a carboxyl group (-COOH) and an amino group ($-NH_2$) attached to a carbon atom. The difference between different amino acids is the variable group (R on diagram) they contain.

Structure of an Amino Acid

R ← variable group
|
$H_2N - C - COOH$
|
H

amino group   carboxyl group

E.g. Structure of Glycine

H
|
$H_2N - C - COOH$
|
H

Glycine is the smallest amino acid — the R group is a hydrogen atom.

Tip: You'll see a lot of words that start with mono, di or poly. <u>Mono</u> refers to <u>one</u> of something, <u>di</u> refers to <u>two</u>, and <u>poly</u> is where there are <u>lots</u>.

Polypeptide formation

Amino acids are linked together by **condensation reactions** to form polypeptides. A molecule of water is released during the reaction. The bonds formed between amino acids are called **peptide bonds**. The reverse reaction happens during digestion — it's called **hydrolysis**.

Tip: Condensation reactions <u>form</u> a water molecule, hydrolysis reactions <u>use</u> a water molecule.

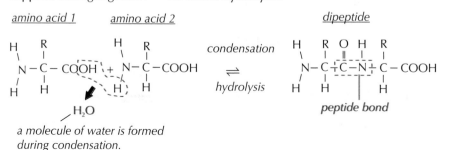

amino acid 1   *amino acid 2*   *dipeptide*

condensation ⇌ *hydrolysis*

peptide bond

a molecule of water is formed during condensation.

Q1 Look at the following amino acid structures.

Glycine

$$H_2N - \overset{\displaystyle H}{\underset{\displaystyle H}{C}} - COOH$$

Alanine

$$H_2N - \overset{\displaystyle CH_3}{\underset{\displaystyle H}{C}} - COOH$$

Valine

$$H_2N - \overset{\displaystyle \overset{\displaystyle CH_3 \quad CH_3}{\underset{\displaystyle }{\underset{\displaystyle CH}{|}}}}{\underset{\displaystyle H}{C}} - COOH$$

Draw the dipeptides and polypeptide that would be formed from a condensation reaction between:

a) glycine and valine.

b) alanine and glycine.

c) glycine, alanine and valine.

Q2 Draw the amino acids produced from the hydrolysis of the dipeptide below.

$$H_2N - \overset{\displaystyle H}{\underset{\displaystyle H}{C}} - \overset{\displaystyle O}{\underset{\displaystyle }{C}} - \overset{\displaystyle H}{\underset{\displaystyle H}{N}} - \overset{\displaystyle CH_2OH}{\underset{\displaystyle H}{C}} - COOH$$

Exam Tip
Remember that in hydrolysis a molecule of water is used, so for Q2 you need to make sure you've added two Hs and one O.

Protein structure

Proteins are big, complicated molecules. They're much easier to explain if you describe their structure in four 'levels'. These levels are a protein's primary, secondary, tertiary and quaternary structures.

Primary structure

This is the sequence of amino acids in the polypeptide chain.

amino acid

Secondary structure

The polypeptide chain doesn't remain flat and straight. Hydrogen bonds form between the amino acids in the chain. This makes it automatically coil into an alpha (α) helix or fold into a beta (β) pleated sheet — this is the secondary structure.

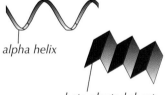
alpha helix

beta pleated sheet

Tip: A hydrogen bond is a relatively weak bond formed between hydrogen atoms and other atoms, e.g. nitrogen or oxygen.

Tertiary structure

The coiled or folded chain of amino acids is often coiled and folded further.
More bonds form between different parts of the polypeptide chain. For proteins made from a single polypeptide chain, the tertiary structure forms their final 3D structure.

one long polypeptide chain

Tip: Think of the tertiary structure like a big, tangled-up spring.

Quaternary structure

Some proteins are made of several different polypeptide chains held together by bonds. The quaternary structure is the way these polypeptide chains are assembled together. For proteins made from more than one polypeptide chain (e.g. haemoglobin, insulin, collagen), the quaternary structure is the protein's final 3D structure.

polypeptide chain

Tip: Not all proteins have a quaternary structure — some are made of only <u>one</u> polypeptide chain.

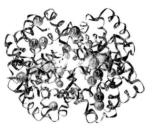

Figure 2: *A molecular model of haemoglobin.*

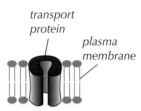

Figure 3: *A transport protein in a plasma membrane.*

transport protein

plasma membrane

Figure 4: *A molecular model of collagen.*

Tip: Don't get the biuret test mixed up with the Benedict's test for sugars on page 36.

Figure 5: *A negative (left) and positive (right) biuret test result.*

Protein shape and function

A protein's shape determines its function. E.g. haemoglobin is a compact, soluble protein, which makes it easy to transport. This makes it great for carrying oxygen around the body (see p. 132). There are loads of different proteins found in living organisms. They've all got different structures and shapes, which makes them specialised to carry out particular jobs.
For example:

Enzymes

They're usually roughly spherical in shape due to the tight folding of the polypeptide chains. They're soluble and often have roles in metabolism, e.g. some enzymes break down large food molecules (digestive enzymes, see p. 28) and other enzymes help to synthesise (make) large molecules.

Antibodies

Antibodies are involved in the immune response. They're made up of two light (short) polypeptide chains and two heavy (long) polypeptide chains bonded together. Antibodies have variable regions (see p. 14) — the amino acid sequences in these regions vary greatly.

Transport proteins

These are present in cell membranes (p. 57). They contain hydrophobic (water hating) and hydrophilic (water loving) amino acids, which cause the protein to fold up and form a channel (see Figure 3). These proteins transport molecules and ions across membranes.

Structural proteins

Structural proteins are physically strong. They consist of long polypeptide chains lying parallel to each other with cross-links between them. Structural proteins include keratin (found in hair and nails) and collagen (found in connective tissue). Collagen has three polypeptide chains tightly coiled together, which makes it strong. This makes it a great supportive tissue in animals.

The biuret test for proteins

If you needed to find out if a substance, e.g. a food sample, contained protein you'd use the biuret test. There are two stages to this test.

1. The test solution needs to be alkaline, so first you add a few drops of sodium hydroxide solution.
2. Then you add some copper(II) sulfate solution.

If protein is present, the solution turns purple. If there's no protein, the solution will stay blue — see Figure 6. The colours can be fairly pale, so you might need to look carefully.

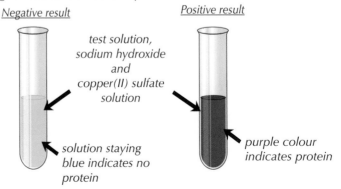

Negative result

Positive result

test solution, sodium hydroxide and copper(II) sulfate solution

solution staying blue indicates no protein

purple colour indicates protein

Figure 6: *A positive and negative biuret test result.*

Practice Questions — Application

A biuret test was carried out to determine which liquids contained protein. The results of the experiment are shown in the table below.

Liquid	Result
De-ionised water	Blue
Cow's milk	Blue
Orange juice	Purple
Orange squash	Blue
Goat's milk	Purple

Q1 Which of the liquids in the table gave a positive test result?

Q2 Suggest why the scientist tested de-ionised water.

Q3 The scientist measured the pH of each liquid after the test. The pH of the cow's milk was below 7, so the scientist marked the test result as void.

    a) Why did they mark the result as void?

    b) Suggest what mistake the scientist might have made during the experiment.

Exam Tip
When a question says 'suggest' you're not expected to know the exact answer — you're expected to use your knowledge to come up with a sensible answer.

Practice Questions — Fact Recall

Q1 What are the monomers of proteins?

Q2 What is a polypeptide?

Q3 Draw the general structure of an amino acid.

Q4 What sort of reaction links amino acids together?

Q5 What is the name of the bond that forms between amino acids?

Q6 Describe the tertiary structure of proteins.

Q7 Explain how the shape of structural proteins make them specialised for their function.

Q8 The biuret test is used to test for proteins.

    a) What is added to the test solution to make it alkaline?

    b) What is added next to the solution?

    c) What would a positive test result look like?

Exam Tip
Make sure you know how to carry out the biuret test, as well as what a positive result and a negative result look like.

Learning Objectives:

- Know the structure of α-glucose as:

- Understand the linking of α-glucose by glycosidic bonds formed by condensation reactions, to form maltose and starch.

- Know that sucrose is a disaccharide formed by condensation of glucose and fructose, and is broken down by sucrase.

- Know that lactose is a disaccharide formed by condensation of glucose and galactose, and is broken down by lactase.

- Understand lactose intolerance.

- Recall the biochemical tests using Benedict's reagent for reducing sugars and non-reducing sugars, and iodine/potassium iodide solution for starch.

- Understand the breakdown of starch, including the role of salivary and pancreatic amylases and of maltase located in the intestinal epithelium.

Specification Reference 3.1.2

3. Carbohydrates

Carbohydrates provide the body with energy. They're found in foods such as bread, pasta and potatoes, but they need to be broken down into monomers before they can be absorbed.

What are carbohydrates made from?

As you know, most carbohydrates are polymers. The monomers that they're made from are monosaccharides, e.g. glucose, fructose and galactose.

Glucose is a hexose sugar — a monosaccharide with six carbon atoms in each molecule. There are two forms of glucose — alpha (α) and beta (β) glucose (see p. 138 for more on β-glucose). For this Unit you need to learn the structure of α-glucose — see Figure 1.

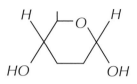

Figure 1: *An α-glucose molecule.*

Carbohydrate formation

Monosaccharides are joined together by **condensation reactions**. During a condensation reaction a molecule of water is released and a **glycosidic bond** forms between the two monosaccharides. A **disaccharide** is formed when two monosaccharides join together. A **polysaccharide** is formed when more than two monosaccharides join together.

┌─ **Example** ─────────────────────────────

Two α-glucose molecules are joined together to form maltose.

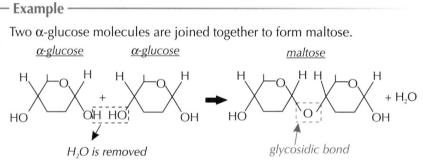

Digestion of carbohydrates

Disaccharides and polysaccharides are often present in the food we eat, so we need to be able to break them down. Luckily we have enzymes released by the intestinal epithelium that break down disaccharides and polysaccharides by **hydrolysis**.

┌─ **Example** ─────────────────────────────

A sucrose molecule is hydrolysed into α-glucose and fructose.

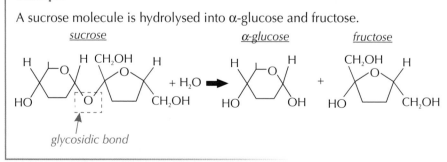

glycosidic bond

Tip: The intestinal epithelium is the membrane that lines the inside of the intestines.

You need to learn the monosaccharides that make up maltose, sucrose and lactose and the enzymes that hydrolyse them. Luckily for you we've put it all in this pretty purple table.

Disaccharide	Hydrolysed by...	Into...
maltose	maltase	glucose + glucose
sucrose	sucrase	glucose + fructose
lactose	lactase	glucose + galactose

Exam Tip
You have to learn these examples for the exam. The enzymes that break them down are easy to remember, but unfortunately there are no shortcuts for learning the monomers.

Practice Questions — Application

Q1 Look at the following monosaccharides.

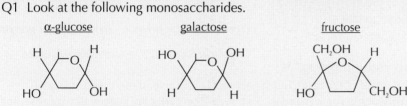

α-glucose   galactose   fructose

a) Draw the disaccharide that would be formed from a condensation reaction between:
 i) α-glucose and galactose
 ii) α-glucose and fructose
b) Draw a polysaccharide made of three α-glucose molecules.

Q2 Draw the monosaccharides produced from hydrolysis of the polysaccharides shown below.

a)

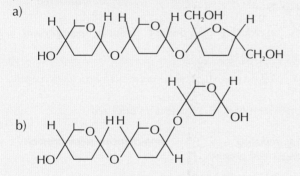

b)

Tip: Structures aren't always drawn with everything on them, e.g. when you get a line with nothing on the end, like this

it just means there's a carbon there, with other elements (like hydrogen) attached to it.

Exam Tip
All you need to remember for questions like Q2 is to split them at the glycosidic bond and add a 'H' to either side.

Lactose-intolerance

Lactose is a sugar found in milk. It's digested by an enzyme called lactase, found in the intestines. If you don't have enough of the enzyme lactase, you won't be able to break down the lactose in milk properly — a condition called lactose-intolerance.

Undigested lactose is fermented by bacteria and can cause a whole host of intestinal complaints such as stomach cramps, excessive flatulence (wind) and diarrhoea.

Milk can be artificially treated with purified lactase to make it suitable for lactose-intolerant people. It's fairly common to be lactose-intolerant though — around 15% of Northern Europeans, 50% of Mediterraneans, 95% of Asians and 90% of people of African descent are lactose intolerant.

Tip: Diarrhoea is caused by having a high concentration of lactose in the intestines. This causes water to move out of the blood and into the intestines (by osmosis). The increase in water means you get runny faeces. Lovely.

The Benedict's test for sugars

Sugar is a general term for monosaccharides and disaccharides. All sugars can be classified as **reducing sugars** or **non-reducing sugars**. If you carry out an experiment on the digestion of carbohydrates you'll need to test for sugars — to do this you use the Benedict's test. The test differs depending on the type of sugar you're testing for.

Reducing sugars

Reducing sugars include all monosaccharides and some disaccharides, e.g. maltose. You add Benedict's reagent (which is blue) to a sample and heat it. If the sample contains reducing sugars it gradually turns brick red due to the formation of a red precipitate — see Figure 2.

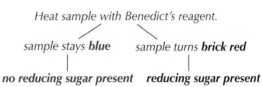

Heat sample with Benedict's reagent.

*sample stays **blue*** → ***no reducing sugar present***

*sample turns **brick red*** → ***reducing sugar present***

Figure 2: *Benedict's test for reducing sugars.*

Tip: If the result is negative for the reducing sugars test, there might still be a non-reducing sugar present.

Non-reducing sugars

If the result of the reducing sugars test is negative, there could still be a non-reducing sugar present. To test for non-reducing sugars, like sucrose, first you have to break them down into monosaccharides. You do this by getting a new sample of the test solution (i.e. not the same one you've already added Benedict's reagent to) and boil it with dilute hydrochloric acid. Then you neutralise it by adding sodium hydrogencarbonate. Finally just carry out the Benedict's test as you would for a reducing sugar — see Figure 3.

Heat sample with Benedict's reagent.

*sample stays **blue*** → ***no reducing sugar present***

*sample turns **brick red*** → ***reducing sugar present***

Boil a new sample with dilute hydrochloric acid then neutralise sample by adding sodium hydrogencarbonate. Heat sample with Benedict's reagent.

*sample stays **blue*** → ***no non-reducing (or reducing) sugar present***

*sample turns **brick red*** → ***non-reducing sugar present***

Figure 3: *Benedict's test for non-reducing sugars.*

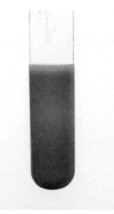

Figure 4: *A brick red colour indicates a positive Benedict's test result.*

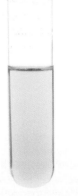

Figure 5: *A blue colour indicates a negative Benedict's test result.*

Practice Questions — Application

Q1 The table shows data from four different Benedict's tests. What conclusions can you draw from each test?

Test	Procedure	Result
1	Sample heated with Benedict's reagent.	Blue
2	Sample heated with Benedict's reagent, (remained blue), then boiled with hydrochloric acid and neutralised. Finally heated with Benedict's reagent.	Red
3	Sample heated with Benedict's reagent, (remained blue), then boiled with hydrochloric acid and neutralised. Finally heated with Benedict's reagent.	Blue
4	Sample heated with Benedict's reagent.	Red

Starch

Starch is made up of a mixture of two polysaccharides — amylose and amylopectin (see p. 139). Both are composed of long chains of α-glucose linked together by glycosidic bonds, formed in condensation reactions.

When starch is digested, it's first broken down into maltose by amylase — an enzyme released by the salivary glands and the pancreas (see p. 28). Maltose is then broken down into α-glucose molecules by maltase — see Figure 6. Maltase is released by the intestinal epithelium.

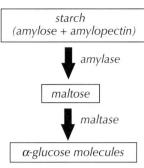

Figure 6: The breakdown of starch.

Tip: You may have noticed that the names of most carbohydrates you've seen so far end with '<u>ose</u>'. Don't be thrown by amylo<u>pectin</u> — pectins are a group of polysaccharides.

Exam Tip
Make sure you always talk about <u>iodine in potassium iodide solution</u>, not just iodine.

The iodine test for starch

If you do any experiment on the digestion of starch and want to find out if any is left, you'll need the iodine test. Just add iodine dissolved in potassium iodide solution to the test sample. If there is starch present, the sample changes from browny-orange to a dark, blue-black colour — see Figure 7.

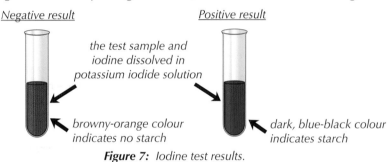

<u>Negative result</u>

<u>Positive result</u>

the test sample and iodine dissolved in potassium iodide solution

browny-orange colour indicates no starch

dark, blue-black colour indicates starch

Figure 7: Iodine test results.

Figure 8: A dark blue-black colour indicates the presence of starch in an iodine test.

Practice Questions — Fact Recall

Q1 Draw the structure of α-glucose.

Q2 What molecule is released during a condensation reaction between two monosaccharides?

Q3 What is the name of the bond that forms between two monosaccharides?

Q4 Which monosaccharides make up the disaccharides:
   a) maltose?
   b) sucrose?
   c) lactose?

Q5 Describe the cause and explain the effect of lactose intolerance.

Q6 Describe how to test for reducing sugars and say what a positive and a negative result would look like.

Q7 What is the end product of starch digestion?

Q8 Name two glands that secrete amylase for starch digestion.

Q9 Describe the method you would use to test for the presence of starch, and say what a positive and a negative result would look like.

- Know that enzymes are catalysts which lower activation energy through the formation of enzyme substrate complexes.
- Understand the lock and key and induced fit models of enzyme action.
- Be able to use the lock and key model to explain the properties of enzymes. Recognise its limitations and be able to explain why the induced fit model provides a better explanation of specific enzyme properties.
- Know how the properties of enzymes relate to their tertiary structure.

Specification Reference 3.1.2

4. Enzymes

Enzymes are proteins that speed up the rate of chemical reactions. Without enzymes, digestion would be a much slower process.

Enzymes as biological catalysts

Enzymes speed up chemical reactions by acting as biological catalysts. They catalyse metabolic reactions in your body, e.g. digestion and respiration. Even your phenotype (physical appearance) is due to enzymes that catalyse the reactions that cause growth and development (see p. 120).

Enzymes are proteins (see p. 32). Enzymes have an **active site**, which has a specific shape. The active site is the part of the enzyme where the substrate molecules (the substance that the enzyme interacts with) bind to. Enzymes are highly specific due to their tertiary structure (see page 40).

How enzymes speed up reactions

In a chemical reaction, a certain amount of energy needs to be supplied to the chemicals before the reaction will start. This is called the **activation energy** — it's often provided as heat. Enzymes lower the amount of activation energy that's needed, often making reactions happen at a lower temperature than they could without an enzyme. This speeds up the rate of reaction.

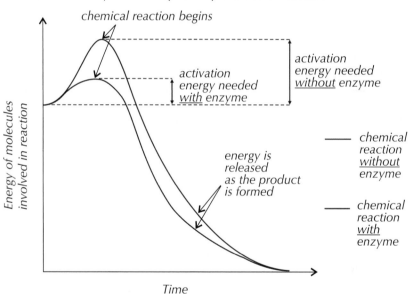

Figure 1: A graph to show the activation energy needed for a reaction with and without an enzyme.

Tip: A catalyst is a substance that speeds up a chemical reaction without being used up in the reaction itself.

Tip: Imagine you have to get to the top of a mountain to start a chemical reaction. It would take a lot of energy to get to the top. An enzyme effectively reduces the height of the mountain, so it doesn't take as much energy to start the reaction.

When a substrate fits into the enzyme's active site it forms an **enzyme-substrate complex** — it's this that lowers the activation energy. Here are two reasons why:

- If two substrate molecules need to be joined, being attached to the enzyme holds them close together, reducing any repulsion between the molecules so they can bond more easily.

- If the enzyme is catalysing a breakdown reaction, fitting into the active site puts a strain on bonds in the substrate, so the substrate molecule breaks up more easily.

Models of enzyme action

Scientists now have a pretty good understanding of how enzymes work. As with most scientific theories, this understanding has changed over time.

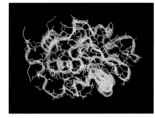

Figure 2: *Computer model of an enzyme-substrate complex. The substrate (yellow) has bound to the enzyme's active site.*

The 'lock and key' model

Enzymes are a bit picky — they only work with substrates that fit their active site. Early scientists studying the action of enzymes came up with the 'lock and key' model. This is where the substrate fits into the enzyme in the same way that a key fits into a lock — the active site and the substrate have a complementary shape.

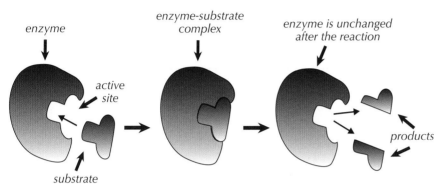

Figure 3: *The 'lock and key' model.*

Scientists soon realised that the lock and key model didn't give the full story. The enzyme and substrate do have to fit together in the first place, but new evidence showed that the enzyme-substrate complex changed shape slightly to complete the fit. This locks the substrate even more tightly to the enzyme. Scientists modified the old lock and key model and came up with the 'induced fit' model.

Exam Tip
When describing enzyme action you need to say the active site and the substrate have a complementary shape, rather than the same shape.

The 'induced fit' model

The 'induced fit' model helps to explain why enzymes are so specific and only bond to one particular substrate. The substrate doesn't only have to be the right shape to fit the active site, it has to make the active site change shape in the right way as well. This is a prime example of how a widely accepted theory can change when new evidence comes along. The 'induced fit' model is still widely accepted — for now, anyway.

Tip: The diagrams on this page show how enzymes break substrates down (e.g. one substrate molecule goes into the active site and two products come out). Enzymes can also catalyse synthesis reactions (e.g. two substrate molecules go into the active site, bind together and one product comes out).

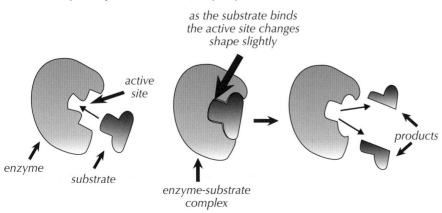

Figure 4: *The 'induced fit' model.*

Enzyme properties

Enzyme properties are related to their tertiary structure. Enzymes are very specific — they usually only catalyse one reaction, e.g. maltase only breaks down maltose, sucrase only breaks down sucrose. This is because only one substrate will fit into the active site. The active site's shape is determined by the enzyme's tertiary structure (which is determined by the enzyme's primary structure). Each different enzyme has a different tertiary structure and so a different shaped active site. If the substrate shape doesn't match the active site, the reaction won't be catalysed — see Figure 5.

Tip: See page 31 for more on the primary and tertiary structure of proteins.

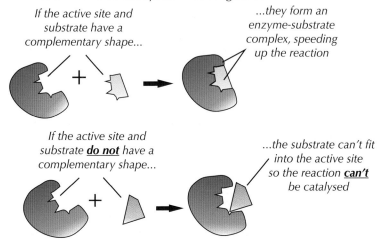

If the active site and substrate have a complementary shape...

...they form an enzyme-substrate complex, speeding up the reaction

*If the active site and substrate **do not** have a complementary shape...*

*...the substrate can't fit into the active site so the reaction **can't** be catalysed*

Figure 5: *An enzyme's active site has a complementary shape to the substrate.*

If the tertiary structure of a protein is altered in any way, the shape of the active site will change. This means the substrate won't fit into the active site and the enzyme will no longer be able to carry out its function. The tertiary structure of an enzyme may be altered by changes in pH or temperature (see pages 41-42). The primary structure (amino acid sequence) of a protein is determined by a gene. If a mutation occurs in that gene, it could change the tertiary structure of the enzyme produced.

Tip: See page 121 for more on mutations.

Practice Questions — Fact Recall

Q1 Look at the graph on the right.

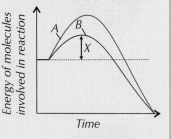

a) Which line shows a reaction with the presence of an enzyme?

b) What does the line labelled X represent?

Q2 Explain, in terms of activation energy, why an enzyme enables reactions to happen at lower temperatures than they could without an enzyme.

Q3 Describe the lock and key model of enzyme action.

Q4 What is the main difference between the lock and key model and the induced fit model?

Q5 What determines the shape of an enzyme's active site?

Q6 Why will an enzyme only bind with one substrate?

Q7 If a mutation occurred in the gene that codes for an enzyme, explain why the enzyme may no longer be able to perform its function.

5. Factors Affecting Enzyme Activity

Learning Objective:

■ Be able to describe and explain the effects of temperature, pH, substrate concentration and competitive and non-competitive inhibitors on enzyme activity.

Specification Reference 3.1.2

Enzymes are great at speeding up reactions, but there are several factors that affect how fast they work.

Measuring enzyme activity

Measuring the rate of a reaction can be done in two ways:

1. Measuring the amount of product produced

There are different molecules present at the end of a chemical reaction than there are at the beginning. By measuring the amount of end product present at different times during the experiment the reaction rate can be calculated.

2. Measuring the amount of substrate left

To produce the end products in a reaction, substrate molecules have to be used up. By measuring the amount of substrate molecules left at different times during the experiment the reaction rate can be calculated.

Temperature

Like any chemical reaction, the rate of an enzyme-controlled reaction increases when the temperature's increased. More heat means more kinetic energy, so molecules move faster. This makes the substrate molecules more likely to collide with the enzymes' active sites. The energy of these collisions also increases, which means each collision is more likely to result in a reaction.

But, if the temperature gets too high, the reaction stops. The rise in temperature makes the enzyme's molecules vibrate more. If the temperature goes above a certain level, this vibration breaks some of the bonds that hold the enzyme in shape. The active site changes shape and the enzyme and substrate no longer fit together. At this point, the enzyme is **denatured** — it no longer functions as a catalyst — see Figure 1.

Tip: In most cases, denaturation permanently changes an enzymes's shape, i.e. it won't go back to normal when the temperature decreases again.

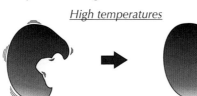

Low temperatures   *High temperatures*

At low temperatures the substrate fits into the active site.

At high temperatures the enzyme vibrates more. This breaks some of the bonds that hold it in shape.

The active site changes shape and the substrate can no longer fit. The enzyme is denatured.

Figure 1: *Effect of temperature on enzyme activity.*

Exam Tip
Make sure you don't say the enzyme's killed by high temperatures — it's denatured.

Every enzyme has an optimum temperature. For most human enzymes it's around 37 °C, but some enzymes, like those used in biological washing powders, can work well at 60 °C.

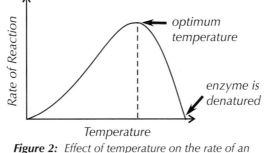

Figure 2: *Effect of temperature on the rate of an enzyme-controlled reaction.*

Exam Tip
You need to understand that different enzymes can have different optimum temperatures, but you don't have to learn any specific optimum temperature values.

pH

All enzymes have an optimum pH value. Most human enzymes work best at pH 7 (neutral), but there are exceptions. Pepsin, for example, works best at pH 2 (acidic), which is useful because it's found in the stomach. Above and below the optimum pH, the H⁺ and OH⁻ ions found in acids and alkalis can disrupt the ionic bonds and hydrogen bonds that hold the enzyme's tertiary structure in place. The enzyme becomes denatured, and the active site changes shape.

Tip: Ionic bonds are chemical bonds between two atoms with opposite charges.

Exam Tip
Don't forget — both a pH that's too high and one that's too low will denature an enzyme, not just one that's too high.

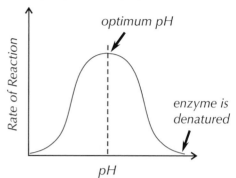

Figure 3: Effect of pH on the rate of an enzyme-controlled reaction.

Substrate concentration

The higher the substrate concentration, the faster the reaction — more substrate molecules means a collision between substrate and enzyme is more likely and so more active sites will be used. This is only true up until a 'saturation' point though. After that, there are so many substrate molecules that the enzymes have about as much as they can cope with (all the active sites are full), and adding more makes no difference — see Figures 4 and 5.

Tip: These graphs show the rate of reaction (i.e. the speed of the reaction). When the line on the graph plateaus it doesn't mean the reaction has stopped, just that it isn't going any faster.

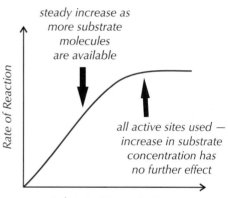

Figure 4: A graph to show the rate of an enzyme-controlled reaction against substrate concentration.

Exam Tip
Don't ever say that the enzymes are used up — say that all the active sites are occupied.

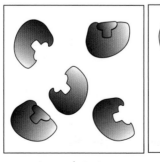 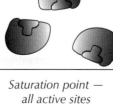 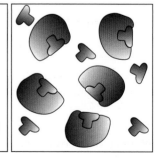

Low substrate concentration — not all active sites are occupied.

Saturation point — all active sites are occupied.

Beyond saturation point — all active sites are occupied and there are spare substrate molecules.

Figure 5: Effect of substrate concentration on occupation of active sites.

Practice Questions — Application

Q1 Hyperthermophillic bacteria are found in hot springs where temperatures reach 80 °C. Psychrotropic bacteria are found in very cold environments. The graph on the right shows the rate of reaction for an enzyme from three different bacteria.

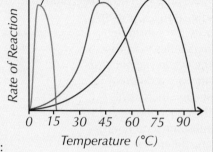

a) Explain which curve on the graph shows the enzyme from:
   i) hyperthermophillic bacteria?
   ii) psychrotropic bacteria?

b) Explain what would happen to enzyme activity for each type of bacteria shown on the graph if they were put into an environment with a temperature range of 60-75 °C.

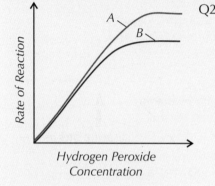

Q2 The graph on the left shows the rate of reaction for the enzyme catalase under two different conditions. Catalase is found in the liver.

a) Explain which curve on the graph represents the reaction with the most catalase present.

b) Both of the curves flatten out. Explain why this is.

Exam Tip
When you're asked to answer questions about a graph, use specific values in your answer where you can.

Enzyme inhibitors

Enzyme activity can be prevented by enzyme inhibitors — molecules that bind to the enzyme that they inhibit. Inhibition can be competitive or non-competitive.

Competitive inhibitors

Competitive inhibitor molecules have a similar shape to that of substrate molecules. They compete with the substrate molecules to bind to the active site, but no reaction takes place. Instead they block the active site, so no substrate molecules can fit in it — see Figure 6.

How much the enzyme is inhibited depends on the relative concentrations of the inhibitor and substrate. If there's a high concentration of the inhibitor, it'll take up nearly all the active sites and hardly any of the substrate will get to the enzyme.

Exam Tip
Don't say that the inhibitor molecule and the substrate have the same shape — they have a <u>similar</u> shape.

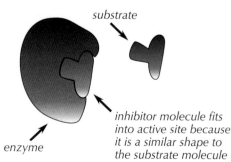

substrate

inhibitor molecule fits into active site because it is a similar shape to the substrate molecule

enzyme

Figure 6: Competitive inhibition.

Non-competitive inhibitors

Non-competitive inhibitor molecules bind to the enzyme away from its
active site. This causes the active site to change shape so the substrate
molecules can no longer bind to it.

They don't 'compete'
with the substrate
molecules to bind to
the active site because
they are a different
shape. Increasing
the concentration of
substrate won't make
any difference —
enzyme activity will still
be inhibited.

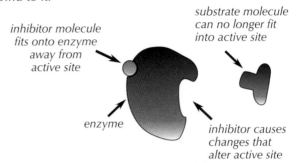

*inhibitor molecule
fits onto enzyme
away from
active site*

*substrate molecule
can no longer fit
into active site*

enzyme

*inhibitor causes
changes that
alter active site*

Figure 7: *Non-competitive inhibition.*

Practice Questions — Application

Methanol is broken down in the body into
formaldehyde. The build up of formaldehyde
can cause death. The enzyme that hydrolyses
the reaction is alcohol dehydrogenase.
The enzyme-substrate complex formed is
shown on the right.

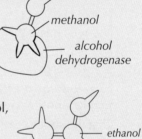

methanol

*alcohol
dehydrogenase*

Q1   A diagram of ethanol is shown below.
     If someone had been poisoned with methanol,
     they could be helped by being given ethanol
     as soon as possible. Explain why.

ethanol

Q2   The graph shows the rate of
     the reaction with no ethanol
     present. Sketch a graph
     with the same axis showing
     the rate of reaction with the
     presence of ethanol.

Rate of Reaction

Methanol Concentration

Practice Questions — Fact Recall

Q1   Explain why an increase in temperature increases the rate of enzyme
     activity.

Q2   Give two factors that may denature an enzyme.

Q3   What happens to an enzyme's shape and function when it is denatured?

Q4   What is meant by the 'saturation point' in an enzyme
     controlled reaction?

Q5   Explain what happens to the rate of a reaction when the substrate
     concentration is increased after the saturation point.

Q6   Where do the following molecules bind to an enzyme:
     a)   a non-competitive inhibitor?
     b)   a competitive inhibitor?

Q7   Explain how non-competitive inhibition prevents enzyme activity.

Section Summary

Make sure you know...

- Many of the molecules in the food we eat are polymers. Polymers are big, insoluble molecules and need to be broken down into smaller, soluble molecules so they can be absorbed and assimilated by the body.
- That the monomers of carbohydrates are monosaccharides and they're made of carbon, hydrogen and oxygen.
- That the monomers of proteins are amino acids and they're made of carbon, hydrogen, oxygen and nitrogen.
- That digestive enzymes catalyse the hydrolysis reactions that break down big molecules into smaller ones.
- The glands involved in digestion — salivary gland and pancreas.
- The structure of the digestive system including the oesophagus, stomach, small and large intestines and rectum.
- That the general structure of an amino acid is: $H_2N-\underset{\underset{H}{|}}{\overset{\overset{R}{|}}{C}}-COOH$
- How condensation reactions link amino acids together with peptide bonds to form polypeptides.
- The relationship between primary, secondary, tertiary and quaternary protein structure.
- That proteins have a variety of functions within all living organisms, and their functions are related to their shape.
- How to carry out a biuret test for proteins and how to interpret the results (blue = negative result and purple = positive result).
- That the structure of α-glucose is:
- How condensation reactions link monosaccharides using glycosidic bonds.
- How the disaccharide sucrose is formed and that it's hydrolysed by sucrase.
- How the disaccharide lactose is formed and that it's hydrolysed by lactase
- What lactose intolerance is — the inability to produce enough of the enzyme lactase.
- How the Benedict's test for sugars is carried out and how to interpret the results.
- How starch is broken down into α-glucose molecules in two steps, by amylase then maltase.
- How the iodine test for starch is carried out and how to interpret the results (blue-black = positive).
- How enzymes catalyse reactions by forming enzyme-substrate complexes and lowering activation energy.
- What the 'lock and key' and induced fit models of enzyme action are.
- Why the properties of enzymes relate to their tertiary structure.
- How temperature, pH, substrate concentration, competitive and non-competitive inhibitors affect enzyme activity.

Exam-style Questions

1 **(a)** Describe the role of salivary glands in digestion.

(3 marks)

(b) Explain how the structure of the stomach makes it suited to its function.

(6 marks)

2 The diagram below shows the disaccharide molecule sucrose.
Sucrose is formed from two monosaccharides.

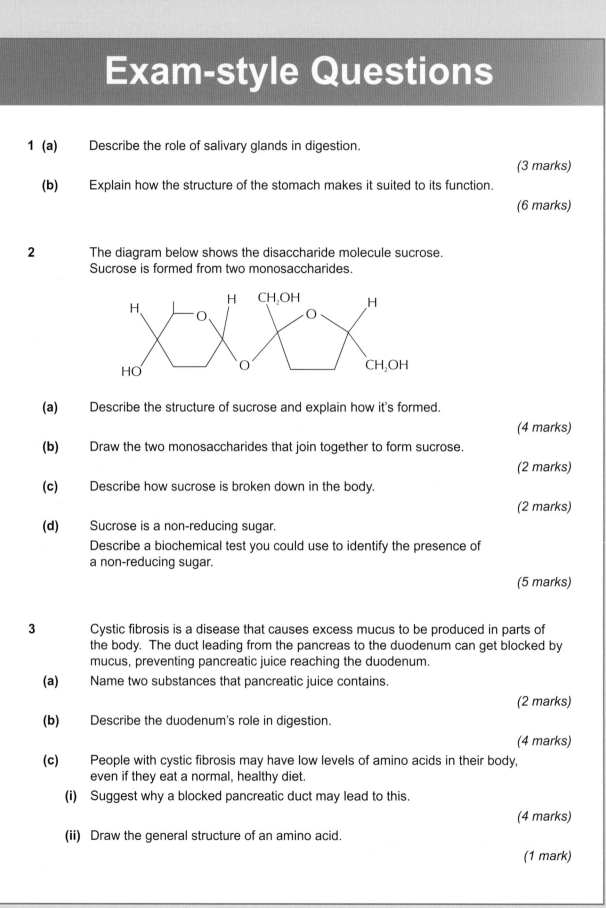

(a) Describe the structure of sucrose and explain how it's formed.

(4 marks)

(b) Draw the two monosaccharides that join together to form sucrose.

(2 marks)

(c) Describe how sucrose is broken down in the body.

(2 marks)

(d) Sucrose is a non-reducing sugar.
Describe a biochemical test you could use to identify the presence of a non-reducing sugar.

(5 marks)

3 Cystic fibrosis is a disease that causes excess mucus to be produced in parts of the body. The duct leading from the pancreas to the duodenum can get blocked by mucus, preventing pancreatic juice reaching the duodenum.

(a) Name two substances that pancreatic juice contains.

(2 marks)

(b) Describe the duodenum's role in digestion.

(4 marks)

(c) People with cystic fibrosis may have low levels of amino acids in their body, even if they eat a normal, healthy diet.

(i) Suggest why a blocked pancreatic duct may lead to this.

(4 marks)

(ii) Draw the general structure of an amino acid.

(1 mark)

4   Triglycerides are a type of fat found in foods. In the stomach, gastric lipase acts as a catalyst to break triglycerides down into diglycerides and fatty acids.

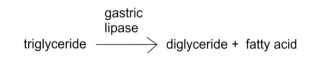

(a)   The graph below shows the rate of reaction for gastric lipase at different pH values.

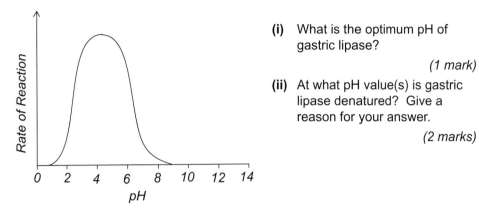

(i)   What is the optimum pH of gastric lipase?

(1 mark)

(ii)   At what pH value(s) is gastric lipase denatured? Give a reason for your answer.

(2 marks)

(iii) Explain what happens when an enzyme is denatured.

(2 marks)

(iv) Suggest two variables you would control if you were investigating the activity of gastric lipase at different pH values.

(2 marks)

(b)   The weight-loss drug, orlistat, stops triglycerides from being broken down. Orlistat is a competitive inhibitor of gastric lipase.

The graph below shows the reaction with and without orlistat present.

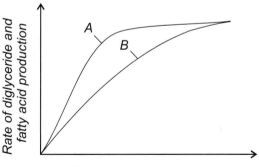

Triglyceride concentration

(i)   Which curve on the graph shows the reaction without the presence of orlistat? Give a reason for your answer.

(1 mark)

(ii)   Explain the action of orlistat in this reaction.

(3 marks)

1. Cell Structure

Learning Objectives:

- Know the appearance, ultrastructure and function of the:
  - plasma membrane, including the cell-surface membrane
  - microvilli
  - nucleus
  - mitochondria
  - lysosomes
  - ribosomes
  - endoplasmic reticulum
  - Golgi apparatus.
- Be able to apply your knowledge of organelles to explain adaptations of other eukaryotic cells.
- Know the structure of an epithelial cell from the small intestine as seen with an optical microscope.
- Understand the role of the microvilli in increasing the surface area of cell-surface membranes.

Specification Reference 3.1.3

You learnt about cell structure at GCSE, but there's a lot more to it at AS...

Cell types

There are two main types of organism — eukaryotes and prokaryotes. Prokaryotic organisms are **prokaryotic cells** (i.e. they're single-celled organisms) and eukaryotic organisms are made up of **eukaryotic cells**. Eukaryotic cells are complex and include all animal and plant cells. Prokaryotic cells are smaller and simpler, e.g. bacteria, see p. 70 for more.

Organelles

Organelles are parts of cells. Each one has a specific function.
If you examine a cell through an electron microscope (see p. 54) you can see its organelles and the internal structure of most of them. Most of what's known about cell structure has been discovered by electron microscope studies.
Figure 1 shows the eukaryotic cell organelles you need to know for Unit 1.

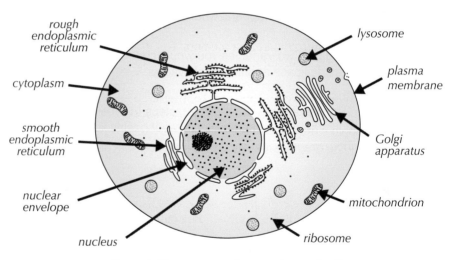

Figure 1: The structure of a typical animal cell.

Functions of organelles

Tip: Don't confuse plasma membranes with epithelial membranes. Plasma membranes surround every cell, epithelial membranes are collections of cells lining places such as the respiratory tract.

Plasma membrane (Also called the cell-surface membrane)

Description
The membrane found on the surface of animal cells and just inside the cell wall of plant cells and prokaryotic cells.
It's made mainly of lipids and protein.

Function
Regulates the movement of substances into and out of the cell. It also has receptor molecules on it, which allow it to respond to chemicals like hormones. See pages 57-58 for more info.

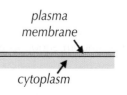

Microvilli

Description

These are folds in the plasma membrane.

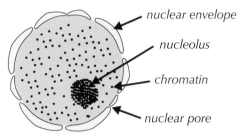

microvillus

plasma membrane

Function

They're found on cells involved in processes like absorption, such as epithelial cells in the small intestine (see p. 27). They increase the surface area of the plasma membrane.

Figure 2: *An electron micrograph of an intestinal cell, showing the microvilli.*

Nucleus

Description

A large organelle surrounded by a nuclear envelope (double membrane), which contains many pores. The nucleus contains chromatin and often a structure called the nucleolus.

nuclear envelope

nucleolus

chromatin

nuclear pore

Function

Chromatin is made from proteins and DNA (DNA controls the cell's activities). The pores allow substances (e.g. RNA) to move between the nucleus and the cytoplasm. The nucleolus makes ribosomes (see below).

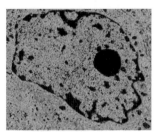

Figure 3: *An electron micrograph of a nucleus, showing the nucleolus, nuclear envelope and nuclear pores.*

Lysosome

Description

A round organelle surrounded by a membrane, with no clear internal structure.

Function

Contains digestive enzymes. These are kept separate from the cytoplasm by the surrounding membrane, and can be used to digest invading cells or to break down worn out components of the cell.

Ribosome

Description

A very small organelle that floats free in the cytoplasm or is attached to the rough endoplasmic reticulum.

small subunit

large subunit

Function

The site where proteins are made.

Tip: Most eukaryotic organelles are surrounded by membranes, which sometimes causes confusion — don't make the mistake of thinking that a diagram of an organelle is a diagram of a whole cell. They're not cells — they're parts of cells.

Endoplasmic reticulum (ER)

Description

There are two types of endoplasmic reticulum: the smooth endoplasmic reticulum (diagram a) is a system of membranes enclosing a fluid-filled space. The rough endoplasmic reticulum (diagram b) is similar, but is covered in ribosomes.

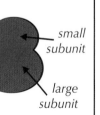

a)

b)

ribosome

fluid

Function

The smooth endoplasmic reticulum synthesises and processes lipids. The rough endoplasmic reticulum folds and processes proteins that have been made at the ribosomes.

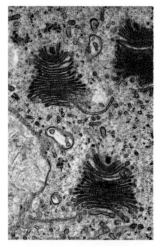

Figure 4: An electron micrograph of Golgi apparatus.

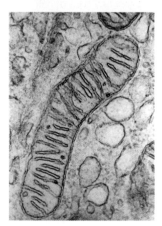

Figure 5: An electron micrograph of a mitochondrion.

Exam Tip
Never say mitochondria produce energy in the exam — they produce ATP or release energy (energy can't be made).

Tip: Mitochondria contain a small amount of DNA (mtDNA), which controls their function.

Exam Tip
You need to learn what an epithelial cell looks like under the microscope for your exams.

Golgi apparatus

Description

A group of fluid-filled flattened sacs.

Function

It processes and packages new lipids and proteins, which are transported elsewhere by vesicles (membrane-bound sacks). It also makes lysosomes.

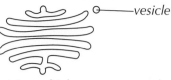

Mitochondrion

Description

They're usually oval-shaped. They have a double membrane — the inner one is folded to form structures called cristae. Inside is the matrix, which contains enzymes involved in respiration.

Function

The site of aerobic respiration. Aerobic respiration produces ATP — a common energy source in the cell. Mitochondria are found in large numbers in cells that are very active and require a lot of energy.

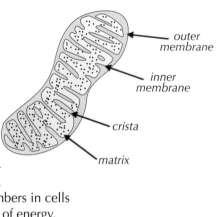

Cell function and organelles

In the exam, you might get a question where you need to apply your knowledge of the organelles in a cell to explain why it's particularly suited to its function. Here are some tips:

- Think about how the structure of the cell might affect its job — e.g. if it's part of an exchange surface it might have organelles that increase the surface area (e.g. microvilli). If it carries things it might have lost some of its organelles to make more room.

- Think about what the cell needs to do its job — e.g. if the cell uses a lot of energy, it'll need lots of mitochondria. If it makes a lot of proteins it'll need a lot of ribosomes.

Examples

Epithelial cells

Epithelial cells in the small intestine are adapted to absorb food efficiently:

- The walls of the small intestine have lots of finger-like projections called villi to increase surface area.

- The cells on the surface of the villi have microvilli to increase surface area even more.

- They also have lots of mitochondria — to provide energy for the transport of digested food molecules into the cell.

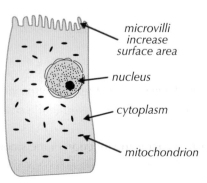

Red blood cells

Red blood cells are adapted to carry oxygen around the body. They have no nucleus to make more room for the oxygen-carrying compound haemoglobin.

Sperm cells

Sperm cells contain a lot of mitochondria to provide the large amounts of energy they need to propel themselves towards an egg.

Practice Questions — Application

Below is a list of cell types and their function.

Cell type	Function
Cardiac muscle cells	Contraction of the heart.
Alveolar macrophage cells	To ingest and digest pathogens invading the lungs.
Beta cells in islets of Langerhans	To produce insulin (a protein).
Proximal tubule epithelial cells	To reabsorb useful molecules filtered out of the blood by the kidneys.

Q1 Name one organelle you would expect to find a lot of in cardiac muscle cells. Give a reason for your answer.

Q2 Suggest how alveolar macrophage cells are adapted to their function in terms of the organelles they contain.

Q3 Name three organelles you would expect to find a lot of in beta cells in the islets of Langerhans.

Q4 Suggest how proximal tubule epithelial cells are adapted to their function in terms of the organelles they contain.

Exam Tip
In the exam they could throw any type of cell at you — don't panic if you haven't heard of it though, just focus on its function and you'll be able to figure out the organelles it needs to do its job.

Practice Questions — Fact Recall

Q1 Give two functions of the plasma membrane.

Q2 Draw a diagram of microvilli, labelling the plasma membrane, the inside of the cell and the outside of the cell.

Q3 The diagram on the right is of a cell nucleus. Name the structures labelled A-D.

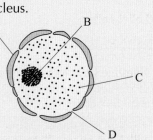

Q4 Describe the functions of the nucleus.

Q5 Give one function of a lysosome.

Q6 Describe how the structure of the rough endoplasmic reticulum is different from the smooth endoplasmic reticulum.

Q7 What is the function of the smooth endoplasmic reticulum?

Q8 Describe the appearance of the Golgi apparatus.

Q9 Draw a labelled diagram to show the structure of a mitochondrion.

Learning Objectives:

- Know the difference between magnification and resolution.
- Know the principles and limitations of transmission and scanning electron microscopes.
- Know how cell fractionation and ultracentrifugation are used to separate cell components.

Specification Reference 3.1.3

Exam Tip

If you find rearranging formulas hard you can use a formula triangle to help. This is the formula triangle for magnification:

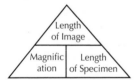

All you do is put your finger over the one you want and read off the formula. E.g. if you want the length of specimen you put your finger over that and it leaves behind length of image ÷ magnification.

2. Investigating Cell Structure

Investigating cells, and what's in them, involves donning your lab coat and digging out your trusty microscope.

Magnification and resolution of microscopes

We all know that microscopes produce a magnified image of a sample, but resolution is just as important...

Magnification

Magnification is how much bigger the image is than the specimen (the sample you're looking at). It's calculated using this formula:

$$\text{magnification} = \frac{\text{length of image}}{\text{length of specimen}}$$

Examples

Calculating magnification

If you have a magnified image that's 5 mm wide and your specimen is 0.05 mm wide the magnification is:

$$\text{magnification} = \frac{\text{length of image}}{\text{length of specimen}}$$
$$= \frac{5}{0.05} = \times 100$$

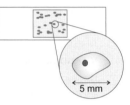

Calculating length of image

If your specimen is 0.1 mm wide and the magnification of the microscope is × 20, then the length of the image is:

$$\text{length of image} = \text{magnification} \times \text{length of specimen}$$
$$= 20 \times 0.1 = 2 \text{ mm}$$

Calculating length of specimen

If you have a magnified image that's 5 mm wide and the magnification is × 50, then the length of the specimen is:

$$\text{length of specimen} = \frac{\text{length of image}}{\text{magnification}}$$
$$= \frac{5}{50} = 0.1 \text{ mm}$$

When you're calculating magnification you need to make sure that all lengths are in the same unit, e.g. all in millimetres. When dealing with microscopes these units can get pretty tiny. The table below shows common units:

Unit	How many millimetres it is:	To convert
Millimetre (mm)	1 mm	
Micrometre (μm)	0.001 mm	÷ 1000
Nanometre (nm)	0.000001 mm	÷ 1000

To convert from a smaller unit to a bigger unit you divide by 1000.
E.g. to convert 6 micrometres to millimetres you divide 6 by 1000 = 0.006 mm.
To go from a bigger unit to a smaller unit you times by 1000.

Resolution

Resolution is how detailed the image is. More specifically, it's how well a microscope distinguishes between two points that are close together. If a microscope lens can't separate two objects, then increasing the magnification won't help.

Tip: A microscope can't distinguish between objects that are smaller than its maximum resolution.

Example

When you look at a car in the dark that's a long way away you see the two headlights as one light. This is because your eyes can't distinguish between the two points at that distance — your eyes produce a low resolution image. When the car gets a bit closer you can see both headlights — a higher resolution image.

Practice Questions — Application

Q1 Image A shows a cartilage cell under a × 3150 microscope.

Image A

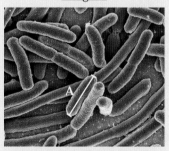

a) What is the diameter of the nucleus (labelled A) in millimetres?

b) What is the diameter of the cell (labelled B) in millimetres?

Q2 A researcher is examining some ribosomes under a microscope. Ribosomes are around 0.00002 mm long. How long will the image appear through a × 40 microscope? Give your answer in millimetres.

Image B

Q3 Image B shows some bacteria. It was taken using a × 7000 microscope. How long is the bacterium labelled A, in micrometres?

Q4 Rhinovirus particles are around 0.023 μm in diameter. What will the diameter of the image be through a × 1500 microscope? Give your answer in millimetres.

Q5 Image C shows a blood clot in an artery (labelled A). The clot is 2 mm in diameter.

a) What is the magnification of the microscope?

b) The diameter of the artery is 3 mm. If the same specimen was examined under a × 50 microscope, what would the diameter of the artery in the image be?

Q6 A mitochondrion is 10 μm long. In a microscope image it is 10 mm. What is the magnification of the microscope?

Image C

Exam Tip
Don't forget that the units need to be the same, e.g. all in millimetres, or all in micrometres.

Types of microscope

Light microscope

They use light (no surprises there). They have a lower resolution than electron microscopes. They have a maximum resolution of about 0.2 micrometres (μm). The maximum useful magnification of a light microscope is about × 1500.

Electron microscope

They use electrons instead of light to form an image. They have a higher resolution than light microscopes so give a more detailed image. They have a maximum resolution of about 0.0001 micrometres (μm). (About 2000 times higher than light microscopes.) The maximum useful magnification of an electron microscope is about × 1 500 000. Electron microscopes produce black and white images, but these are often coloured using a computer. The images can sometimes contain artefacts (e.g. dust or scratches) left over from preparing the specimen — these can affect the clarity and reliability of the image.

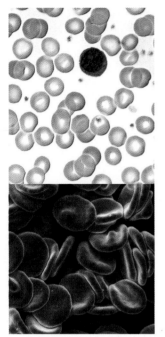

Figure 2: Red blood cells seen under a light microscope (top) and an electron microscope (bottom).

	Light microscope	Electron microscope
Magnification	Lower (maximum of × 1500)	Higher (maximum of × 1 500 000)
Resolution	Lower (maximum of 0.2 μm)	Higher (maximum of 0.0001 μm)

Figure 1: Comparison table of light and electron microscope features.

Types of electron microscope

There are two types of electron microscope:

Transmission electron microscopes (TEMs)

TEMs use electromagnets to focus a beam of electrons, which is then transmitted through the specimen. Denser parts of the specimen absorb more electrons, which makes them look darker on the image you end up with. TEMs are good because they give high resolution images, so you can use them to look at smaller objects. But you've got to view the specimen in a vacuum, so they're no good for looking at living organisms. They can also only be used on thin specimens.

Scanning electron microscopes (SEMs)

SEMs scan a beam of electrons across the specimen. This knocks off electrons from the specimen, which are gathered in a cathode ray tube to form an image. The images you end up with show the surface of the specimen and they can be 3-D. SEMs are good because they can be used on thick specimens. But they give lower resolution images than TEMs and still can't be used on living organisms.

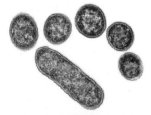

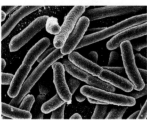

Figure 4: A TEM (top), and SEM (bottom) of E.coli bacteria.

	TEMs	SEMs
Advantages	Give high resolution images, so shows small objects.	Can be used on thick specimens. Can be 3-D.
Disadvantages	Can only be used on thin specimens. Can only be used on non-living specimens.	Give lower resolution images than TEMs. Can only be used on non-living specimens.

Figure 3: Comparison table of TEM and SEM features.

Cell fractionation

Suppose you wanted to look at some organelles under an electron microscope. First you'd need to separate them from the rest of the cell — you can do this by cell fractionation. There are three steps to this technique:

1. Homogenisation — breaking up the cells

Homogenisation can be done in several different ways, e.g. by vibrating the cells or by grinding the cells up in a blender. This breaks up the plasma membrane and releases the organelles into a solution.

The solution is kept ice cold, to reduce the activity of enzymes that break down the organelles. The solution also has to be isotonic — this means it has the same concentration of chemicals as the cells being broken down. It has to be isotonic to prevent the organelles bursting or shrivelling due to movement of water (in or out) by osmosis.

Tip: There's loads more about osmosis on page 63.

2. Filtration — getting rid of the big bits

Next, the homogenised cell solution is filtered through a gauze to separate any large cell debris or tissue debris, like connective tissue, from the organelles. The organelles are much smaller than the debris, so they pass through the gauze.

Tip: Filtration separates cell debris from the organelles, it doesn't separate out the different organelles (that's the job of ultracentrifugation).

3. Ultracentrifugation — separating the organelles

After filtration, you're left with a solution containing a mixture of organelles. To separate a particular organelle from all the others you use ultracentrifugation:

Figure 5: A centrifuge.

- The cell fragments are poured into a tube. The tube is put into a centrifuge (a machine that separates material by spinning) and is spun at a low speed. The heaviest organelles, like nuclei, get flung to the bottom of the tube by the centrifuge. They form a thick sediment at the bottom — the pellet. The rest of the organelles stay suspended in the fluid above the sediment — the supernatant.

- The supernatant is drained off, poured into another tube, and spun in the centrifuge at a higher speed. Again, the heaviest organelles, this time the mitochondria, form a pellet at the bottom of the tube. The supernatant containing the rest of the organelles is drained off and spun in the centrifuge at an even higher speed.

- This process is repeated at higher and higher speeds, until all the organelles are separated out — see Figure 6. Each time, the pellet at the bottom of the tube is made up of lighter and lighter organelles.

The organelles are separated in order of mass (from heaviest to lightest) — this order is usually: nuclei, then mitochondria, then lysosomes, then endoplasmic reticulum, and finally ribosomes.

Exam Tip
You can remember the order the organelles separate out in (Nuclei, Mitochondria, Lysosomes, ER, Ribosomes) using "Naughty Monkeys Like Eating Red Raspberries".

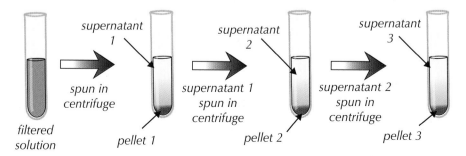

filtered solution

spun in centrifuge

supernatant 1

pellet 1

supernatant 1 spun in centrifuge

supernatant 2

pellet 2

supernatant 2 spun in centrifuge

supernatant 3

pellet 3

Figure 6: Ultracentrifugation.

Practice Questions — Application

Tip: For Q1, you need to think about the advantages and disadvantages of each type of microscope.

Q1 Suggest what type of microscope you would use in each of the following scenarios. Give a reason for each answer.

a) Studying how *E.coli* bacteria replicate.

b) Studying the 3-D structure of red blood cells.

c) Studying virus particles that are 0.1 μm in diameter.

Q2 The diagram below shows the first few steps in ultracentrifugation.

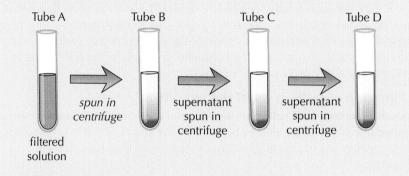

Which organelles would you expect to find in:

a) Tube A

b) The pellet in Tube B

c) The supernatant in Tube D

Practice Questions — Fact Recall

Q1 What is the formula for calculating the magnification of a microscope?

Q2 What is resolution of a microscope?

Q3 What is the maximum resolution for:

a) A light microscope,

b) An electron microscope?

Q4 Which has a higher maximum magnification, a light microscope or an electron microscope?

Q5 What type of microscope would you use to study an object that is 0.001 μm long?

Q6 How do transmission electron microscopes work?

Q7 How do scanning electron microscopes work?

Q8 Give one advantage and one disadvantage of TEMs.

Q9 Give one advantage of SEMs over TEMs.

Q10 Give two ways homogenisation for cell fractionation is done.

Q11 Why is the homogenised solution kept ice cold?

Q12 Describe what happens at the filtration step of cell fractionation and explain why it is carried out.

Q13 Describe ultracentrifugation in detail.

3. Plasma Membranes

Plasma membranes are the boundaries of cells, but there's an awful lot more to them that...

Functions of the plasma membrane

In order to survive and carry out their functions, cells need to take in substances like glucose and oxygen, and get rid of substances like urea and carbon dioxide. As the cell boundary, one of the plasma membrane's main functions is to control what substances enter or leave the cell. The membrane also plays an important role in cell communication and recognition.

Plasma membrane structure

The structure of all membranes is basically the same. They're composed of lipids (mainly a type called phospholipids), proteins and carbohydrates (usually attached to proteins or lipids).

In 1972, the **fluid mosaic model** was suggested to describe the arrangement of molecules in the membrane. In the model, phospholipid molecules form a continuous, double layer (called a bilayer). This layer is 'fluid' because the phospholipids are constantly moving. Protein molecules are scattered through the layer, like tiles in a mosaic — see Figure 1.

Tip: See p. 60 for more on phospholipids.

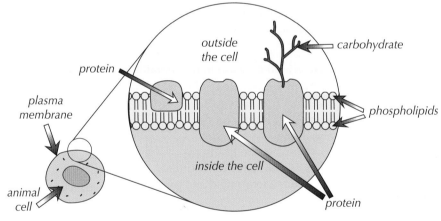

Figure 1: The fluid mosaic model of membrane structure.

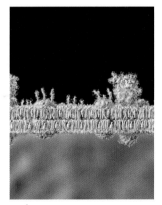

Figure 2: A computer model of membrane structure.

The fluid mosaic model and membrane properties

You might get a question in the exam where you need to use your knowledge of the fluid mosaic model to explain why the plasma membrane has various properties. You can't go far wrong if you learn these points:

Controls entry and exit

Some proteins in the membrane allow the passage of large or charged water-soluble substances that would otherwise find it difficult to cross the membrane. Different cells have different proteins to carry out this function — e.g. the membrane of a nerve cell has sodium-potassium carrier proteins (which help to conduct nerve impulses) and muscle cells have calcium protein channels (which are needed for muscle contraction).

Tip: There's more on carrier proteins and protein channels on page 65.

Learning Objectives:

- Know the arrangement of phospholipids, proteins and carbohydrates in the fluid-mosaic model of membrane structure.
- Be able to use the fluid-mosaic model to explain appropriate properties of plasma membranes.

Specification Reference 3.1.3

Forms a barrier against water-soluble substances

Phospholipid molecules have a 'head' and a 'tail' (see Figure 2). The head is hydrophilic — it attracts water. The tail is hydrophobic — it repels water.

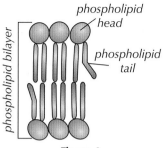

Figure 3:
Phospholipid bilayer.

The molecules automatically arrange themselves into a bilayer — the heads face out towards the water on either side of the membrane. The centre of the bilayer is hydrophobic so the membrane doesn't allow water-soluble substances (like ions) through it — it acts as a barrier to these substances.

Allows cell communication

Membranes contain receptor proteins. These allow the cell to detect chemicals released from other cells. The chemicals signal to the cell to respond in some way, e.g. the hormone insulin binds to receptors in the membranes of liver cells — this tells the liver cells to absorb glucose. This cell communication is vital for the body to function properly. Different cells have different receptors present in their membranes.

Allows cell recognition

Some proteins and lipids in the plasma membrane have short carbohydrate chains attached to them — they're called **glycoproteins** and **glycolipids**. These molecules tell white blood cells that the cell is your own. White blood cells only attack cells that they don't recognise as self (e.g. those of microorganisms like bacteria).

Is fluid

The phospholipids in the plasma membrane make the bilayer quite fluid. Cholesterol molecules fit in between the phospholipids and reduce membrane fluidity — the more cholesterol molecules there are, the less fluid the membrane becomes. Cholesterol is important as it makes the cell membrane more rigid and prevents it from breaking up.

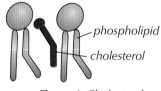

Figure 4: Cholesterol in the membrane.

Practice Questions — Fact Recall

Q1 Describe the structure of the plasma membrane according to the fluid mosaic model.

Q2 How does the plasma membrane control what enters and leaves the cell?

Q3 Explain the meaning of the terms 'hydrophilic' and hydrophobic'.

Q4 Explain why the plasma membrane is an effective barrier against water-soluble substances.

Q5 Describe the function of the following components of the plasma membrane:

　　a) receptor proteins,

　　b) glycoproteins,

　　c) cholesterol.

4. Lipids in Membranes

Lipids are pretty important molecules in the human body — they're one of the main components of plasma membranes for a start...

Triglycerides

The lipids in membranes aren't triglycerides, but you need to know about triglycerides before you can understand phospholipids.

Triglycerides have one molecule of glycerol with three fatty acids attached to it. Fatty acid molecules have long 'tails' made of hydrocarbons. The tails are 'hydrophobic' (they repel water molecules). These tails make lipids insoluble in water.

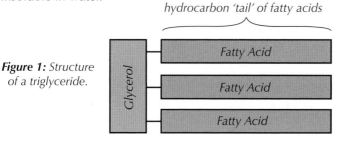

hydrocarbon 'tail' of fatty acids

Figure 1: *Structure of a triglyceride.*

Learning Objectives:

- Know that glycerol and fatty acids combine by condensation to produce triglycerides.
- Know that the R-group of a fatty acid may be saturated or unsaturated.
- Know that in phospholipids, one of the fatty acids of a triglyceride is substituted by a phosphate group.
- Know the emulsion test for lipids.

Specification Reference 3.1.3

Fatty acids

All fatty acids have the same basic structure, but the hydrocarbon tail varies — see Figure 2.

There are two kinds of fatty acids — saturated and unsaturated. The difference is in their hydrocarbon tails.

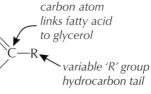

carbon atom links fatty acid to glycerol

variable 'R' group hydrocarbon tail

Figure 2: *Basic structure of a fatty acid.*

Tip: Hydrocarbons are chains of hydrogen and carbon atoms. The variable 'R' group can be any hydrocarbon.

Saturated fatty acids

Saturated fatty acids don't have any double bonds between their carbon atoms. The fatty acid is 'saturated' with hydrogen.

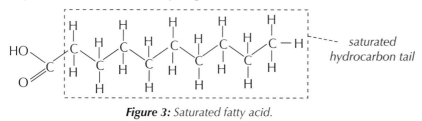

saturated hydrocarbon tail

Figure 3: *Saturated fatty acid.*

Exam Tip
Remember:
Saturated fatty acids have Single bonds.
Unsaturated fatty acids have doUble bonds.

Unsaturated fatty acids

Unsaturated fatty acids do have double bonds between carbon atoms, which cause the chain to kink.

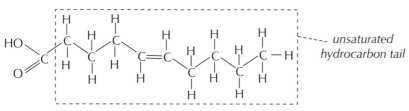

unsaturated hydrocarbon tail

Figure 4: *Unsaturated fatty acid.*

Tip: Unsaturated fatty acids affect the fluidity of plasma membranes. The more unsaturated fatty acids there are in the phospholipid bilayer, the more fluid the membrane.

Tip: There's more about condensation reactions on page 30.

Triglyceride formation

Triglycerides are formed by condensation reactions. Figure 5 shows a fatty acid joining to a glycerol molecule. An **ester bond** forms between the two molecules, releasing a molecule of water — this is a condensation reaction. This process happens twice more to form a triglyceride.

Tip: You can pretty much ignore the 'R' group on the fatty acid — it never gets involved in the reaction.

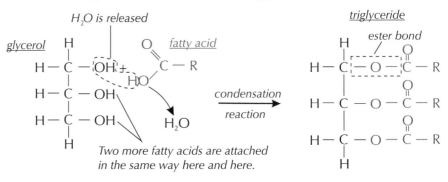

Figure 5: Triglyceride formation.

Phospholipids

The lipids in plasma membranes are mainly phospholipids. Phospholipids are pretty similar to triglycerides except one of the fatty acid molecules is replaced by a phosphate group. The phosphate group is hydrophilic and the fatty acid tails are hydrophobic. This is important in the plasma membrane (see p. 57).

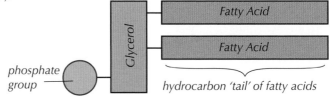

Figure 6: Structure of a phospholipid.

The emulsion test for lipids

If you wanted to find out if there was any fat in a particular food you could do the **emulsion test**:

- Shake the test substance with ethanol for about a minute, then pour the solution into water.
- Any lipid will show up as a milky emulsion — see Figures 7 and 8.
- The more lipid there is, the more noticeable the milky colour will be.

Figure 7: A positive result using the emulsion test.

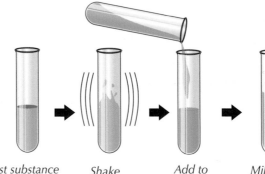

| Test substance and ethanol | Shake | Add to water | Milky colour indicates lipid |

Figure 8: The emulsion test for lipids.

Q1 The table below shows the structures of three fatty acids.

Name:	Structure:
Propanoic acid	CH_3CH_2COOH
Palmitic acid	$CH_3(CH_2)_{14}COOH$
Stearic acid	$CH_3(CH_2)_{16}COOH$
Oleic acid	$CH_3(CH_2)_7CH=CH(CH_2)_7COOH$

a) Identify the 'R' groups in each of the fatty acids in the table.

b) Draw the triglyceride that would be formed from a condensation reaction between glycerol and propanoic acid.

c) Unsaturated fatty acids will decolourise iodine solution. Which of the fatty acids in the table above will produce a positive result when added to iodine solution?

Tip: For Q1 b), think about which part of the fatty acid molecule reacts with glycerol.

Q2 A triglyceride is shown on the right. Draw one molecule of the fatty acid that makes up the hydrocarbon tail.

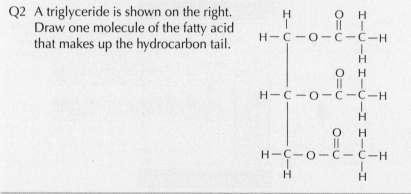

Q1 What are the components of a triglyceride?

Q2 Draw the basic structure of a fatty acid.

Q3 Explain the difference between a saturated fatty acid and an unsaturated fatty acid.

Q4 Name the small molecule released during a condensation reaction to form a triglyceride.

Q5 Describe the structure of a phospholipid.

Q6 A student carries out an emulsion test on a food sample.

a) What is the student testing for?

b) Describe how the student should carry out the test and what he should expect to see if the result is positive.

- Know that diffusion is the passive movement of substances down a concentration gradient.

- Understand how surface area, difference in concentration and the thickness of the exchange surface affect the rate of diffusion.

- Know that osmosis is a special case of diffusion in which water moves from a solution of higher water potential to a solution of lower water potential through a partially permeable membrane.

- Recall the term isotonic.

- Understand the role of carrier proteins and protein channels in facilitated diffusion.

- Understand the role of carrier proteins and the transfer of energy in the transport of substances against a concentration gradient.

- Know the absorption of the products of carbohydrate digestion.

- Understand the roles of diffusion, active transport and co-transport involving sodium ions in the absorption of these products.

Specification Reference 3.1.3

5. Exchange Across Plasma Membranes

There are many ways substances move in and out of cells across the membrane. First up, diffusion and osmosis.

Diffusion

Diffusion is the net movement of particles (molecules or ions) from an area of higher concentration to an area of lower concentration. Molecules will diffuse both ways, but the net movement will be to the area of lower concentration. This continues until particles are evenly distributed throughout the liquid or gas. The concentration gradient is the path from an area of higher concentration to an area of lower concentration. Particles diffuse down a concentration gradient.

Diffusion is a passive process — no energy is needed for it to happen. Particles can diffuse across plasma membranes, as long as they can move freely through the membrane. E.g. oxygen and carbon dioxide molecules are small enough to pass easily through spaces between phospholipids.

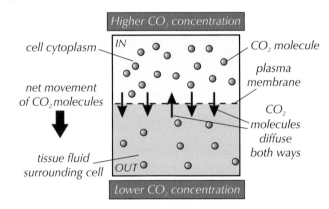

Figure 1: Diffusion of carbon dioxide across the plasma membrane.

Factors affecting the rate of diffusion

There are three main factors that affect the rate of diffusion:

- The concentration gradient — the higher it is, the faster the rate of diffusion.

- The thickness of the exchange surface — the thinner the exchange surface (i.e. the shorter the distance the particles have to travel), the faster the rate of diffusion.

- The surface area — the larger the surface area (e.g. of the plasma membrane), the faster the rate of diffusion.

┌─ Example ─────────────────────────

Some cells (e.g. epithelial cells in the small intestine) have microvilli — projections formed by the plasma membrane folding up on itself (see p.49). Microvilli give the cell a larger surface area — in human cells microvilli can increase the surface area by about 600 times. A larger surface area means that more particles can be exchanged in the same amount of time — increasing the rate of diffusion.

Osmosis

Osmosis is the diffusion of water molecules across a partially permeable membrane, from an area of higher water potential (i.e. higher concentration of water molecules) to an area of lower water potential (i.e. lower concentration of water molecules). Water potential is the potential (likelihood) of water molecules to diffuse out of or into a solution.

A partially permeable membrane allows some molecules through it, but not all. The plasma membrane is partially permeable. Water molecules are small and can diffuse easily through the plasma membrane, but large solute molecules can't.

Pure water has a water potential of zero. Adding solutes to pure water lowers its water potential — so the water potential of any solution is always negative. The more negative the water potential, the stronger the concentration of solutes in the solution.

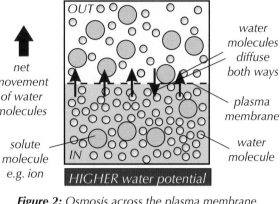

Figure 2: Osmosis across the plasma membrane.

Exam Tip
You should always use the term <u>water potential</u> in the exam — never say water concentration.

Tip: Osmosis is a special case of diffusion.

Tip: Another way of looking at it is that pure water has the highest water potential and all solutions have a lower water potential than pure water.

Example

Glass A contains pure water — it's got a water potential of zero.

Glass B contains a solution of orange squash. The orange squash molecules are a solute. They lower the concentration of the water molecules. This means that the water potential of the orange squash is lower than the water potential of pure water.

If two solutions have the same water potential they're said to be **isotonic**. Cells in an isotonic solution won't lose or gain any water — there's no net movement of water molecules because there's no difference in water potential between the cell and the surrounding solution.

If a cell is placed in a solution that has a higher water potential it will swell as water moves into it by osmosis. Solutions with a higher water potential compared with the inside of the cell are called **hypotonic**. If a cell is placed in a solution that has a lower water potential it may shrink as water moves out of it by osmosis. Solutions with a lower water potential than the cell are called **hypertonic**.

Exam Tip
You're not expected to learn what hypotonic and hypertonic mean, but it helps to be familiar with them.

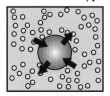

Cell in an <u>isotonic</u> solution — no net movement of water.

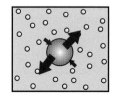

Cell in a <u>hypertonic</u> solution — net movement of water <u>out</u> of the cell.

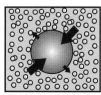

Cell in a <u>hypotonic</u> solution — net movement of water <u>into</u> the cell.

Practice Questions — Application

Q1 The photograph on the right shows ink diffusing through a beaker of water. Explain what is happening to the ink molecules.

Q2 Carbon dioxide is a waste product of respiration and must be removed from cells. How will each of the following affect the rate of diffusion of carbon dioxide across a plasma membrane? Explain your answer in each case.

a) Increasing the thickness of the cell membrane.

b) Increasing the number of folds in the cell membrane.

c) Reducing the concentration of carbon dioxide outside of the cell.

Q3 Describe the movement of water molecules in each of the following situations:

a) Human cheek cells with a water potential of -300 kPa are placed in a salt solution with a water potential of -325 kPa.

b) Apple slices with a water potential of -750 kPa are placed in a beaker of pure water.

c) Orange squash with a water potential of -450 kPa is sealed in a length of Visking tubing and suspended in a solution of equal water potential.

Q4 Potato cells with a water potential of -350 kPa are placed in sucrose solutions with varying water potentials. The water potential of each solution is shown in the table below.

Solution	Water potential
1	-250 kPa
2	-500 kPa
3	-1000 kPa

a) After 15 minutes, the potato cells in solution 1 have increased in volume. Explain why this is the case.

b) Predict whether the cells in solutions 2 and 3 will increase or decrease in volume. Explain your answers.

Tip: Water potential is usually measured in kilopascals (or kPa). It's actually a unit of pressure.

Tip: Visking tubing is a partially permeable membrane — it's used a lot in osmosis and diffusion experiments.

Tip: Remember, a higher water potential is closer to 0 (the water potential of pure water).

Facilitated diffusion

Some larger molecules (e.g. amino acids, glucose) and charged atoms (e.g. chloride ions) can't diffuse directly through the phospholipid bilayer of the cell membrane. Instead they diffuse through proteins in the cell membrane — this is called facilitated diffusion.

Like diffusion, facilitated diffusion moves particles down a concentration gradient, from a higher to a lower concentration. It's also a passive process — it doesn't use energy. There are two types of protein involved — carrier proteins and protein channels.

Exam Tip
Always say <u>down</u> the concentration gradient in the exam, not across or along — or you won't get the marks.

Carrier proteins

Carrier proteins move large molecules into or out of the cell, down their concentration gradient. Different carrier proteins facilitate the diffusion of different molecules. Here's how they work:

- First, a large molecule attaches to a carrier protein in the membrane.
- Then, the protein changes shape.
- This releases the molecule on the opposite side of the membrane — see Figure 3.

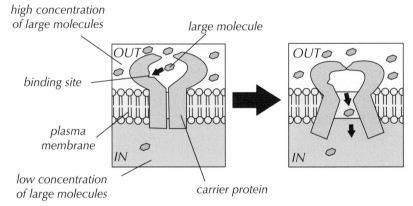

Figure 3: Movement of a molecule by carrier proteins.

Tip: Carrier proteins and protein channels (see below) are called transport proteins.

Protein channels

Protein channels form pores in the membrane for charged particles to diffuse through (down their concentration gradient). Different protein channels facilitate the diffusion of different charged particles.

Tip: Charged particles are things like sodium and potassium ions.

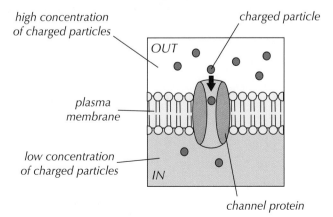

Figure 4: Movement of charged particles by protein channels.

Figure 5: Computer model showing a cross section of a protein channel in the phospholipid bilayer.

Active transport

Active transport uses energy to move molecules and ions across plasma membranes, against a concentration gradient. Carrier proteins and co-transporters are involved in active transport.

Carrier proteins

The process is pretty similar to facilitated diffusion — a molecule attaches to the carrier protein, the protein changes shape and this moves the molecule across the membrane, releasing it on the other side — see Figure 6.
The only difference is that energy is used (usually from ATP produced in mitochondria — see page 50), to move the solute against its concentration gradient.

Exam Tip
It's easy to get facilitated diffusion and active transport confused because they both use proteins to transport molecules. But active transport is the only one that uses energy to do so.

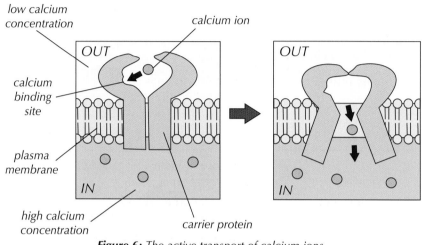

Figure 6: The active transport of calcium ions.

Co-transporters

Co-transporters are a type of carrier protein. They bind two molecules at a time. The concentration gradient of one of the molecules is used to move the other molecule against its own concentration gradient.

Figure 7 shows the co-transport of sodium ions and glucose. Sodium ions move into the cell down their concentration gradient. This moves glucose into the cell too, against its concentration gradient.

Tip: It's the glucose that's being actively transported here, not the sodium ions.

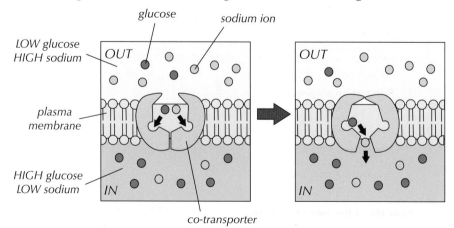

Figure 7: The co-transport of glucose and sodium ions.

Type of transport:	Description
Diffusion	▪ Net movement of particles from an area of higher concentration to an area of lower concentration. ▪ Passive process — doesn't require energy.
Osmosis	▪ Movement of water molecules across a partially permeable membrane from an area of higher water potential to an area of lower water potential. ▪ Passive process — doesn't require energy.
Facilitated diffusion	▪ Net movement of particles from an area of higher concentration to an area of lower concentration. ▪ Uses carrier proteins and protein channels to aid the diffusion of large molecules and charged atoms through the plasma membrane. ▪ Passive process — doesn't require energy.
Active transport	▪ Movement of molecules against a concentration gradient. ▪ Uses carrier proteins and co-transporters to transport molecules. ▪ Active process — requires energy.

Figure 8: Summary table of exchange mechanisms.

Exam Tip
Make sure you know that active transport is the only process that uses energy.

Practice Questions — Application

ATP is produced by mitochondria during aerobic respiration. The overall equation for this process can be written as:

glucose + oxygen → carbon dioxide + water + ATP

The graph below shows the relationship between the relative rates of oxygen consumption and the active transport of sodium ions across epithelial cells.

Q1 a) Describe the relationship shown by the graph.

b) Suggest an explanation for this relationship.

Q2 What effect would the rate of the facilitated diffusion of sodium ions have on the rate of oxygen consumption?

Q3 Suggest one other factor that may affect the rate of sodium ion active transport.

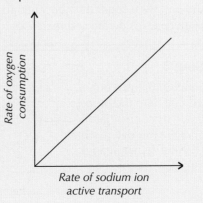

Exam Tip
Questions asking you to describe and explain graphical relationships are dead common in exams — make sure you're comfortable with doing them.

Tip: There's more on the products of carbohydrate breakdown on page 34.

Exam Tip
You need to learn this example. Make sure you know exactly which processes are involved at each stage.

EXAMPLE: absorption of glucose

All these processes — diffusion, facilitated diffusion and active transport — are essential in the body. For example, they're needed to absorb the products of carbohydrate digestion across the intestinal epithelium cells. Glucose is a product of carbohydrate digestion — it's absorption into the blood stream involves two main stages:

Stage 1: diffusion into the blood

When carbohydrates are first broken down, there's a higher concentration of glucose in the small intestine than in the blood — there's a concentration gradient. Glucose moves across the epithelial cells of the small intestine into the blood by diffusion. When the concentration in the lumen becomes lower than in the blood diffusion stops.

Stage 2: active transport

The remaining glucose is absorbed by active transport with sodium ions. Here's how it works:

Step 1

Sodium ions are actively transported out of the small intestine epithelial cells, into the blood, by the sodium-potassium pump.

This creates a concentration gradient — there's now a higher concentration of sodium ions in the small intestine lumen than inside the cell.

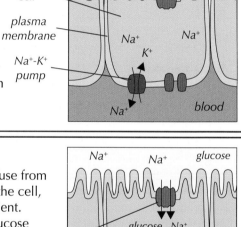

Step 2

This causes sodium ions to diffuse from the small intestine lumen into the cell, down their concentration gradient. They do this via the sodium-glucose co-transporter proteins.

The co-transporter carries glucose into the cell with the sodium. As a result the concentration of glucose inside the cell increases.

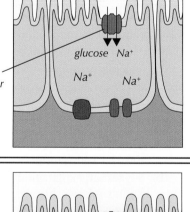

Tip: Remember, co-transporters use the concentration gradient of one molecule (in this case the sodium ions) to move another molecule against its concentration gradient (in this case glucose).

Step 3

Glucose diffuses out of the cell, into the blood, down its concentration gradient through a protein channel, by facilitated diffusion.

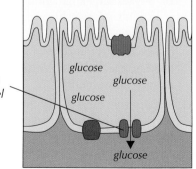

Q1   What is diffusion?

Q2   Is diffusion an active or passive process?

Q3   Describe the difference between simple diffusion through a plasma membrane and facilitated diffusion through a plasma membrane.

Q4   Give three factors that affect the rate of diffusion.

Q5   Define osmosis.

Q6   Define the term 'water potential'.

Q7   The plasma membrane is a partially permeable membrane. What does this mean?

Q8   Summarise the similarities and differences between facilitated diffusion and active transport.

Q9   Describe how the following are used to transport substances across the cell membrane during active transport:

   a) carrier proteins.

   b) protein channels.

   c) co-transporters.

Q10 When carbohydrates are first broken down, glucose diffuses directly across the epithelium cells in the small intestine into the blood.

   a) Explain why this process eventually stops.

   b) By what process is glucose transported from the lumen of the small intestine into the epithelial cells after this point?

Q11 Why are sodium ions important in the transport of glucose from the small intestine into the blood?

Q12 Describe the role of facilitated diffusion in the transport of glucose from the small intestine into the blood.

Exam Tip
Make sure you know the definitions of diffusion and osmosis off by heart.

- Know that the cholera bacterium is an example of a prokaryotic organism.

- Know the structure of prokaryotic cells to include cell wall, cell-surface membrane, capsule, circular DNA, flagella and plasmid.

- Understand that cholera bacteria produce toxins which increase secretion of chloride ions into the lumen of the intestine. This results in severe diarrhoea.

- Understand the use of oral rehydration solutions (ORS) in the treatment of diarrhoeal diseases.

- Be able to discuss the applications and implications of science in developing improved oral rehydration solutions.

- Be able to discuss the ethical issues associated with trialling improved oral rehydration solutions on humans.

Specification Reference 3.1.3

Exam Tip
Questions on the differences between prokaryotic cells and eukaryotic cells (see p.48) come up quite a bit in exams — make sure you know what they are.

6. Cholera

Cholera is a pretty nasty disease, but the good news is we know what causes it and how to cure it...

What is cholera?

Cholera is a disease caused by the bacterium *Vibrio cholerae*, a prokaryotic organism (see below). The bacteria infect the small intestine and produce a toxin that disrupts osmosis in the intestinal cells. The result of this is watery diarrhoea and vomiting.

Every year between three and five million people worldwide contract cholera. It's spread through contaminated food and water and is common in developing countries where populations are overcrowded and sanitation is poor. If left untreated, cholera can quickly cause severe dehydration and death — around 100 000 people die from the disease each year. But with proper treatment to replace the fluids and salts lost in diarrhoea, most people are able to make a full recovery.

Prokaryotic cell structure

Prokaryotes are single-celled organisms, e.g. bacteria. Prokaryotic cells are much smaller and simpler than eukaryotic cells — and they don't have any membrane-bound organelles (like a nucleus). You need to know the structure of a prokaryotic cell and what all the different organelles inside are for — see Figure 1.

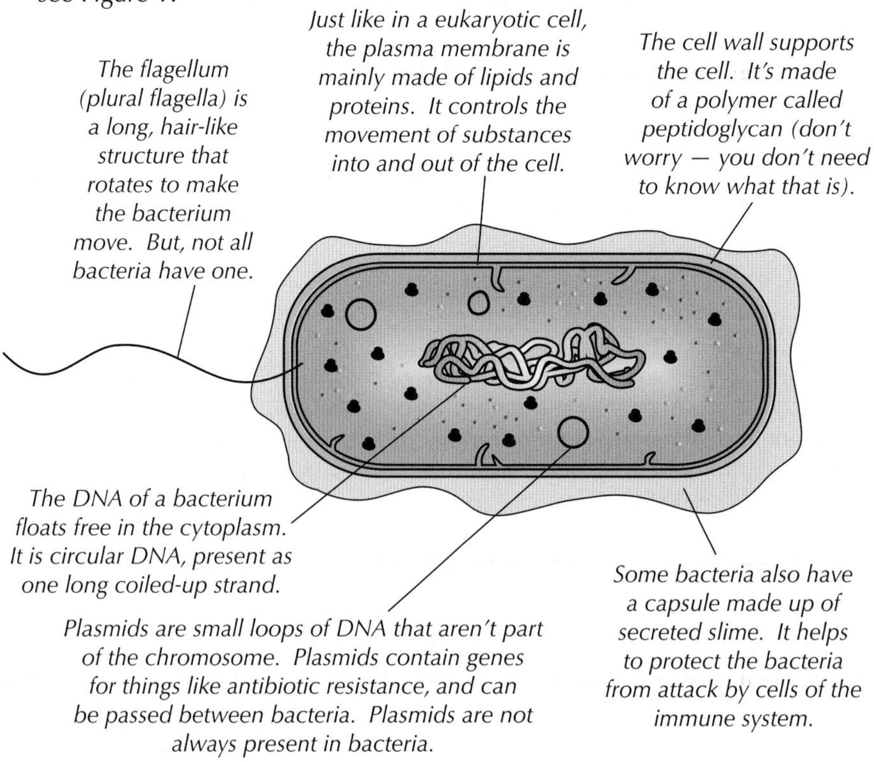

The flagellum (plural flagella) is a long, hair-like structure that rotates to make the bacterium move. But, not all bacteria have one.

Just like in a eukaryotic cell, the plasma membrane is mainly made of lipids and proteins. It controls the movement of substances into and out of the cell.

The cell wall supports the cell. It's made of a polymer called peptidoglycan (don't worry — you don't need to know what that is).

The DNA of a bacterium floats free in the cytoplasm. It is circular DNA, present as one long coiled-up strand.

Plasmids are small loops of DNA that aren't part of the chromosome. Plasmids contain genes for things like antibiotic resistance, and can be passed between bacteria. Plasmids are not always present in bacteria.

Some bacteria also have a capsule made up of secreted slime. It helps to protect the bacteria from attack by cells of the immune system.

Figure 1: *The structure of a prokaryotic cell.*

Of all the features described in Figure 1, only the plasma membrane is also found in eukaryotic cells. (Some eukaryotic cells do have a cell wall, e.g. plant cells, but it isn't made from peptidoglycan.)

Cholera toxin

Cholera bacteria produce a toxin when they infect the body.
This toxin causes a fair old bit of havoc...

- The toxin causes chloride ion protein channels in the plasma membranes of the small intestine epithelial cells to open.

- Chloride ions move into the small intestine lumen. The build up of chloride ions lowers the water potential of the lumen.

- Water moves out of the blood, across the epithelial cells, and into the small intestine lumen by osmosis (to even up the water concentration).

- The massive increase in water secretion into the intestine lumen leads to really, really, really bad diarrhoea — causing the body to become extremely dehydrated.

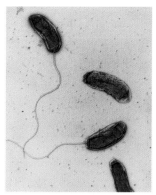

Figure 2: A TEM of Vibrio cholerae.

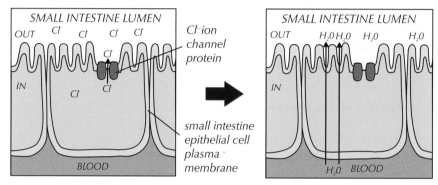

Figure 3: How the cholera toxin causes diarrhoea.

Oral rehydration solutions

People suffering from diarrhoeal diseases like cholera need to replace all the fluid that they've lost in the diarrhoea. The quickest way to do this is by inserting a drip into a person's vein. However, not everywhere in the world has access to drips, so oral rehydration solutions are used instead.

An oral rehydration solution (ORS) is a drink that contains large amounts of salts (such as sodium ions and chloride ions) and sugars (such as glucose and sucrose) dissolved in water. Sodium ions are included to increase glucose absorption (sodium and glucose are co-transported into the epithelium cells in the intestine — see p. 68). Getting the concentration of the ORS right is essential for effective treatment. An ORS is a very cheap treatment and the people administering it don't require much training. This makes it great for treating diarrhoeal diseases in developing countries (where they're a huge problem).

Tip: Glucose is absorbed into the epithelium cells and lowers the water potential of the cells to below that of the intestines. This causes water to move out of the intestines and into the epithelium cells, then the blood by osmosis — replacing the water lost in diarrhoea.

Testing new oral rehydration solutions

ORS are so important in treating diarrhoeal disease that research into the development of new, improved ORS is always being carried out.
But before a new ORS can be put into use, scientists have to show that it's more effective than the old ORS and that it's safe. This is done by clinical testing on humans. There are some ethical issues associated with trialling ORS:

Diarrhoeal diseases mostly affect children, so many trials involve children. Parents decide whether the child will participate in the trial. The child doesn't make their own decision — some people think this is unethical. But scientists believe the treatment must be trialled on children if it's to be shown to be effective against a disease that mainly affects children.

Figure 4: A child in Uganda receiving ORS.

Clinical trials usually involve a blind trial. This is where some patients who are admitted into hospital with diarrhoeal diseases are given the standard ORS and others are given the new ORS. This means that the two can be compared. It's called a blind trial because the patients don't know which treatment they've been given. Some people don't agree with this — they think that people have the right to know and decide on the treatment that they're going to have. Scientists argue that a blind trial is important to eliminate any bias that may skew the data as a result of patients knowing which treatment they've received.

When a new ORS is first trialled, there's no way of knowing whether it'll be better than the current ORS — there is a risk of the patient dying when the original, better treatment was available.

Practice Questions — Fact Recall

Q1 Give three organelles found in a prokaryotic cell and describe the function of each one.

Q2 Explain how the cholera toxin causes diarrhoea.

Q3 What is an oral rehydration solution (ORS) and what is it used for?

Q4 Discuss why some people feel that testing a new oral rehydration solution on a patient with a diarrhoeal disease is unethical.

Section Summary

Make sure you know:

- The structure, function and appearance of the plasma membrane, micovilli, nucleus, mitochondria, lysosomes, ribosomes, endoplasmic reticulum and golgi apparatus.
- The structure of an epithelial cell in the small intestine, as seen under a light microscope.
- How to apply your knowledge of organelles to explain why different cells are suited to their function.
- How to calculate magnification using magnification = length of image ÷ length of specimen.
- The difference between magnification (how much bigger the sample is) and resolution (how detailed).
- The pros and cons of SEMs and TEMs.
- How cell fractionation separates out organelles — homogenisation, filtration and ultracentrifugation.
- The fluid mosaic model for plasma membranes — phospholipid bilayer, proteins, carbohydrates.
- How the fluid mosaic model explains different membrane properties.
- The basic structure of triglycerides (glycerol and three fatty acids) and how they're formed.
- The basic structure of fatty acids, including the difference between saturated and unsaturated.
- The basic structure of a phospholipid — glycerol, two fatty acids and a phosphate group.
- How to carry out the emulsion test — shake sample with ethanol, add to water, milky = lipid present.
- The definitions of diffusion and osmosis, and the factors that affect the rate of diffusion.
- What facilitated diffusion and active transport are, and the role of proteins in these processes.
- How the products of carbohydrate digestion, such as glucose, are absorbed into the body.
- That the cholera bacteria is a prokaryotic organism.
- The structure of prokaryotic cells, including the cell wall, cell-surface membrane, capsule, circular-DNA, flagella and plasmids.
- How the toxin produced by the cholera bacteria causes severe diarrhoea.
- How oral rehydration solutions are used to treat diarrhoeal diseases.
- How oral rehydration solutions are developed and tested (including the ethics of testing them).

Exam-style Questions

1 A scientist is studying secretory epithelial cells from the stomach under a light microscope. The microscope has a magnification of × 100 and a resolution of 0.2 μm.

(a) (i) The ribosomes in the epithelial cells are 25 nm in diameter. Will the scientist be able to see them using the light microscope? Explain your answer.

(2 marks)

(ii) The scientist sees an image of an epithelial cell that is 4 mm in diameter. Calculate the actual diameter of the cell.

(2 marks)

(b) One of the main functions of secretory epithelial cells in the stomach is to produce and secrete digestive enzymes. Suggest one organelle that is likely to be present in large numbers in the epithelial cells to aid this function. Explain your choice.

(2 marks)

(c) The scientist also separated the organelles by cell fractionation in order to study each one individually. Describe and explain the process of cell fractionation.

(6 marks)

2 The graph below shows how a person's blood glucose concentration changes during a five hour period.

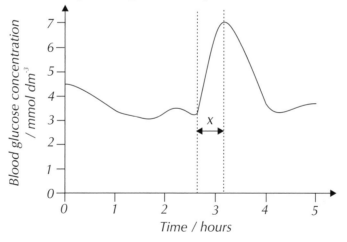

(a) (i) What is the change in blood glucose concentration during the period marked 'X'?

(1 mark)

(ii) Explain the change in blood glucose concentration during the period marked 'X'.

(1 mark)

(iii) Suggest what will happen to the glucose concentration in the small intestine during the same period. Explain your answer.

(2 marks)

(b) Describe how glucose moves out of the lumen of the small intestine and into the blood stream against its concentration gradient.

(5 marks)

3   A group of students investigated the water potential of potato cells.

They cut cubes of potato of equal size and shape, weighed them and placed a single cube into one of four different concentrations of sucrose solution.
One cube was placed in pure water.

They re-weighed each of the cubes every hour and after 12 hours the mass of all the cubes remained constant. The overall change in mass for each cube is shown in the graph below.

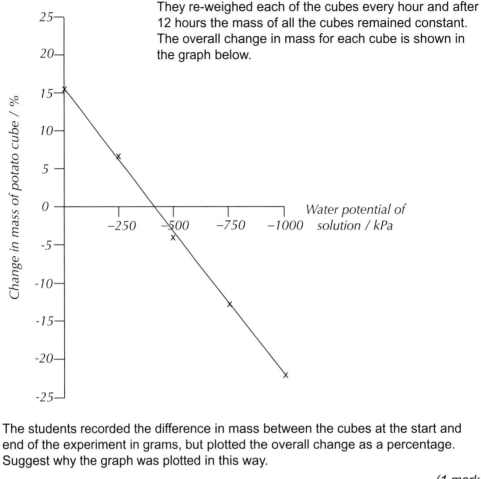

(a)   The students recorded the difference in mass between the cubes at the start and end of the experiment in grams, but plotted the overall change as a percentage. Suggest why the graph was plotted in this way.

(1 mark)

(b)   What was the change in mass for the potato cube placed in pure water?

(1 mark)

(c) (i)   Explain why the cubes in the –500, –750 and –1000 kPa solutions lost mass.

(2 marks)

   (ii)   Use the graph to estimate the water potential of the potato cells.

(1 mark)

(d)   Suggest how the students could make their results more reliable.

(1 mark)

(e)   If the experiment was repeated with cubes that had a larger surface area would you expect the mass of all the cubes to become constant before 12 hours, at 12 hours or after 12 hours? Explain your answer.

(2 marks)

1. Lung Function

The role of your respiratory system is to supply your blood with oxygen, which then gets delivered to all the cells in your body.

The lungs

Humans need to get oxygen into the blood (for respiration) and they need to get rid of carbon dioxide (made by respiring cells). This is where breathing (or ventilation as it's sometimes called) and the lungs come in.

Lung structure

As you breathe in, air enters the trachea (windpipe). The trachea splits into two bronchi — one bronchus leading to each lung. Each bronchus then branches off into smaller tubes called bronchioles. The bronchioles end in small 'air sacs' called alveoli — see Figure 1. This is where gases are exchanged (see page 77). The ribcage, intercostal muscles and diaphragm all work together to move air in and out.

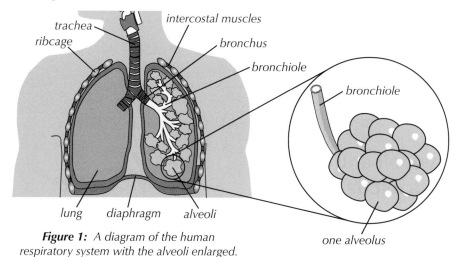

Figure 1: *A diagram of the human respiratory system with the alveoli enlarged.*

Ventilation

Ventilation consists of inspiration (breathing in) and expiration (breathing out).

Inspiration

- The intercostal and diaphragm muscles contract.
- This causes the ribcage to move upwards and outwards and the diaphragm to flatten, increasing the volume of the thorax (the space where the lungs are).
- As the volume of the thorax increases the lung pressure decreases (to below atmospheric pressure).
- This causes air to flow into the lungs — see next page, Figure 3.
- Inspiration is an active process — it requires energy.

Learning Objectives:

- Know the gross structure of the human gas exchange system limited to: the alveoli, bronchioles, bronchi, trachea and lungs.
- Understand the mechanism of breathing.
- Understand the exchange of gases in the lungs.
- Know the essential features of the alveolar epithelium as a surface over which gas exchange takes place.

Specification Reference 3.1.4

Figure 2: *A coloured chest X-ray showing the airways in the lungs (pink).*

Tip: Air always flows from areas of <u>high</u> pressure to areas of <u>low</u> pressure.

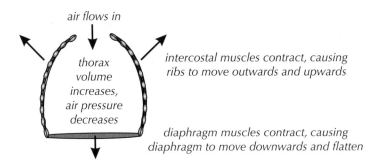

air flows in

thorax volume increases, air pressure decreases

intercostal muscles contract, causing ribs to move outwards and upwards

diaphragm muscles contract, causing diaphragm to move downwards and flatten

Figure 3: Diagram showing what happens during inspiration.

Tip: It's the movement of the ribcage and diaphragm and the change in lung pressure that causes air to flow in and out — not the other way round.

Expiration

- The intercostal and diaphragm muscles relax.
- The ribcage moves downwards and inwards and the diaphragm becomes curved again.
- The thorax volume decreases, causing the air pressure to increase (to above atmospheric pressure).
- Air is forced out of the lungs — see Figure 4.
- Expiration is a passive process — it doesn't require energy.

Tip: Remember, when the diaphragm contracts, it's flat. When it relaxes, it bulges upwards. Think of it like trying to hold your stomach in — you contract your muscles to flatten your stomach and relax to release it.

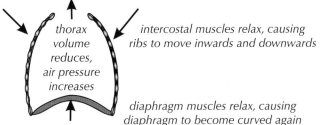

air is forced out

thorax volume reduces, air pressure increases

intercostal muscles relax, causing ribs to move inwards and downwards

diaphragm muscles relax, causing diaphragm to become curved again

Figure 4: Diagram showing what happens during expiration.

Alveoli and gas exchange

Lungs contain millions of microscopic air sacs where gas exchange occurs — called alveoli. The alveoli are surrounded by a network of capillaries — see Figure 6.

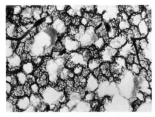

Figure 5: A light micrograph of capillaries surrounding alveoli.

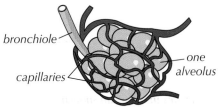

bronchiole

capillaries

one alveolus

Figure 6: Alveoli covered in a network of capillaries.

Alveoli structure

Each alveolus is made from a single layer of thin, flat cells called alveolar epithelium. The walls of the capillaries are made from capillary endothelium — see Figure 7.

The walls of the alveoli contain a protein called elastin. Elastin is elastic — it helps the alveoli to return to their normal shape after inhaling and exhaling air.

Tip: There's more on different types of epithelial tissue on p.50.

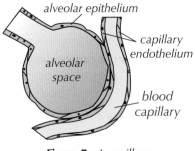

alveolar epithelium

capillary endothelium

alveolar space

blood capillary

Figure 7: A capillary next to an alveolus.

Gas exchange in the alveoli

Oxygen (O_2) diffuses out of the alveoli, across the alveolar epithelium and the capillary endothelium, and into a compound called haemoglobin in the blood. Carbon dioxide (CO_2) diffuses into the alveoli from the blood, and is breathed out — see Figure 8.

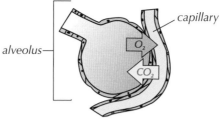

Figure 8: *Gaseous exchange between an alveolus and a capillary.*

Tip: Don't forget, gases pass through <u>two</u> layers of cells (the alveolar epithelium and the capillary endothelium).

Tip: Haemoglobin is found in red blood cells. There's more about it on page 132.

Factors affecting the rate of diffusion

Alveoli have features that speed up the rate of diffusion so gases can be exchanged quickly:

- A thin exchange surface — the alveolar epithelium is only one cell thick. This means there's a short diffusion pathway (which speeds up diffusion).

- A large surface area — there's a large number of alveoli. This means there's a large surface area for gas exchange.

There's also a steep concentration gradient of oxygen and carbon dioxide between the alveoli and the capillaries, which increases the rate of diffusion. This is constantly maintained by the flow of blood and ventilation — see Figure 9.

Tip: Diffusion is the net movement of particles from an area of higher concentration to an area of lower concentration — see page 62 for more.

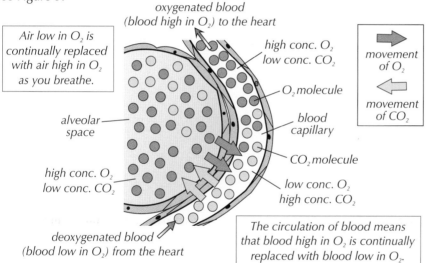

Figure 9: *Diagram showing how O_2 moves from an area of high concentration (inside the alveolus) to low concentration (in the deoxygenated blood).*

Practice Questions — Application

Q1 The diagram below shows a capillary next to an alveolus. Blood flows from X to Y.

a) Which arrow, 1 or 2, indicates the movement of carbon dioxide?

b) At which letter, A, B or C, would you find the highest concentration of oxygen?

c) Blood takes 2 s to flow from X to Y. The distance between X and Y is 0.82 mm. Calculate the speed of blood flow from X to Y, giving your answer in mm s^{-1}.

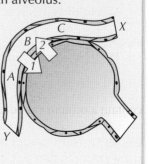

Exam Tip
You need to be able to use maths in the exam — whatever the topic.

Q2 A mountain climber is climbing at altitude, where there's less oxygen. Suggest how this will affect gas exchange in the alveoli.

Q3 One of the effects of severe obesity is that the sufferer cannot fully inhale. Suggest the effect this would have on the rate of diffusion of oxygen.

Q4 The pictures on the right show light micrographs of healthy lung tissue (top) and diseased lung tissue from a patient with emphysema (bottom). The alveoli appear white.

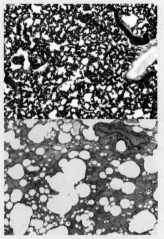

a) Describe the main difference between the healthy lung tissue and the diseased lung tissue.

b) Use your answer to part a) to explain why people with emphysema have a lower level of oxygen in the blood than normal.

Exam Tip
Don't panic if a question asks you about a disease you've never heard of — just apply your knowledge of what you've learnt about how lungs normally work and you'll be able to work out the answer.

Practice Questions — Fact Recall

Q1 The diagram below shows the structure of the human respiratory system. Write down the names of the structures, A to H.

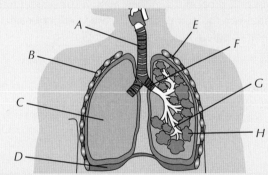

Q2 Describe what happens to make the volume of the thorax increase during inspiration.

Q3 The picture on the right shows the thorax. Which stage of ventilation (inspiration or expiration) does the picture show? Give a reason for your answer.

Q4 Is inspiration an active process or a passive process?

Q5 Describe how oxygen gets from the lungs into the blood.

Q6 Describe the features of alveoli and explain how they affect the rate of diffusion.

Exam Tip
If an exam question asks you about the factors that affect diffusion, remember they speed up or slow down diffusion — don't write about them making diffusion 'better' or 'worse' or else you won't get the marks.

2. Measuring Lung Function

Scientists and doctors measure lung function to see whether a person's lungs are functioning normally or not.

Pulmonary ventilation (PV)

Pulmonary ventilation is a measure of lung function — it's the volume of air taken into the lungs in one minute, measured in dm^3 min^{-1}. You need to learn the equation to calculate it:

> **Pulmonary Ventilation = Tidal volume × Ventilation rate**

Tidal volume is the volume of air in each breath.
Ventilation rate is the number of breaths per minute.

Tip: dm^3 min^{-1} is cubic decimetres per minute. 1 dm^3 is the same as 1 litre, so you might also see PV measured in litres min^{-1}.

Example — calculating pulmonary ventilation

Tidal volume is usually about 0.4 dm^3.
Ventilation rate for a person at rest is about 15 breaths.
So for a normal person at rest...

$$\text{pulmonary ventilation} = \text{tidal volume} \times \text{ventilation rate}$$
$$= 0.4 \ dm^3 \times 15 \ min^{-1}$$
$$= 6 \ dm^3 \ min^{-1}$$

Spirometer traces

A spirometer is a fancy machine that's used to measure the volume of air breathed in and out. It produces a graph called a spirometer trace. You can figure out both tidal volume and ventilation rate from a spirometer trace and use this information to calculate pulmonary ventilation.

Exam Tip
Try using this formula triangle to work out PV, tidal volume or ventilation rate:

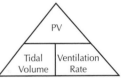

Just put your finger over the one you want and read off the formula.

Example — calculating PV from a spirometer trace

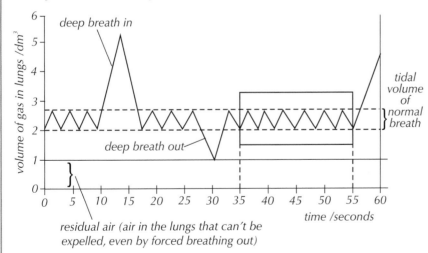

deep breath in

deep breath out

tidal volume of normal breath

residual air (air in the lungs that can't be expelled, even by forced breathing out)

Figure 1: A spirometer trace.

You can calculate the PV in the boxed area of the trace like this:

- Tidal volume in boxed area = 2.7 − 2 = 0.7 dm^3
- Ventilation rate in boxed area = 6 breaths in 20 s = 18 breaths in 1 minute (6 × 3 = 18) = 18 min^{-1}
- PV = tidal volume × ventilation rate = 0.7 × 18 = 12.6 dm^3 min^{-1}

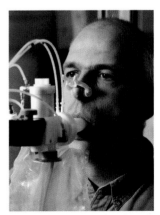

Figure 2: Testing a patient's respiratory function using a spirometer.

Practice Questions — Application

Q1 a) A doctor measures a patient's lung function. She measures the volume of air in each breath as 0.5 dm³. The patient takes 24 breaths in 90 seconds. Calculate their pulmonary ventilation.

b) The doctor measures another patient's lung function. They take 70 breaths in 300 seconds and their PV is 7.84 dm³ min⁻¹. Calculate their tidal volume.

c) The final patient has 0.41 dm³ air in each breath. His PV is 8.2 dm³ min⁻¹. Calculate his ventilation rate.

Tip: Use the formula triangle on the previous page to help you with these calculations.

Q2 The graph below shows the volume of gas in a person's lungs at rest.

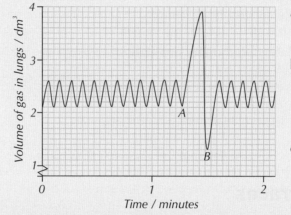

a) What happened between points A and B?

b) What is the person's residual volume? Give your answers in litres.

c) Use the graph to calculate PV.

Q3 The graph below shows the volume of gas in another person's lungs. They started exercising after 30 seconds.

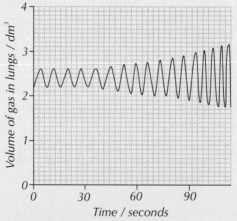

Exam Tip
Make sure you look carefully at the axes of any graph you get in the exam. For example, it could be the volume of gas in the spirometer, not the lungs, that's plotted on the y-axis.

a) Describe and explain two features of the graph which show that the person is exercising.

b) Calculate the percentage increase in tidal volume, from when the person is at rest to when they are breathing most deeply.

c) Use the information in the graph to explain how exercise affects pulmonary ventilation.

Practice Questions — Fact Recall

Q1 Give the definition of the following:
a) pulmonary ventilation,
b) tidal volume,
c) ventilation rate.

Q2 What are the units of pulmonary ventilation?

Q3 Give the equation for calculating pulmonary ventilation.

3. Lung Diseases

Unfortunately, lungs don't always work perfectly. There are various lung diseases that affect ventilation and reduce the rate of gas exchange between the alveoli and the capillaries. Here are the ones you need to know about...

Pulmonary tuberculosis (TB)

Pulmonary tuberculosis is a lung disease caused by the bacterium *Mycobacterium tuberculosis*.

Infection

When someone becomes infected with tuberculosis bacteria, immune system cells build a wall around the bacteria in the lungs. This forms small, hard lumps known as tubercles — see Figure 1. Infected tissue within the tubercles dies and the gaseous exchange surface is damaged, so tidal volume is decreased.

Tuberculosis also causes fibrosis (see next page), which further reduces the tidal volume. If the bacteria enter the bloodstream, they can spread to other parts of the body.

Symptoms

Common symptoms include a persistent cough, coughing up blood and mucus, chest pains, shortness of breath and fatigue. Sufferers may also have a fever. Many lose weight due to a reduction in appetite.

Many people with tuberculosis are asymptomatic — they're infected but they don't show any symptoms, because the infection is in an inactive form. People who are asymptomatic are unable to pass the infection on. But if they become weakened, for example by another disease or malnutrition, then the infection can become active. They'll show the symptoms and be able to pass on the infection.

Transmission

TB is transmitted by droplet infection — when an infected person coughs or sneezes, tiny droplets of saliva and mucus containing the bacteria are released from their mouth and nose (see Figure 2). If an uninfected person breathes in these droplets, the bacteria are passed on.

Tuberculosis tends to be much more widespread in areas where hygiene levels are poor and where people live in crowded conditions. TB can be prevented with the BCG vaccine, and can be treated with antibiotics.

Learning Objectives:

- Know the course of infection, symptoms and transmission of pulmonary tuberculosis.

- Know the effects of fibrosis, asthma and emphysema on lung function.

- Be able to explain the symptoms of diseases and conditions affecting the lungs in terms of gas exchange and respiration.

Specification Reference 3.1.4

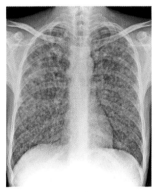

Figure 1: *A coloured X-ray of a patient with pulmonary tuberculosis. The tubercles are shown in pink.*

Figure 2: *A high speed photograph of a sneeze.*

Practice Questions — Application

Q1 Which one of the spirometer traces below is from a patient with TB, A or B? Give a reason for your answer.

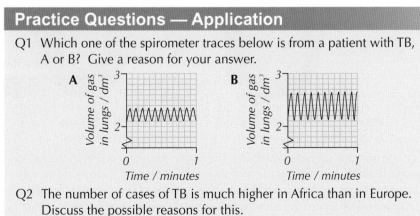

Q2 The number of cases of TB is much higher in Africa than in Europe. Discuss the possible reasons for this.

Fibrosis

Fibrosis is the formation of scar tissue in the lungs (see Figure 3). This can be the result of an infection or exposure to substances like asbestos or dust. Scar tissue is thicker and less elastic than normal lung tissue. This means that the lungs are less able to expand and so can't hold as much air as normal — the tidal volume is reduced. It's also harder to force air out of the lungs due to the loss of elasticity.

Fibrosis reduces the rate of gas exchange in the alveoli because diffusion is slower across a thicker scarred membrane. Less oxygen is able to diffuse into the bloodstream, the body cells receive less oxygen and the rate of aerobic respiration in cells is reduced. This means less energy is released and sufferers often feel tired and weak.

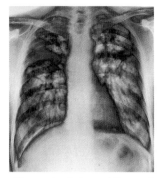

Figure 4: *Coloured X-ray of a patient with lung fibrosis. Scar tissue between the alveoli is shown in red.*

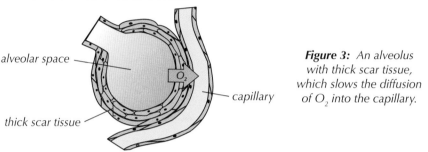

alveolar space

thick scar tissue

capillary

Figure 3: *An alveolus with thick scar tissue, which slows the diffusion of O_2 into the capillary.*

As well as fatigue and weakness, symptoms of fibrosis include shortness of breath, a dry cough, chest pain. Fibrosis sufferers have a faster breathing rate than normal — to get enough air into their lungs to oxygenate their blood.

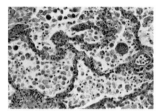

Figure 5: *A light micrograph of fibrosis in lung tissue. The dark bands show the thick scar tissue.*

Asthma

Asthma is a respiratory condition where the airways become inflamed and irritated. The causes vary from case to case but it's usually because of an allergic reaction to substances such as pollen and dust.

During an asthma attack, the smooth muscle lining the bronchioles contracts and a large amount of mucus is produced (see Figure 6). This causes constriction of the airways, making it difficult for the sufferer to breathe properly. Air flow in and out of the lungs is severely reduced, so less oxygen enters the alveoli and moves into the blood. This means the body cells receive less oxygen and the rate of aerobic respiration in cells is reduced.

Tip: An asthma attack narrows the bronchioles, not the trachea or alveoli.

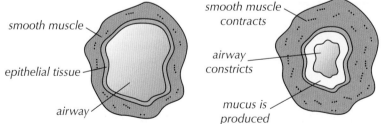

smooth muscle

epithelial tissue

airway

smooth muscle contracts

airway constricts

mucus is produced

Figure 6: *A cross section through a healthy bronchiole (left) and a bronchiole of someone suffering from an asthma attack (right).*

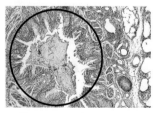

Figure 7: *A lung section showing a constricted bronchiole (circled).*

Symptoms include wheezing (the sound you hear when someone has difficulty breathing), a tight chest and shortness of breath. During an attack the symptoms come on very suddenly. They can be relieved by drugs (often in inhalers) which cause the muscle in the bronchioles to relax, opening up the airways.

Emphysema

Emphysema is a lung disease caused by smoking or long-term exposure to air pollution — foreign particles in the smoke (or air) become trapped in the alveoli. This causes inflammation, which attracts phagocytes to the area.

The phagocytes produce an enzyme that breaks down the protein elastin — see page 76. Loss of elastin means the alveoli can't recoil to expel air as well (it remains trapped in the alveoli). It also leads to destruction of the alveoli walls, which reduces the surface area of the alveoli — see Figure 8. This reduces the rate of gas exchange in the alveoli, similar to fibrosis and asthma. The lack of oxygen reaching the cells leaves sufferers feeling tired and weak (again, just like in fibrosis).

Symptoms of emphysema include shortness of breath and wheezing. People with emphysema have an increased breathing rate as they try to increase the amount of air (containing oxygen) reaching their lungs.

Tip: A phagocyte is a type of white blood cell that carries out phagocytosis — see page 12 for more.

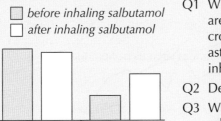

an alveolus

less surface area for gas exchange

Figure 8: *Cross-section of healthy alveoli (top) and damaged alveoli (bottom).*

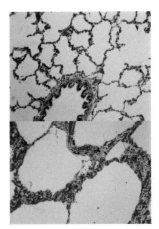

Figure 9: *Light micrographs of healthy lung tissue (top) and diseased lung tissue in a patient with emphysema (bottom).*

Practice Questions — Application

The graph below shows the median area of a bronchial cross-section in healthy volunteers and in people with asthma. The areas were measured both before and after a drug called salbutamol was inhaled.

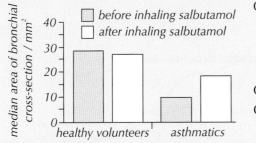

Q1 What was the median area of a bronchial cross-section in the asthmatics before inhaling salbutamol?

Q2 Describe the data.

Q3 What do you think salbutamol is used for? Explain your answer.

Practice Questions — Fact Recall

Q1 Name the bacterium that causes pulmonary tuberculosis.

Q2 Describe in detail how TB is transmitted.

Q3 How can TB be prevented?

Q4 A person with fibrosis has a reduced tidal volume. Explain why.

Q5 Explain why the rate of gaseous exchange in someone with fibrosis is slower than in a healthy person.

Q6 What is asthma?

Q7 Explain how the symptoms of an asthma attack can be relieved.

Q8 Name one cause of emphysema.

Q9 Give two symptoms of emphysema.

4. Interpreting Lung Disease Data

Learning Objectives:

- Be able to interpret data relating to the effects of pollution and smoking on the incidence of lung disease.
- Be able to analyse and interpret data associated with specific risk factors and the incidence of lung disease.
- Be able to recognise correlations and causal relationships.

Specification Reference 3.1.4

It's common for exam questions to include a graph or two, so you could well get asked to interpret some data on lung diseases.

HOW SCIENCE WORKS

Risk factors, correlation and cause

All diseases have factors that will increase a person's chance of getting that disease. These are called **risk factors**. For example, it's widely known that if you smoke you're more likely to get lung cancer (smoking is a risk factor for lung cancer). This is an example of a **correlation** — a link between two things (see page 5). However, a correlation doesn't always mean that one thing causes the other. Smokers have an increased risk of getting cancer but that doesn't necessarily mean smoking causes the disease — there are lots of other factors to take into consideration.

You need to be able to describe and analyse data given to you in your exams. Over the next three pages are some examples of the kind of thing you might get.

Tip: 'Incidence' just means the number of new cases of a disease.

Tip: A risk factor is just something that <u>increases</u> the chance of getting a disease. Having a risk factor doesn't mean you'll definitely get the disease though, it just makes it more likely.

Exam Tip
Always read graph axes and figure labels carefully. For example, this graph shows the rate per 100 000 population — so in 1982, 80 men per 100 000 people died of lung cancer in Northern Ireland.

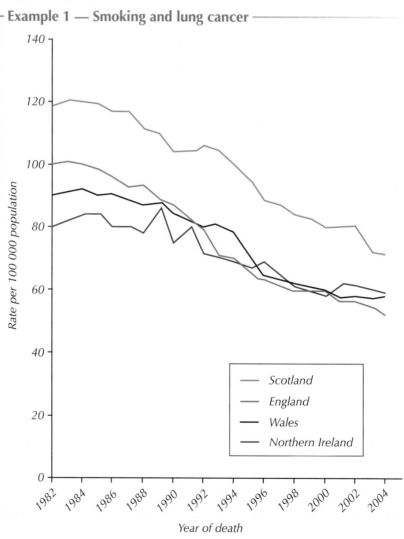

Example 1 — Smoking and lung cancer

Figure 1: A graph of age-standardised mortality rates for male lung cancer in England, Scotland, Wales and Northern Ireland.

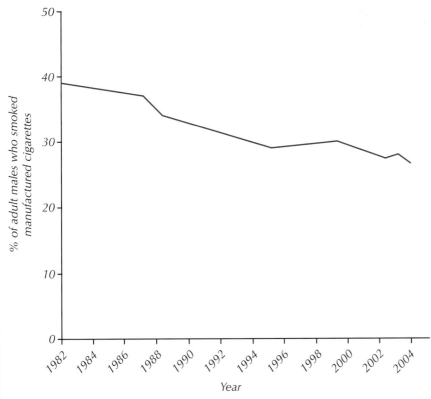

Figure 2: A graph to show the percentage of males aged 16 and over who smoked manufactured cigarettes in Great Britain.

You might be asked to:

1. Describe the data

Figure 1 shows that the male lung cancer mortality (death) rate decreased between 1982 and 2004 for each of the countries shown. Easy enough so far.

Figure 2 shows that the number of adult males in Great Britain (England, Wales and Scotland) who smoke decreased between 1982 and 2004.

2. Draw conclusions

You need to be careful what you say here. There's a correlation (link) between the number of males who smoked and the mortality rate for male lung cancer. But you can't say that one caused the other. There could be other reasons for the trend, e.g. deaths due to lung cancer may have decreased because less asbestos was being used in homes (not because fewer people were smoking).

Other points to consider

Figure 1 shows mortality (death) rates. The rate of cases of lung cancer may have been increasing but medical advances may mean more people were surviving (so only mortality was decreasing).

It would also be helpful to know more about how the information was collected. For example, the graph in Figure 2 was probably produced by doing a survey. But we don't know how big the sample size was or how the men chosen to take part were picked — if the sample size was too small or the men weren't chosen at random, then the results may not be very reliable.

Exam Tip
It's always a good idea to pick out some numbers from a graph when describing data.

Tip: Mortality rate is the number of deaths in a population in a set period of time (e.g. a year). Morbidity rate is the number of people with a disease in a population in a set period of time.

Example 2 — Air pollution and asthma

Figure 3 shows the number of new cases of asthma per 100 000 of the population diagnosed in the UK from 1996 to 2000. Figure 4 shows the emissions (in millions of tonnes) of sulfur dioxide (an air pollutant) from 1996 to 2000 in the UK.

Tip: Figure 4 shows sulfur dioxide emissions in millions of tonnes. So there were 2 million tonnes of emissions in 1996 — not 2 tonnes.

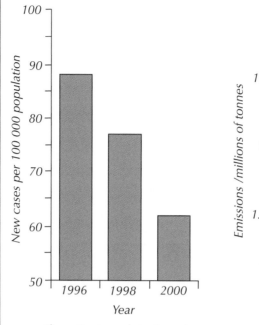

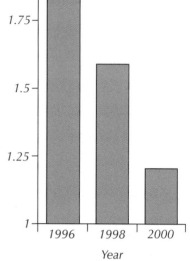

Figure 3: *A graph to show the rates of new cases of asthma 1996-2000 in the UK.*

Figure 4: *A graph to show the emission of sulfur dioxide between 1996 and 2000 in the UK.*

You might be asked to describe the data...

Figure 3 shows that the number of new cases of asthma in the UK fell between 1996 and 2000, from 87 to 62 per 100 000 people.

Figure 4 shows that the emissions of sulfur dioxide in the UK fell between 1996 and 2000, from 2 to 1.2 million tonnes.

... or draw conclusions

Tip: There's loads more about interpreting data on pages 3-5.

Be careful what you say when drawing conclusions. Here there's a link between the number of new cases of asthma and emissions of sulfur dioxide in the UK — the rate of new cases of asthma has fallen as sulfur dioxide emissions have fallen. You can't say that one causes the other though because there could be other reasons for the trend, e.g. the number of new cases of asthma could be falling due to the decrease in the number of people smoking. You can't say the reduction in asthma cases is linked to a reduction in air pollution (in general) either as only sulfur dioxide levels were studied.

Other points to consider:

Tip: Always try to think about other factors that could be affecting results.

Figure 3 shows new cases of asthma. The rate of new cases may be decreasing but existing cases may be becoming more severe. The emissions were for the whole of the UK but air pollution varies from area to area, e.g. cities tend to be more polluted. The asthma data doesn't take into account any other factors that may increase the risk of developing asthma, e.g. allergies, smoking, etc.

The graph below shows the per capita consumption of tobacco and the death rates for COPD (chronic obstructive pulmonary disease, which includes emphysema) from 1945 to 1998 in Australia.

Tip: <u>Per capita</u> basically just means <u>per person</u>.

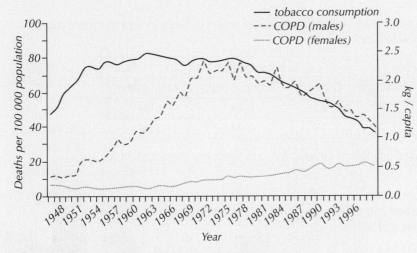

Q1 Describe in detail the trend in male COPD.

Q2 A scientist concludes from this data that COPD in women is not caused by smoking. Discuss this claim.

Section Summary

Make sure you know...

- The structure of the human gas exchange system, from the trachea to the alveoli.
- How the ribcage, intercostal muscles and diaphragm all work together during ventilation.
- About the exchange of oxygen and carbon dioxide in the alveoli.
- The features of alveoli that affect the rate of diffusion — a thin exchange surface, a large surface area and a steep concentration gradient of oxygen and carbon dioxide.
- The importance of blood circulation and ventilation in maintaining the steep concentration gradient of oxygen and carbon dioxide between the alveoli and the capillaries.
- That pulmonary ventilation is the volume of air taken into the lungs in one minute, tidal volume is the volume of air in each breath and ventilation rate is the number of breaths per minute.
- That pulmonary ventilation = tidal volume × ventilation rate.
- The units of pulmonary ventilation ($dm^3 \ min^{-1}$), tidal volume (dm^3) and ventilation rate (min^{-1}).
- How to work out tidal volume and ventilation rate from a graph.
- That pulmonary tuberculosis (TB), fibrosis, asthma and emphysema are all lung diseases.
- The course of infection, symptoms and transmission of TB.
- The effects of fibrosis, asthma and emphysema on lung function.
- How to interpret data on lung disease and explain what the data shows.
- The difference between correlation (a link between two things) and cause (one thing makes the other thing happen).
- How to draw conclusions from data on lung disease.

Exam-style Questions

1   The table below shows the approximate composition of oxygen and carbon dioxide in inhaled and exhaled air.

	% composition			
	Nitrogen	Oxygen	Carbon dioxide	Other gases
Inhaled air	78	21	0.04	0.96
Exhaled air	78	17	4.04	0.96

(a) (i) Express the ratio of oxygen in inhaled air to oxygen in exhaled air in its simplest form.

(1 mark)

(ii) Describe and explain the difference between the composition of inhaled air and the composition of exhaled air.

(3 marks)

(b)   Describe the processes of inspiration and expiration.

(6 marks)

(c)   Oxygen tents contain a higher percentage of oxygen than normal air.
Patients suffering from fibrosis may benefit from being inside an oxygen tent.

(i) What is fibrosis?

(1 mark)

(ii) Explain what effect fibrosis has on gaseous exchange in the alveoli.

(2 marks)

(iii) Suggest how being in an oxygen tent might benefit a patient with fibrosis.

(2 marks)

2   The photographs on the right show a scanning electron micrograph of alveoli in a healthy human lung (left) and the effects of emphysema on the alveoli (right). The magnification is x 60.

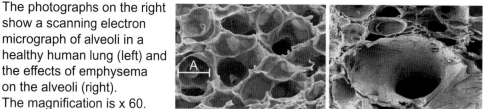

(a)   Calculate the actual width of the labelled alveolus, A. Give your answer in μm.

(2 marks)

(b)   Describe one difference between the healthy alveoli and the diseased alveoli, and explain what effect this would have on gaseous exchange in the alveoli.

(3 marks)

(c) (i) Give one cause of emphysema.

(1 mark)

(ii) Give one symptom of emphysema and explain why this symptom occurs.

(2 marks)

3   A spirometer trace of a person at rest is shown on the right.

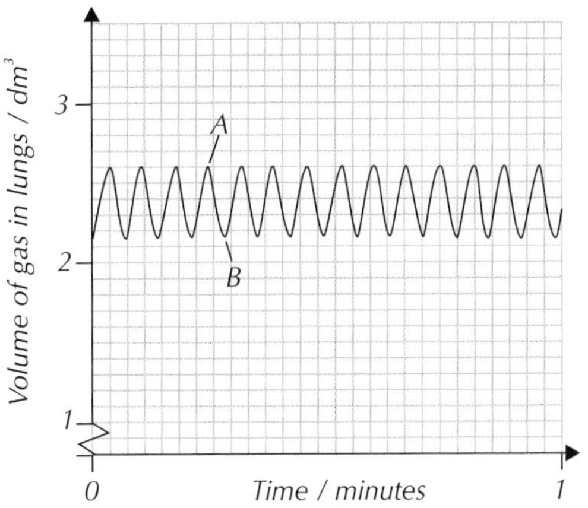

(a)   What happened between points A and B?

(1 mark)

(b)   Calculate the person's tidal volume.

(1 mark)

(c)   Suggest how the person's pulmonary ventilation would change if they were to start exercising. Explain your answer.

(3 marks)

(d)   The person suffers from asthma. Occasionally they have an asthma attack.

   (i)   Describe what happens in the respiratory system when someone has an asthma attack.

(3 marks)

   (ii)   Give one way in which you would expect the graph above to differ during an asthma attack, and explain the cause of this difference.

(2 marks)

   (iii)   Someone having an asthma attack may use an inhaler containing muscle relaxant drugs. Suggest how the drugs might relieve the symptoms of an asthma attack.

(1 mark)

4   The graph on the right shows the number of reported cases of tuberculosis (TB) in the UK between 2000 and 2009.

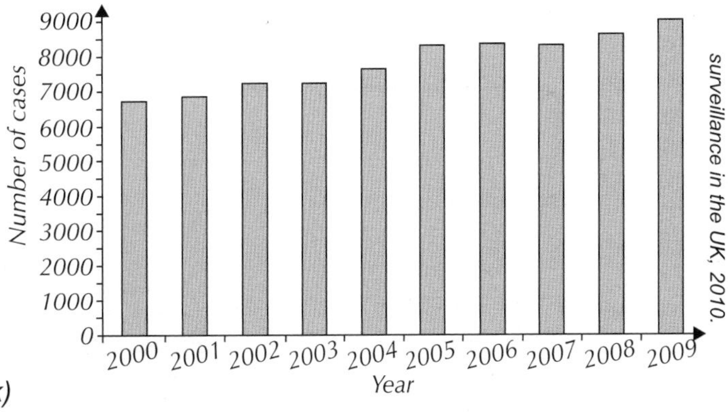

Figure adapted from Tuberculosis in the UK: Annual report on tuberculosis surveillance in the UK, 2010.

(a) (i)   Describe the trend in the number of reported TB cases in the UK between 2000 and 2009.

(1 mark)

   (ii)   Calculate the approximate percentage increase in the number of cases of reported TB in the UK between 2003 and 2009. Show your working.

(2 marks)

   (iii)   A newspaper headline states that "The number of TB cases in England is predicted to rise by 33% by the year 2018". Discuss this claim using the information in the graph.

(3 marks)

(b)   The incidence of TB in the UK is comparatively low. Discuss the reasons why the UK has a comparatively low incidence of TB.

(5 marks)

Tip: Right side of the heart = deoxygenated blood (blue). Left side of the heart = oxygenated blood (pink).

Lungs

Rest of Body

1. The Heart

Your heart is responsible for pumping blood all around your body, through your blood vessels. So it's quite important really...

The structure of the heart

Figure 1 below shows the internal structure of the heart.
The right side pumps deoxygenated blood to the lungs and the left side pumps oxygenated blood to the whole body. Note — the left and right sides are reversed on the diagram, cos it's the left and right of the person that the heart belongs to.

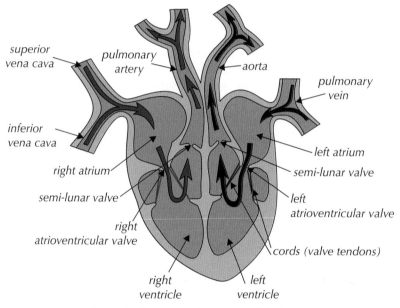

Figure 1: The internal structure of the heart.

Each bit of the heart is adapted to do its job effectively.

- The **left ventricle** of the heart has thicker, more muscular walls than the right ventricle, because it needs to contract powerfully to pump blood all the way round the body. The right side only needs to get blood to the lungs, which are nearby.

- The **ventricles** have thicker walls than the atria, because they have to push blood out of the heart whereas the atria just need to push blood a short distance into the ventricles.

- The **atrioventricular (AV) valves** link the atria to the ventricles and stop blood flowing back into the atria when the ventricles contract.

- The **semi-lunar (SL) valves** link the ventricles to the pulmonary artery and aorta, and stop blood flowing back into the heart after the ventricles contract.

- The **cords** attach the atrioventricular valves to the ventricles to stop them being forced up into the atria when the ventricles contract.

Heart valves

The valves only open one way — whether they're open or closed depends on the relative pressure of the heart chambers. If there's higher pressure behind a valve, it's forced open, but if pressure is higher in front of the valve it's forced shut — see Figure 2.

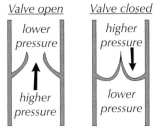

Valve open   *Valve closed*

lower pressure   higher pressure

higher pressure   lower pressure

Figure 2: *Diagram showing how heart valves open and close.*

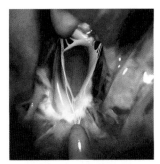

Figure 3: *A heart valve.*

Control of heart beat

Cardiac (heart) muscle is 'myogenic' — this means that it can contract and relax without receiving signals from nerves. This pattern of contractions controls the regular heartbeat.

The process starts in the **sino-atrial node (SAN)**, which is in the wall of the right atrium. The SAN is like a pacemaker — it sets the rhythm of the heartbeat by sending out regular waves of electrical activity to the atrial walls. This causes the right and left atria to contract at the same time. A band of non-conducting collagen tissue prevents the waves of electrical activity from being passed directly from the atria to the ventricles. Instead, these waves of electrical activity are transferred from the SAN to the **atrioventricular node (AVN)**.

The AVN is responsible for passing the waves of electrical activity on to the bundle of His. But, there's a slight delay before the AVN reacts, to make sure the ventricles contract after the atria have emptied. The **bundle of His** is a group of muscle fibres responsible for conducting the waves of electrical activity to the finer muscle fibres in the right and left ventricle walls, called the **Purkyne fibres**. The Purkyne fibres carry the waves of electrical activity into the muscular walls of the right and left ventricles, causing them to contract simultaneously, from the bottom up.

Exam Tip
You should always use the phrase 'waves of electrical activity'. Don't use 'signals' or 'waves of excitement' or 'messages'.

Exam Tip
Remember that there's a delay before the AVN reacts. Don't write in the exam that there is a delay in the wave of electrical activity reaching the AVN.

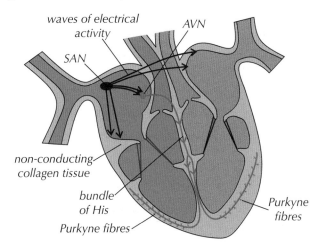

waves of electrical activity   AVN

SAN

non-conducting collagen tissue

bundle of His

Purkyne fibres

Purkyne fibres

Figure 4: *The pathway of electrical activity in the heart.*

Tip: Remember the route of the waves of electrical activity by Silly Ants Have Pants — SAN, AVN, bundle of His, Purkyne fibres.

Cardiac output

Cardiac output is the volume of blood pumped by the heart per minute (measured in cm^3 per minute). It's calculated using this formula:

cardiac output = stroke volume × heart rate

- **Heart rate** — the number of heartbeats per minute. You can measure your heart rate by feeling your pulse, which is basically surges of blood forced through the arteries by the heart contracting.
- **Stroke volume** — the volume of blood pumped during each heartbeat, measured in cm^3.

Examples

Calculating cardiac output

If you have a stroke volume of 70 cm^3 and a heart rate of 75 beats per minute, your cardiac output is:

cardiac output = stroke volume × heart rate
$$= 70 \times 75 = 5250 \ cm^3 \text{ per minute}$$

Calculating stroke volume

If you have a heart rate of 80 beats per minute and a cardiac output of 5440 cm^3 per minute, your stroke volume is:

$$\text{stroke volume} = \frac{\text{cardiac output}}{\text{heart rate}} = \frac{5440}{80} = 68 \ cm^3$$

Calculating heart rate

If you have a stroke volume of 68 cm^3 and a cardiac output of 4896 cm^3 per minute, your heart rate is:

$$\text{heart rate} = \frac{\text{cardiac output}}{\text{stroke volume}} = \frac{4896}{68} = 72 \text{ beats per minute}$$

Practice Questions — Application

Q1 Some people suffer from valve regurgitation. This is where the heart valves don't close properly. Describe the effect that valve regurgitation of the semi-lunar valves would have on blood flow in the heart.

Q2 If you have a stroke volume of 61 cm^3 and a heart rate of 79 beats per minute, what is your cardiac output?

Q3 If you have a stroke volume of 72.5 cm^3 and a cardiac output of 5075 cm^3 per minute, what is your heart rate?

Q4 If you have a heart rate of 75 beats per minute and a cardiac output of 5175 cm^3 per minute, what is your stroke volume?

Q5 If you have a stroke volume of 0.067 L and a heart rate of 76 beats per minute, what is your cardiac output?

Q6 If you have a stroke volume of 0.071 L and a cardiac output of 5538 cm^3 per minute, what is your heart rate?

Q7 If you have a heart rate of 74 beats per minute and a cardiac output of 5402 cm^3 per minute, what is your stroke volume in litres?

Tip: Cardiac output increases when you exercise.

Exam Tip
Use the formula triangle below to help you rearrange the formula for cardiac output.

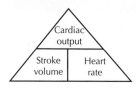

Put your finger over the bit of the triangle that corresponds to what you want to find, then read off the correct formula.

Tip: Convert litres to cm^3 by multiplying by 1000, e.g. 0.07 L × 1000 = 70 cm^3. Convert cm^3 to litres by dividing by 1000, e.g. 68 cm^3 ÷ 1000 = 0.068 L.

Exam Tip
Don't forget that stroke volume needs to be in cm^3, in order to work out cardiac output in cm^3 per minute.

The cardiac cycle

The cardiac cycle is an ongoing sequence of contraction and relaxation of the atria and ventricles that keeps blood continuously circulating round the body. The volume of the atria and ventricles changes as they contract and relax. Pressure changes also occur, due to the changes in chamber volume (e.g. decreasing the volume of a chamber by contraction will increase the pressure of a chamber). The cardiac cycle can be simplified into three stages.

Tip: Cardiac contraction is also called systole, and relaxation is called diastole.

1. Ventricles relax, atria contract

The ventricles are relaxed. The atria contract, decreasing the volume of the chamber and increasing the pressure inside the chamber. This pushes the blood into the ventricles. There's a slight increase in ventricular pressure and chamber volume as the ventricles receive the ejected blood from the contracting atria.

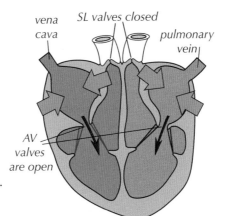

vena cava — SL valves closed — pulmonary vein

AV valves are open

Tip: Contraction of the atria or ventricles is a bit like squeezing a balloon — the size of the balloon decreases and the pressure inside it increases.

2. Ventricles contract, atria relax

The atria relax. The ventricles contract (decreasing their volume), increasing their pressure. The pressure becomes higher in the ventricles than the atria, which forces the AV valves shut to prevent back-flow. The pressure in the ventricles is also higher than in the aorta and pulmonary artery, which forces open the SL valves and blood is forced out into these arteries.

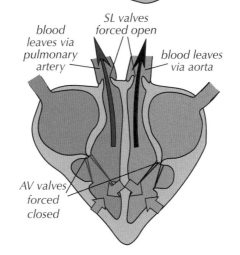

blood leaves via pulmonary artery — SL valves forced open — blood leaves via aorta

AV valves forced closed

Tip: Remember that if there's a higher pressure in front of a valve it's forced shut and if there's a higher pressure behind a valve it's forced open (see page 91).

3. Ventricles relax, atria relax

The ventricles and the atria both relax. The higher pressure in the pulmonary artery and aorta closes the SL valves to prevent back-flow into the ventricles.

Blood returns to the heart and the atria fill again due to the higher pressure in the vena cava and pulmonary vein. In turn this starts to increase the pressure of the atria. As the ventricles continue to relax, their pressure falls below the pressure of the atria and so the AV valves open. This allows blood to flow passively (without being pushed by atrial contraction) into the ventricles from the atria. The atria contract, and the whole process begins again.

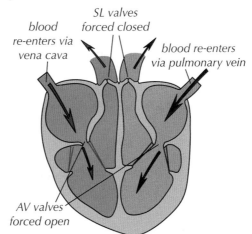

blood re-enters via vena cava — SL valves forced closed — blood re-enters via pulmonary vein

AV valves forced open

Exam Tip
When writing about the cardiac cycle in the exam, make sure you always name the valves.

Tip: Remember that it's the change in volume in a chamber that causes the change in pressure — see page 93.

Tip: At point A, the AV valves are shut because the pressure is higher in front of the AV valves, i.e. in the ventricles.

Tip: mmHg is a unit of measurement for pressure. It means millimetres of mercury.

Interpreting data on the cardiac cycle

You may well be asked to analyse or interpret data about the changes in pressure and volume during the cardiac cycle. Here are two examples of the kind of things you might get:

Example 1

If you get a graph you could be asked questions like this:

When does blood start flowing into the aorta?
At point A, the ventricles are contracting (and the AV valves are shut), forcing blood into the aorta.

Why is ventricular volume decreasing at point B?
The ventricles are contracting, reducing the volume of the chamber.

Are the semi-lunar valves open or closed at point C? Closed.
The ventricles are relaxed and refilling, so the pressure is higher in the pulmonary artery and aorta, forcing the SL valves closed.

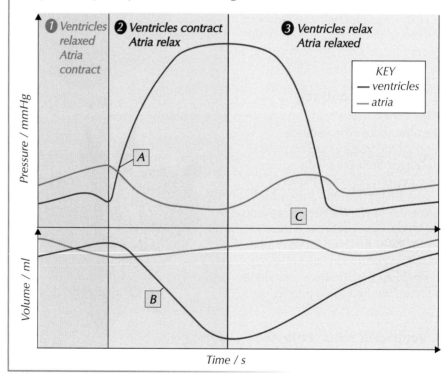

Example 2

You may have to describe the changes in pressure and volume shown by a diagram, like the one below. In this diagram the AV valves are open. So you know that the pressure in the atria is higher than in the ventricles. So you also know that the atria are contracting because that's what causes the increase in pressure.

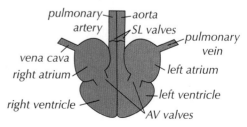

Exam Tip
In the exam, the heart might not always be drawn like the one we've shown on the right. Don't let this throw you — just look to see where the valves are and whether they're opened or closed, then answer the questions.

Practice Questions — Application

The diagram below shows pressure changes in the cardiac cycle.

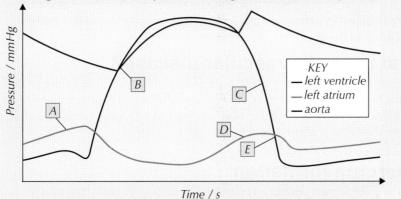

Time / s

Q1 Why is the atrial pressure increasing at point A?

Q2 Is the semi-lunar valve open or closed at point B?
Explain your answer.

Q3 Why is the ventricular pressure decreasing at point C?

Q4 Why is the atrial pressure increasing at point D?

Q5 Is the atrioventricular valve open or closed at point E?
Explain your answer.

Tip: The left ventricle has a thicker wall than the right ventricle and so it contracts more forcefully. This means the pressure is higher in the left ventricle (and in the aorta).

Exam Tip
In the exam, if you're given a graph like the one on the left, make sure you read the key carefully so that you don't get the lines mixed up and answer the question incorrectly.

Practice Questions — Fact Recall

Q1 Which side of the heart pumps deoxygenated blood?

Q2 The diagram on the right shows the heart. Name the structures labelled A to H.

Q3 Why does the left ventricle of the heart have thicker, more muscular walls than the right ventricle?

Q4 a) Name the valves that link the ventricles to the aorta and pulmonary artery.

b) What is the function of these valves?

Q5 Cardiac muscle is described as 'myogenic'. Explain what this means.

Q6 What is the function of the SAN?

Q7 Name the tissue that prevents electrical signals passing directly from the atria to the ventricles.

Q8 Describe the role of the bundle of His.

Q9 State the formula for working out cardiac output.

Q10 What is the cardiac cycle?

Q11 When the atria contract, describe the pressure and volume changes that take place in the atria.

Tip: To answer Q3 on the left, think about where the left and right ventricles are pumping blood to.

Exam Tip
Make sure you learn the formula for cardiac output — you won't be given it in the exam.

Learning Objectives:
- Know that atheroma is the presence of fatty material within the walls of arteries.
- Understand the link between atheroma and the increased risk of aneurysm and thrombosis.
- Know what myocardial infarction is and how it's caused in terms of an interruption to the blood flow to heart muscle.

Specification Reference 3.1.5

2. Cardiovascular Disease

Your circulatory system keeps you going by constantly supplying all parts of your body with oxygen and glucose for respiration. However, sometimes things can go wrong...

What is cardiovascular disease?

Cardiovascular disease is a general term used to describe diseases associated with the heart and blood vessels. Cardiovascular diseases include aneurysms, thrombosis and myocardial infarction — see page 97. Most cardiovascular disease starts with atheroma formation.

Atheroma formation

The wall of an artery is made up of several layers (see p. 166). The endothelium (inner lining) is usually smooth and unbroken. If damage occurs to the endothelium (e.g. by high blood pressure), white blood cells (mostly macrophages) and lipids (fat) from the blood, clump together under the lining to form fatty streaks.

Over time, more white blood cells, lipids and connective tissue build up and harden to form a fibrous plaque called an atheroma — see Figure 1. This plaque partially blocks the lumen of the artery and restricts blood flow, which causes blood pressure to increase.

Exam Tip
In the exam, don't write that atheromas are made up of fatty acids — they're made up of fatty material (lipids).

Exam Tip
Remember that atheromas form under the endothelium of an <u>artery</u>. Don't write that they form in veins, capillaries or blood vessels.

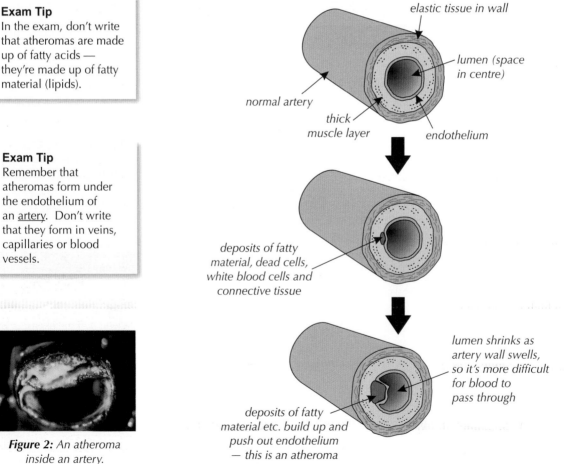

Figure 2: An atheroma inside an artery.

Figure 1: The process of atheroma formation.

Aneurysm

An aneurysm is a balloon-like swelling of the artery. It starts with the formation of atheromas. Atheroma plaques damage and weaken arteries. They also narrow arteries, increasing blood pressure. When blood travels through a weakened artery at high pressure, it may push the inner layers of the artery through the outer elastic layer to form an aneurysm. This aneurysm may burst, causing a haemorrhage (bleeding).

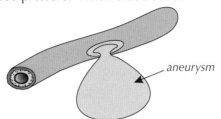

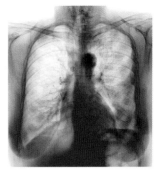

Figure 3: An x-ray of an aneurysm (red balloon) in the aorta.

Thrombosis

Thrombosis is the formation of a blood clot. It also starts with the formation of atheromas. An atheroma plaque can rupture (burst through) the endothelium (inner lining) of an artery. This damages the artery wall and leaves a rough surface. Platelets and fibrin (a protein) accumulate at the site of damage and form a **blood clot** (a thrombus). This blood clot can cause a complete blockage of the artery, or it can become dislodged and block a blood vessel elsewhere in the body. Debris from the rupture can cause another blood clot to form further down the artery.

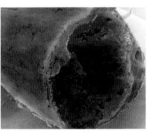

Figure 5: A blood clot in an artery.

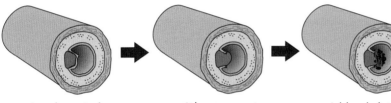

| An atheroma forms. | Atheroma ruptures the endothelium. | A blood clot forms. |

Figure 4: Formation of a blood clot.

Myocardial infarction (heart attack)

The heart muscle is supplied with blood by the **coronary arteries** — see Figure 7. This blood contains the oxygen needed by heart muscle cells to carry out respiration. If a coronary artery becomes completely blocked (e.g. by a blood clot) an area of the heart muscle will be totally cut off from its blood supply, receiving no oxygen. This causes a myocardial infarction — more commonly known as a heart attack — see Figure 6.

A heart attack can cause damage and death of the heart muscle. Symptoms include pain in the chest and upper body, shortness of breath and sweating. If large areas of the heart are affected complete heart failure can occur, which is often fatal.

Exam Tip
To gain full marks for explaining how a myocardial infarction is caused, you need to be specific about where the blockage is, i.e. in the coronary arteries.

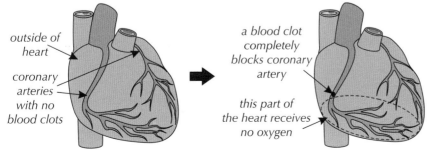

Figure 6: How a heart attack is caused.

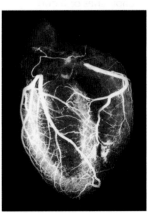

Figure 7: The coronary arteries.

Practice Questions — Application

Q1 A stroke occurs when the blood supply to part of the brain is cut off. It can be caused by an artery to the brain bursting and leading to a haemorrhage (bleeding). Suggest what disease might have caused this artery to burst.

Q2 Thrombocytosis is where a person has an abnormally high level of platelets in their blood. Explain whether this would be likely to increase or decrease a person's risk of thrombosis.

Q3 Angina is chest pain caused by the coronary arteries becoming narrowed by atheromas.

a) Describe how an atheroma can form in a coronary artery.

b) Suggest what heart problem a person with angina is at an increased risk of suffering from.

Q4 Aspirin can be used in low doses to reduce the risk of a person suffering from a heart attack. Aspirin inhibits the production of thromboxane. Thromboxane causes platelets to clump together at the site of damage on an artery wall. Use your knowledge to explain how aspirin can reduce the risk of suffering from a heart attack.

Exam Tip
Don't be put off by an unfamiliar context in an exam question — it will still be testing a point on the specification. For example, Q3 on the right is about angina, but it's testing what you know about atheroma formation and its effects.

Practice Questions — Fact Recall

Q1 What is an atheroma?

Q2 Where exactly does an atheroma form in an artery?

Q3 Give two effects an atheroma has on the artery it's in.

Q4 The diagram below shows an artery.
Name the structures labelled A to C.

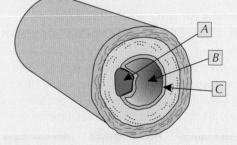

Q5 a) What is an aneurysm?

b) How is an aneurysm formed?

Q6 What is the name given to the formation of a blood clot?

Q7 What is the name of the arteries that supply the heart muscle with blood?

Q8 What is a myocardial infarction?

Tip: Don't get atheromas mixed up with aneurysms. An atheroma can lead to the formation of an aneurysm.

Tip: To help you answer Q6 on the right, remember that a blood clot can also be called a thrombus.

3. Risk Factors and Coronary Heart Disease (CHD)

Learning Objectives:

- Know the following risk factors associated with coronary heart disease: high blood pressure, blood cholesterol, diet and cigarette smoking.
- Be able to describe and explain data relating to the relationship between specific risk factors and the incidence of coronary heart disease.

Specification Reference 3.1.5

There are quite a few things that increase your risk of getting atheromas in your coronary arteries, like smoking and too much salt in your diet. So, avoid these risk factors, and you'll lower your risk.

What is coronary heart disease?

Coronary heart disease is when the coronary arteries have lots of atheromas in them, which restricts blood flow to the heart. It's a type of cardiovascular disease.

Atheromas can also cause blood clots to form (see p. 96). A blood clot could block flow of blood to the heart muscle, possibly resulting in myocardial infarction (see p. 97).

Common risk factors

High blood pressure

High blood pressure increases the risk of damage to the coronary artery walls. Damaged walls have an increased risk of atheroma formation, causing a further increase in blood pressure. So anything that increases blood pressure also increases the risk of CHD, e.g. being overweight, not exercising and excessive alcohol consumption.

Figure 1: The link between high blood pressure, CHD and myocardial infarction.

Exam Tip
It's not a good idea to write about high blood pressure 'putting a strain on the heart' — you need to be more technically accurate and write about it increasing the risk of damage to artery walls.

High blood cholesterol and poor diet

If the blood cholesterol level is high (above 240 mg per 100 cm³) then the risk of coronary heart disease is increased. This is because cholesterol is one of the main constituents of the fatty deposits that form atheromas.

A diet high in **saturated fat** is associated with high blood cholesterol levels. A diet high in **salt** also increases the risk of cardiovascular disease because it increases the risk of high blood pressure.

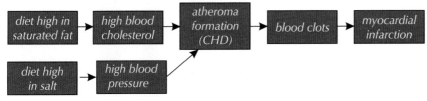

Figure 2: The link between a diet high in saturated fat or salt, CHD and myocardial infarction.

Exam Tip
Don't refer to atheromas 'furring up arteries' — they are fibrous plaques (containing fatty material) that narrow the lumen of arteries.

Exam Tip
In the exam, don't write about 'bad cholesterol' — you won't get a mark for it.

Cigarette smoking

Both carbon monoxide and nicotine, found in cigarette smoke, increase the risk of coronary heart disease and myocardial infarction.

Carbon monoxide combines with haemoglobin and reduces the amount of oxygen transported in the blood, and so reduces the amount of oxygen available to tissues. If heart muscle doesn't receive enough oxygen it can lead to a heart attack.

Tip: A risk factor is something that increases your chance of developing a disease.

Smoking also decreases the amount of antioxidants in the blood — these are important for protecting cells from damage. Fewer antioxidants means cell damage in the coronary artery walls is more likely, and this can lead to atheroma formation.

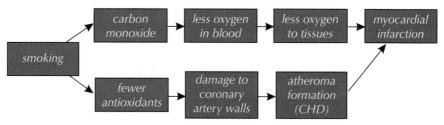

Figure 3: The link between smoking, CHD and myocardial infarction.

Reducing the risk

Most of these factors are within our control — a person can choose to smoke, eat fatty foods, etc. However, some risk factors can't be controlled, such as having a genetic predisposition to coronary heart disease or having high blood pressure as a result of another condition, e.g. some forms of diabetes. Even so, the risk of developing CHD can be reduced by removing as many risk factors as you possibly can.

Interpreting data on risk factors and CHD

Take a look at the following example of the sort of study you might see in your exam.

Example

The graph shows the results of a study involving 34 439 male British doctors. Questionnaires were used to find out the smoking habits of the doctors. The number of deaths among the participants from ischaemic heart disease (coronary heart disease) was counted, and adjustments were made to account for differences in age.

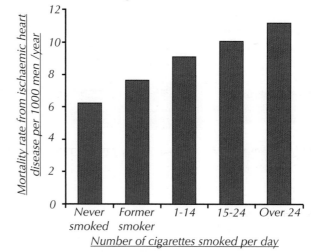

Here are some of the things you might be asked to do:

Describe the data — The number of deaths from ischaemic heart disease increased as the number of cigarettes smoked per day increased. Fewer former smokers and non-smokers died of ischaemic heart disease than smokers.

Draw conclusions — The graph shows a positive correlation between the number of cigarettes smoked per day by male doctors and the mortality rate from ischaemic heart disease.

Explain the link — You may get asked to explain the link between the risk factor under investigation (smoking) and CHD. E.g. carbon monoxide in cigarette smoke combines with haemoglobin, reducing the amount of oxygen transported in the blood. This reduces the amount of oxygen available to tissues, including heart muscle, which could lead to a heart attack. You would also talk about antioxidants (see previous page).

Check any conclusions are valid — make sure the conclusions match the data, e.g. this study only looked at male doctors — no females were involved, so you can't say that this trend is true for everyone. Also, you couldn't say smoking more cigarettes causes an increased risk of heart disease. The data shows deaths only and specifically from ischaemic heart disease. It could be that the morbidity rate (the number who have heart disease) decreases with the number of cigarettes a day. But you can't tell that from this data.

Comment on the reliability of the results — For example:

- A large sample size was used — 34 439, which increases reliability.
- People (even doctors) can tell porkies on questionnaires, reducing the reliability of results.

Practice Questions — Application

In a US study, a computer model was used to predict how interventions to reduce some CHD risk factors could affect the number of new cases of CHD per year. The results are shown in the graph below. The results for reducing salt intake are based on the highest estimates from the study.

Q1 Describe the effect that reducing salt intake by 1 g per day could have on the number of new cases of CHD per year in the US.

Q2 How many fewer new cases of CHD could there be by reducing BMI by 5% in obese adults, compared to reducing tobacco use/exposure by 50%?

Q3 Use evidence from the graph to suggest which intervention the US public should be encouraged to carry out and why.

Q4 a) Describe the trend shown on the graph between reducing salt intake and the number of new cases of CHD per year.

   b) Explain this trend.

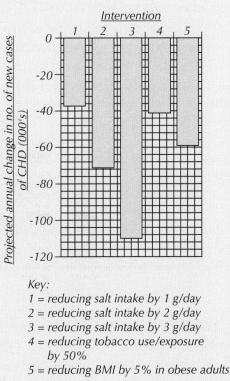

Key:
1 = reducing salt intake by 1 g/day
2 = reducing salt intake by 2 g/day
3 = reducing salt intake by 3 g/day
4 = reducing tobacco use/exposure by 50%
5 = reducing BMI by 5% in obese adults

Tip: An intervention to reduce a risk factor could be a change in diet or lifestyle.

Tip: You need to be really careful when reading complex graphs — make sure you pay attention to the key and axes, so that you know exactly what the graph is showing you.

Tip: BMI (body mass index) is the relationship between weight and height — it's used as a measure of obesity.

Practice Questions — Fact Recall

Q1 What is coronary heart disease?

Q2 Explain how high blood cholesterol leads to an increased risk of having a heart attack.

Q3 a) Explain a way in which smoking leads to an increased risk of coronary heart disease.

    b) Carbon monoxide is found in cigarette smoke. Explain how carbon monoxide leads to an increased risk of having a heart attack.

Q4 a) Explain how high blood pressure leads to an increased risk of coronary heart disease.

    b) Give three things that can cause an increase in blood pressure.

Section Summary

Make sure you know...

- The internal structure of the heart — vena cava, pulmonary artery, aorta, pulmonary vein, right atrium, left atrium, semi-lunar valves, atrioventricular valves, cords, right ventricle and left ventricle.
- That the right side of the heart pumps deoxygenated blood and the left side pumps oxygenated blood.
- How heart valves work — if there's a higher pressure behind a valve, it's forced open, but if pressure is higher in front of the valve it's forced shut.
- That the heart muscle is myogenic — it can contract and relax without receiving signals from nerves.
- The roles of the following structures in controlling the heartbeat: SAN — sets the heartbeat rhythm, AVN — passes on the waves of electrical activity to the bundle of His, Bundle of His — passes on the waves of electrical activity to the Purkyne fibres, Purkyne fibres — pass on the waves of electrical activity to the muscular walls of the right and left ventricles.
- What cardiac output is and the equation: cardiac output = stroke volume × heart rate.
- The cardiac cycle, including pressure changes, volumes changes and valve movements.
- How to analyse and interpret data relating to pressure and volume changes during the cardiac cycle.
- That an atheroma is a hard, fibrous plaque under the endothelium of an artery. It's formed from the build up of white blood cells, lipids and connective tissue at the site where an artery is damaged.
- That an aneurysm is a balloon-like swelling of an artery. It's caused by blood pushing the inner layer of the artery out through the elastic layer, at a weakened site along the artery wall.
- That thrombosis is the formation of a blood clot — fibrin and platelets accumulate at a site of damage along the artery wall, to form a blood clot.
- That myocardial infarction is a heart attack, caused by a coronary artery becoming completely blocked, so that part of the heart muscle receives no oxygen.
- The risk factors of CHD — high blood pressure, diet, blood cholesterol and cigarette smoking.
- How to describe and explain data on the relationship between risk factors and CHD.

Exam-style Questions

1   The diagram below shows the three main stages of the cardiac cycle.

1. Ventricles relax, atria contract

2. Ventricles contract, atria relax

3. Ventricles relax, atria relax

(a)   Describe and explain the pressure changes in the atria in the first and second stages of the cardiac cycle.

(4 marks)

(b) (i)   Name the valves that connect the atria to the ventricles and describe their function.

(2 marks)

   (ii)   During stages one and two, are these valves open or closed? Explain your answer(s).

(2 marks)

(c)   During stage three, why does the pressure of the atria increase?

(1 mark)

(d)   The volume of blood pumped from each turn of the cardiac cycle is called the stroke volume. A hospital patient has a heart rate of 76 beats per minute and a cardiac output of 5.244 L per minute. Calculate their stroke volume.

(2 marks)

2   A scientist was investigating the link between poor diet and coronary heart disease (CHD). He took 1000 British men, aged 40-60 years old and put them into two groups. One group were given dietary information on how to reduce their risk of CHD, e.g. by lowering their saturated fat intake. The other group weren't given any information. The scientist recorded any deaths from CHD over ten years.

(a)   What is the name given to the group of men who weren't given any information?

(1 mark)

(b)   Give two ways in which the study could have been made more reliable.

(2 marks)

(c)   Explain how a diet high in saturated fat and high in salt can lead to an increase in atheromas in the coronary arteries.

(5 marks)

(d)   Other than a poor diet, give two more risk factors for coronary heart disease.

(2 marks)

3   Some people suffer from a disease called third-degree atrioventricular block —
the waves of electrical activity from the sino-atrial node (SAN) are not relayed to
the atrioventricular node (AVN). A pacemaker can be fitted to take over this role.
The diagram below shows a heart with a pacemaker attached.

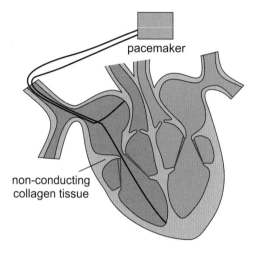

(a)   On the diagram label the position of the AVN, the right ventricle
and the pulmonary vein.

(3 marks)

(b)   What is the purpose of the non-conducting collagen tissue
shown on the diagram?

(1 mark)

(c)   Explain why the pacemaker must be programmed to have a delay
between receiving waves of electrical activity from the SAN and
activating the AVN?

(2 marks)

(d)   Describe the passage of the waves of electrical activity from the
AVN to rest of the heart, causing the ventricles to contract.

(3 marks)

4   Glyceryl trinitrate is the active chemical in a spray used to relieve chest pain in
people with coronary heart disease. It works by widening the coronary arteries.

(a)   Suggest why a person with coronary heart disease would benefit from a
drug that widens the coronary arteries.

(1 mark)

(b)   People with coronary heart disease have an increased risk of blood clots.
Explain how a blood clot is formed.

(3 marks)

(c)   Chest pain could be the sign of a myocardial infarction.
Explain how a myocardial infarction is caused.

(3 marks)

1. Causes of Variation

Variety is the spice of life. When you look around, no two individuals are exactly the same... this is because of variation.

Variation

Variation is the differences that exist between individuals.
There are two types:

Interspecific

The variation that exists between different species.
For example, horses vary from ducks, which vary from mice.

Intraspecific

The differences that occur within a species. For example, the number of 'eyes' on peacocks' feathers, or the length of giraffes' necks.

Causes of intraspecific variation

Although individuals of the same species may appear similar, no two individuals are exactly alike. Variation can be caused by genetic factors, environmental factors or both.

Genetic factors

All the members of a species have the same genes — that's what makes them the same species. But individuals within a species can have different versions of those genes — called **alleles**. The alleles an organism has make up its **genotype**. Different genotypes result in variation in **phenotype** — the characteristics displayed by an organism.

┌─ Examples ─────────────────────

Variation in humans caused by genetic factors include:

- Eye colour (which can be blue, green, grey, brown),
- Blood type (O, A, B or AB).

You inherit your genes from your parents. This means genetic variation is inherited.

Environmental factors

The appearance (phenotype) of an individual is also affected by the environment.

┌─ Examples ─────────────────────

- Plant growth is affected by the amount of minerals, such as nitrate and phosphate, available in the soil.
- Fur colour of the Himalayan rabbit is affected by temperature. Most of the rabbits' fur is white except the ears, nose, feet and tail, which are black (see Figure 1). The black colour only develops in temperatures below 25 °C. If a patch of their white fur is shaved and a cold pad applied to the shaved area, the hair that grows back will be black.

Learning Objectives:

- Know that variation exists between members of a species.
- Know that similarities and differences between individuals within a species may be the result of genetic factors, differences in environmental factors, or a combination of both.
- Be able to appreciate the tentative nature of any conclusions that can be drawn relating to the causes of variation.

Specification Reference 3.2.1

Tip: Take a look at page 120 for more on alleles.

Tip: Don't get inter- and intra-specific variation mixed up. If you're struggling, just remember — int**er** means diff**er**ent species. intr**a** means the s**a**me species.

Figure 1: *The black colour of a Himalayan rabbit's fur is affected by the environment.*

Figure 2: *These identical twins have different hairstyles so show environmental variation.*

Tip: Expression of most genes is influenced by the environment in some way or other.

- Identical twins are genetically identical — they have the same alleles, so any differences between them will be due to the environment (see Figure 2). For example, they may have had different illnesses that affected their development or, if they grew up in different areas, they may have different accents.

Genes and the environment

Variation is often a combination of genetic and environmental factors. An individual may have the genetic information for a particular characteristic, but environmental factors may affect the expression of this characteristic.

┌ **Examples** ─────────────────────────

- A person might have the genes to potentially grow to be six foot tall. Whether or not they grow to this height will depend on environmental factors such as their diet and health.
- The amount of melanin (pigment) people have in their skin is partially controlled by their genes, but skin colour is also influenced by the amount of sunlight a person is exposed to.

Drawing conclusions about the causes of variation

In any group of individuals there's a lot of variation — think how different all your friends are. It's not always clear whether the variation is caused by genes, the environment or both. Scientists draw conclusions based on the information they have until new evidence comes along that challenges it — have a look at these two examples:

┌ **Example 1 — Overeating** ─────────────

Overeating was thought to be caused only by environmental factors, like an increased availability of food in developed countries. It was later discovered that food consumption increases brain dopamine levels in animals. Once enough dopamine was released, people would stop eating.

Researchers discovered that people with one particular allele had 30% fewer dopamine receptors. They found that people with this particular allele were more likely to overeat — they wouldn't stop eating when dopamine levels increased. Based on this evidence, scientists now think that overeating has both genetic and environmental causes.

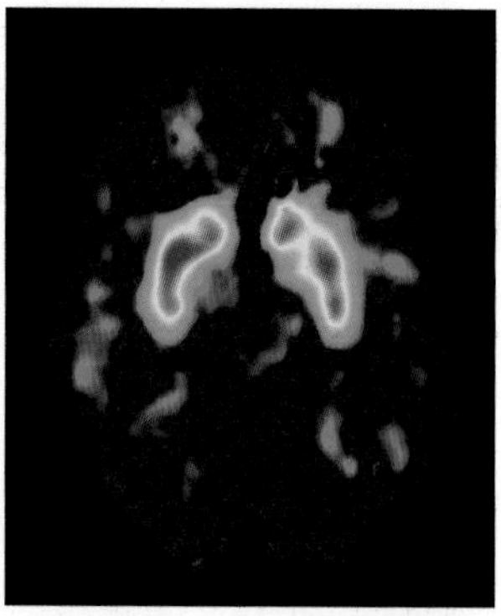

Figure 3: *A coloured PET scan showing a slice through the brain. Brighter areas show high dopamine activity.*

┌ **Example 2 — Antioxidants** ─────────────

Many foods in our diet contain antioxidants — compounds that are thought to play a role in preventing chronic diseases. Foods such as berries contain high levels of antioxidants. Scientists thought that the berries produced by different species of plant contained different levels of antioxidants because of genetic factors.

But experiments that were carried out to see if environmental conditions affected antioxidant levels found that environmental conditions caused a great deal of variation. Scientists now believe that antioxidant levels in berries are due to both genetic and environmental factors.

Twin studies

Studies of identical twins are extremely useful when trying to determine what's due to environmental factors and what's due to genetic factors. These twins are genetically identical, so any differences in phenotype must be entirely due to environmental factors. If a characteristic is very similar in identical twins, genetics probably plays a more important role. But if a characteristic is different between the twins, the environment must have a larger influence.

Practice Question — Application

Q1 A twin study was performed to determine whether head circumference is influenced mainly by environmental factors or by genetic factors. 25 pairs of identical twins were selected for the study and the mean difference in the head circumference of each pair was calculated. The same was done for 25 pairs of non-identical siblings and 25 pairs of unrelated individuals. The results are shown on the right.

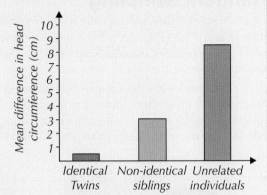

a) Describe the data.

b) Do you think that genetic or environmental factors have a larger effect on head circumference? Explain your answer.

A similar study was performed on adults to determine the effects of genetic and environmental factors on activity levels. Pairs of identical twins, pairs of non-identical siblings and pairs of unrelated individuals were asked to wear a pedometer and the mean difference in steps taken per day was recorded. The results are shown on the right.

c) Explain what the results show about the role of genetics in determining activity levels.

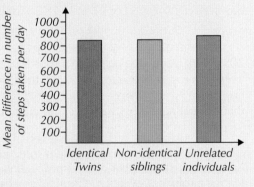

Tip: It's not always clear what the main cause if variation is, so you need to be careful when drawing any conclusions about variation.

Practice Questions — Fact Recall

Q1 What is interspecific variation?

Q2 What is intraspecific variation?

Q3 Give one example of a characteristic that is only influenced by genetic factors.

Q4 Give one example of a characteristic that is influenced by both genetic factors and environmental factors.

2. Investigating Variation

Sometimes it's helpful to know whether variations in a population are primarily due to genetics or the environment. The next few pages are all about how variation is studied and how data on variation is analysed.

Population samples

When studying variation you usually only look at a sample of the population, not the whole thing. For most species it would be too time-consuming or impossible to catch all the individuals in the group. So samples are used as models for the whole population.

Random sampling

Because sample data will be used to draw conclusions about the whole population, it's important that it accurately represents the whole population and that any patterns observed are tested to make sure they're not due to chance.

To make sure the sample isn't **biased**, it should be random. For example, if you were looking at plant species in a field you could pick random sample sites by dividing the field into a grid and using a random number generator to select coordinates — see Figure 1.

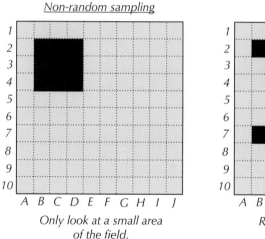
Non-random sampling
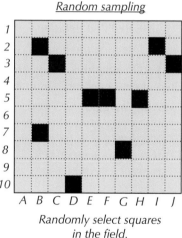
Random sampling

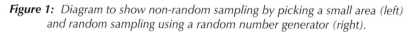

Only look at a small area of the field.

Randomly select squares in the field.

Figure 1: *Diagram to show non-random sampling by picking a small area (left) and random sampling using a random number generator (right).*

To ensure any variation observed in the sample isn't just due to chance, it's important to analyse the results statistically. This allows you to be more confident that the results are true and therefore will reflect what's going on in the whole population.

Analysing and interpreting variation data

You might be asked to analyse and interpret data relating to interspecific and intraspecific variation in your exam. Often this will involve:

- Describing data.

- Drawing conclusions.

- Suggesting reasons for any differences.

The examples on the next page will give you an idea of what you might get...

The graph below shows the growth of two different species of plant in the same environment. You might be asked to:

Describe the data...

- The largest number of plants are 30-39 cm tall for species A and 10-19 cm tall for species B.

- Species A plants range in height from 20-59 cm but the range is larger for species B (0-59 cm).

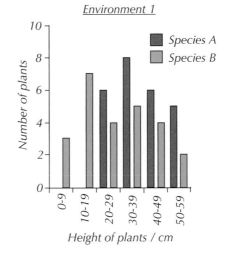

Environment 1

...or draw conclusions

There is interspecific variation in plant height — Species A plants are generally taller than Species B. Both species show intraspecific variation — plant height varies for both species. There is more intraspecific variation in species B — the range of heights is bigger.

Tip: Questions where you have to describe a graph come up on exams a lot — so make sure you know the key features to describe.

Tip: The range is the difference between the biggest and the smallest number.

...or suggest a reason for the differences

A and B are separate species, grown in the same area. This means their genes are different but their environment is the same. So any interspecific variation in height is down to genetic factors, not the environment.

The graph below shows the same two species of plant but grown in a different environment than in the first graph. You might be asked to:

Describe the data...

- E.g. the largest number of plants are 40-49 cm tall for species A and 20-29 cm tall for species B.

- The range in height is 20-59 cm for species A and 10-59 cm for species B.

- You may have to compare the data between the two graphs. E.g. for species A, the plants are generally taller in environment 2. The range in height has stayed the same. For species B, the plants are also generally taller in environment 2, but the range in height is smaller.

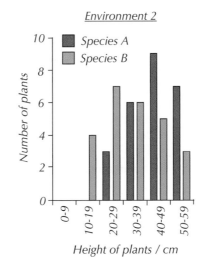

Environment 2

Tip: When comparing two data sets, remember to mention things that are the same as well as things that are different.

...or draw conclusions and suggest a reason for the differences

- Both species are generally taller in environment 2 than in environment 1. So, variation in height is affected by environmental factors.

- Species A shows similar height variation in both environments. The variation in species B differs between the two environments. This suggests that environmental factors influence height more in species B.

Mean and standard deviation

You can use the mean and standard deviation to measure how much variation there is in a sample.

Mean

The mean value tells you the average of the values collected in a sample. It can be used to tell if there is variation between samples.

┌─ **Examples** ────────────────────────────────────

- The mean height of a species of tree in woodland A = 26 m, woodland B = 32 m and woodland C = 35 m. So the mean height varies.

- The mean number of leaves on a clover plant in field X = 3, field Y = 3 and field Z = 3. So the mean number of leaves does not vary.
└──

Most samples will include values either side of the mean, so you end up with a bell-shaped graph — this is called a **normal distribution** (see Figure 2). A normal distribution is symmetrical about the mean.

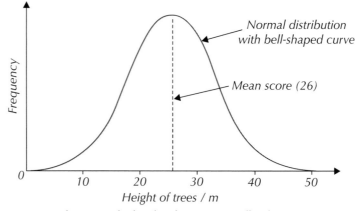

Normal distribution with bell-shaped curve

Mean score (26)

Figure 2: The height of trees in woodland A.

Standard deviation

The standard deviation tells you how much the values in a single sample vary. It's a measure of the spread of values about the mean. Sometimes you'll see the mean written as, for example, 9 ± 3. This means that the mean is 9 and the standard deviation is 3, so the values range from 6 to 12.

Both of the examples below show a normal distribution. However, the values in a sample can vary a little or a lot:

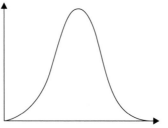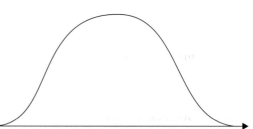

When all the values are similar, so vary little, the graph is steep and the standard deviation is small.

When all the values vary a lot, the graph is fatter and the standard deviation is large.

Tip: If you've forgotten how to calculate the mean, you just add all the values together and divide by the number of values that there are.

Tip:
Normal distribution (symmetrical):

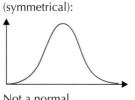

Not a normal distribution (skewed):

Exam Tip
You won't get marks for describing the standard deviation as the spread of results — it's the spread of values <u>about the mean</u>.

Exam Tip
Don't worry — you don't need to be able to calculate standard deviation in the exam.

Height of trees in
woodland A:
mean = 26,
standard deviation = 3

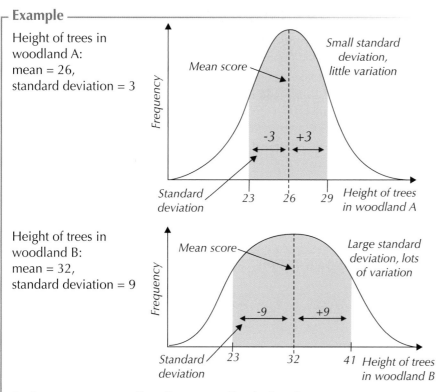

Height of trees in
woodland B:
mean = 32,
standard deviation = 9

So the trees are generally taller in woodland B but there's a greater variation
in height, compared to species A.

Tip: Values with a
larger standard deviation
show greater variation.

Practice Questions — Application

The graph below shows the wing spans of two different species of bird,
both of which live in the same area of woodland.

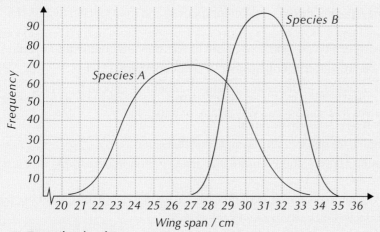

Q1 a) Describe the data.

b) Which species shows a greater variation in wingspan?
Explain your answer.

c) Suggest a reason for the difference in wing span between
species A and B. Give a reason for your answer.

Q2 How much longer is species B's mean wing span than species A's?
Give your answer as a percentage.

Exam Tip
Always show your
working in calculation
questions — don't just
guess an answer. You'll
pick up marks for using
the correct method,
even if your final answer
is wrong.

Q1 Explain why scientists generally only look at a sample of a population and not the whole population.

Q2 How can you make sure that a sample isn't biased?

Q3 Which of the graphs below (A,B or C) show the shape of a normal distribution curve?

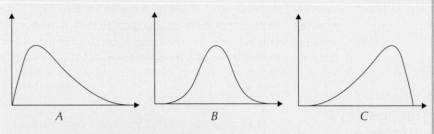

Q4 Which of the following graphs (A, B or C) has the highest standard deviation?

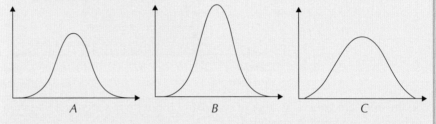

Section Summary

Make sure you know...

- That variation is the differences that exist between individuals.
- The two types of variation — interspecific (between different species) and intraspecific (within the same species).
- That the two main causes of intraspecific variation are genetic factors and environmental factors.
- That variation is often due to a combination of both genetic and environmental factors.
- The difficulties scientists face when trying to determine whether variation is caused by genes, the environment or both.
- That scientists use population samples to study variation.
- The importance of random sampling to ensure that a sample isn't biased.
- The importance of analysing results statistically, to ensure that any variation in the sample isn't just due to chance.
- How to analyse and interpret data on interspecific and intraspecific variation, e.g. by describing the data, drawing conclusions and suggesting reasons for any differences.
- That the mean tells you the average of the values collected in a sample.
- That a normal distribution is a bell-shaped curve that is symmetrical about the mean.
- That the standard deviation is a measure of the spread of values about the mean.
- That a large standard deviation means the values in a sample show a lot of variation, and a small standard deviation means the values show little variation.

Exam-style Questions

1   A group of scientists is trying to develop a new strain of wheat that grows successfully in an area of Africa with low rainfall. They begin by testing two different species. To compare them, the scientists take a random sample of plants from each species. The plants are grown in the same environment and the scientists monitor how long each plant can survive without water. The results are shown below.

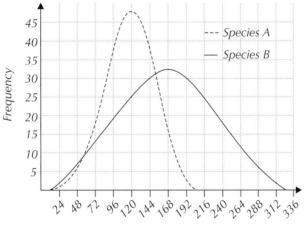

Number of hours survived without water

(a)   Evaluate the method used by the scientists.

(4 marks)

(b)   Study the graph shown above.

Describe the similarities and differences between species A and B.

(3 marks)

(c)   Explain the likely cause of the variation between the two species.

(1 mark)

(d)   The scientists must choose one species to take to Africa for further testing.
Discuss the reasons for and against selecting species B.

(2 marks)

The scientists try to increase survival of their chosen species by inserting two genes for drought-resistance from other plants. The results are shown in the table.

Gene	Mean no. days survived without water (± standard deviation)
X	20 (±4.3)
Y	26 (±1.2)
X and Y combined	24 (±5.4)

(e)   What information does standard deviation give?

(1 mark)

(f)   Which gene(s) should the scientists introduce into their chosen plant?
Explain your answer.

(2 marks)

2   The graph below shows how the incidence of breast cancer in women is
affected by age and family history. First degree relatives include mothers,
sisters and daughters.

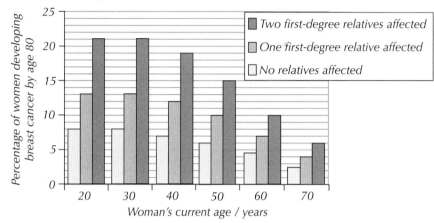

(a)   Approximately what percentage of 30 year old women with two first-degree relatives
affected with breast cancer will develop breast cancer by the age of 80?

(1 mark)

The graph below shows how the incidence of breast cancer in women is
affected by alcohol consumption.

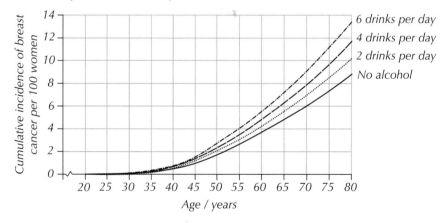

(b)   How is the incidence of breast cancer different for a 70 year old woman
who drinks no alcohol compared to one who drinks 6 drinks per day?

(2 marks)

(c)   What can you conclude about the causes of breast cancer from these two graphs?
Give evidence from the graphs to support your answer.

(5 marks)

1. DNA

DNA (deoxyribonucleic acid) is one of the most important molecules in a cell — and you need to learn all about its structure and function.

DNA function

DNA contains your genetic information — that's all the instructions needed to grow and develop from a fertilised egg to a fully grown adult.

DNA structure

DNA has a **double helix** structure. This means that a DNA molecule is formed from two separate strands which are coiled around each other to form a spiral (see Figure 1). The strands are polynucleotides. They're made up of lots of nucleotides joined together in a long chain.

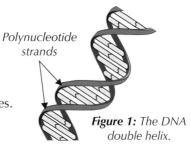

Polynucleotide strands

Figure 1: *The DNA double helix.*

Nucleotide structure

Each nucleotide is made from a phosphate group, a pentose sugar (with 5 carbon atoms) and a nitrogenous **base**.

The sugar in DNA nucleotides is a **deoxyribose sugar**. Each nucleotide has the same sugar and phosphate. The base on each nucleotide can vary though. There are four possible bases — adenine (A), thymine (T), cytosine (C) and guanine (G). The structure of a nucleotide is illustrated in Figure 2.

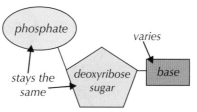

phosphate
varies
stays the same
deoxyribose sugar
base

Figure 2: *A DNA nucleotide.*

Polynucleotide strands

Many nucleotides join together to form the polynucleotide strands. The nucleotides join up between the phosphate group of one nucleotide and the sugar of another, creating a **sugar-phosphate backbone** — see Figure 3.

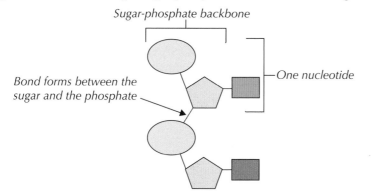

Sugar-phosphate backbone

One nucleotide

Bond forms between the sugar and the phosphate

Figure 3: *Structure of a polynucleotide strand.*

Learning Objectives:

- Know the double helix structure of DNA, including:
  - the components of DNA nucleotides: deoxyribose, phosphate and the bases adenine, cytosine, guanine and thymine.
  - how the two sugar-phosphate backbones are held together by hydrogen bonds between base pairs.
  - how specific base pairing works.
- Understand how the structure of DNA enables it to act as a stable information-carrying molecule.
- Know that in eukaryotes, DNA is linear and associated with proteins.
- Know that in prokaryotes, DNA molecules are smaller, circular and are not associated with proteins.

Specification Reference 3.2.2

Exam Tip
If they ask you to name the components of a DNA nucleotide in the exam, you must specify that the sugar is deoxyribose — or you won't get the marks.

Specific base pairing

Two DNA polynucleotide strands join together by hydrogen bonds between the bases. Each base can only join with one particular partner — this is called **specific base pairing**. Adenine always pairs with thymine (A - T) and guanine always pairs with cytosine (G - C) — see Figure 4.

Tip: If you're struggling to remember which base pairs with which, just think — you eat Apple Turnover with Gloopy Custard.

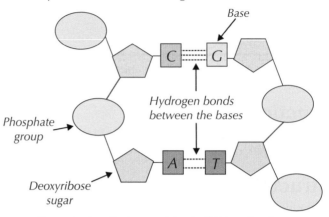

Figure 4: Specific base pairing in DNA molecules.

Figure 6: X-ray diffraction picture of DNA. The cross of bands shows that the molecule is a helix.

Summary

If you tie all this information together, you end up with a DNA molecule that looks like the one in Figure 5. You'll come across this type of diagram a lot in exams so make sure you can label all the important bits.

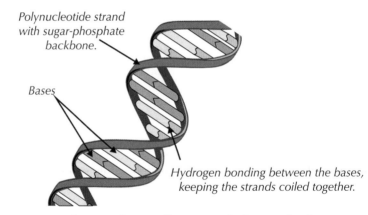

Figure 5: The overall structure of a DNA molecule.

Figure 7: Watson and Crick, two of the scientists who discovered the structure of DNA, and their model of the DNA double helix.

Structure vs. function

The structure of DNA makes it great at carrying out its function — storing genetic information. For example...

- The double-helix structure makes DNA very stable in the cell. This means the DNA doesn't break down or get easily damaged — if it did, important information could be lost.

- The DNA molecules are very long and are coiled up very tightly, so a lot of genetic information can fit into a small space in the cell nucleus (see next page).

- DNA molecules have a paired structure, which makes it much easier to copy itself. This is called semi-conservative replication (see p. 143). It's important for cell division (see p. 146) and for passing genetic information from generation to generation (see pages 122-123).

Tip: The structure of a nucleotide and the arrangement of the DNA double helix is the same in all living organisms.

DNA storage

Although the structure of DNA is the same in all organisms, eukaryotic and prokaryotic cells store DNA in slightly different ways.

Tip: Eukaryotic cells include animal and plant cells. Prokaryotic cells are generally bacteria. See pages 48 and 70 for more.

Eukaryotic cells

Eukaryotic cells contain linear DNA molecules that exist as chromosomes — thread-like structures, each made up of one long molecule of DNA. The DNA molecule is really long so it has to be wound up so it can fit into the nucleus. The molecule is wound around proteins (called **histones**). Histone proteins also help to support the DNA. The DNA (and protein) is then coiled up very tightly to make a compact chromosome (see Figure 8).

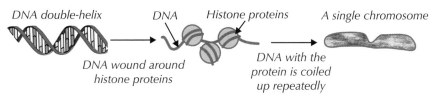

Figure 8: Storage of DNA in eukaryotes.

Prokaryotic cells

Prokaryotes also carry DNA as chromosomes — but the DNA molecules are shorter and circular. The DNA isn't wound around proteins — it condenses to fit in the cell by **supercoiling** (see Figure 9).

Tip: Prokaryotes don't have a nucleus. Their DNA floats freely in the cytoplasm.

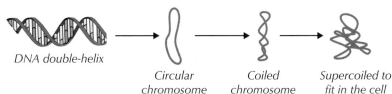

Figure 9: Storage of DNA in prokaryotes.

Practice Questions — Application

Q1 Here are the base sequences of two short stretches of DNA. For each one, write down the sequence of bases they would pair up with:

a) ACTGTCGTAGTCGATGCTA

b) TGCACCATGTGGTAAATCG

Q2 Scientists analysed a section of double stranded DNA. There were 68 bases in total (34 base pairs) and 22 of the bases were adenine. How many of the bases were:

a) thymine?   b) cytosine?   c) guanine?

Practice Questions — Fact Recall

Q1 The diagram shows a DNA nucleotide. Name parts A, B and C.

Q2 Name the pentose sugar found in DNA.

Q3 Describe how nucleotides join together in a polynucleotide.

Q4 Describe three ways in which DNA is adapted to perform its function.

Q5 How is the storage of DNA in prokaryotes different from that in eukaryotes?

Exam Tip
Questions on the structure of DNA are easy marks in the exam — and they come up a lot. Make sure you know the structure inside out.

- Know that genes are sections of DNA that contain coded information as a specific sequence of bases.

- Know that genes code for polypeptides.

- Know that a sequence of three bases, called a triplet, codes for a specific amino acid.

- Know that the base sequence of a gene determines the amino acid sequence in a polypeptide.

- Know that in eukaryotes, much of the nuclear DNA does not code for polypeptides. There are, for example, introns within genes and multiple repeats between genes.

- Know that genes determine the nature and development of organisms.

- Know that a gene occupies a fixed position, called a locus, on a particular strand of DNA.

- Know that the base sequence of a gene can change as a result of a mutation, producing one or more alleles of the same gene.

- Know that differences in base sequences of alleles of a single gene may result in non-functional proteins, including non-functional enzymes.

Specification Reference 3.2.2

2. Genes

Cells contain lots of DNA, but only a small amount of it carries genetic information. The most important parts of a DNA molecule are the genes.

What are genes?

Genes are sections of DNA. They're found on chromosomes. Genes code for proteins (polypeptides) — they contain the instructions to make them.

Making proteins using genes

Proteins are made from amino acids. Different proteins have a different number and order of amino acids. It's the order of nucleotide bases in a gene that determines the order of amino acids in a particular protein. Each amino acid is coded for by a sequence of three bases (called a **triplet**) in a gene. Different sequences of bases code for different amino acids.

┌─ Examples ─────────────────────────────

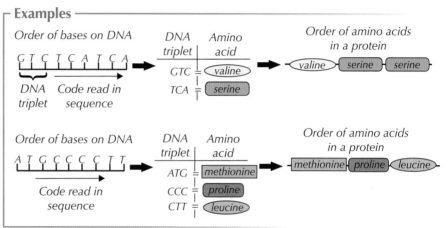

The code in DNA is degenerate. This means that more than one base triplet can code for the same amino acid. That's because there are more possible combinations of three bases than there are amino acids (there are 64 triplets and only 20 amino acids).

┌─ Examples ─────────────────────────────

The amino acid proline (often shortened to 'Pro') can be coded for by four different base triplets: CCT, CCC, CCA, and CCG. Glutamine (Gln) can be coded for by two different triplets: CAA and CAG.

Practice Questions — Application

Q1 The table below shows five amino acids and some of the triplets that code for them:

Amino Acid:	His	Arg	Gly	Tyr	Cys
DNA triplet:	CAT	AGA	GGC	TAC	TGC

Use the table to:

(a) determine the DNA sequence that would code for the following amino acid sequences:

(i) His - Arg - His - Gly - Cys - Arg - Tyr - Tyr - Gly - Arg

(ii) Tyr - Cys - Arg - Arg - Gly - Cys - Gly - Tyr - His - Gly

(b) determine the amino acid sequence coded for by the following DNA sequences:

(i) GGC - TAC - GGC - CAT - AGA - AGA - TGC - TAC - CAT

(ii) CAT - TAC - TAC - AGA - GGC - TGC - CAT - AGA - GGC

Q2 Protein X is known to contain 1 valine, 2 threonines and 3 leucines. The base sequence of the gene encoding protein X is given below:

ACT - TTG - TTG - GTC - ACT - TTG

Using the information above, complete the following table.

Amino Acid:	Valine	Threonine	Leucine
DNA triplet:			

Exam Tip
Questions relating DNA base sequences to amino acid sequences are pretty common in exams — so make sure you can answer these ones.

Non-coding DNA

Genes in eukaryotic DNA contain sections that don't code for amino acids. These sections of DNA are called **introns** (all the bits that do code for amino acids are called **exons**). Introns are removed during protein synthesis — see Figure 1. Their purpose isn't known for sure.

Eukaryotic DNA also contains regions of **multiple repeats** outside of genes. These are DNA sequences that repeat over and over. For example: CCTTCCTTCCTT. These areas don't code for amino acids either. This is illustrated in Figure 1.

Tip: Don't get confused between introns and exons. Just remember — INtrons INterrupt the exons, which code for protein.

Tip: Actual genes are much, much longer than this — thousands of base pairs.

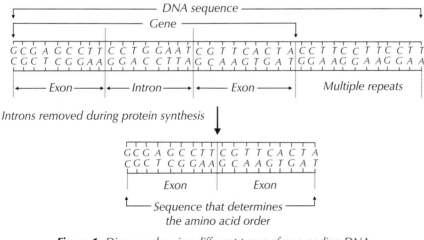

Tip: Remember, only exons code for proteins.

Figure 1: Diagram showing different types of non-coding DNA.

Practice Questions — Application

The diagram below shows the sequence of a short stretch of DNA:

Gene

ACTGTAT CGTATCGC TGATCGA TGCTCG ATGTCTA GCGCGCGCGC
| Exon | Intron | Exon | Intron | Exon |

Q1 Write down the base sequence that actually determines the order of amino acids in the protein.

Q2 a) How many bases long is the region of multiple repeats?

b) Write down the base sequence that is repeated in this region.

Genes and development

Enzymes speed up most of our metabolic pathways — the chemical reactions that occur in the body. These pathways determine how we grow and develop. Because enzymes control the metabolic pathways, they contribute to our development, and ultimately what we look like (our phenotype).

All enzymes are proteins, which are built using the instructions contained within genes. The order of bases in the gene decides the order of amino acids in the protein and so what type of protein (or enzyme) is made.

So, our genes help to determine our nature, development and phenotype because they contain the information to produce all our proteins and enzymes. Here's a nice summary for you:

```
DNA sequence determines
amino acid sequence.
        ↓
Proteins and enzymes formed.
        ↓
Enzymes control metabolic pathways.
        ↓
Metabolic pathways help determine
nature and development.
```

Figure 2: *Labradors with different enzymes for coat colour.*

Example

In Labradors, coat colour is determined by a combination of genes. The genes code for different enzymes, which convert a substance called dopaquinone into different coloured pigments. Depending on the enzymes that are coded for, a Labrador's coat can end up yellow, brown or black.

Alleles

A gene can exist in more than one form. These forms are called alleles. The order of bases in each allele is slightly different, so they code for slightly different versions of the same characteristic.

Example

The gene that codes for blood type exists as one of three alleles — one codes for type O, another for type A and the other for type B.

Tip: So remember — an allele is a form of a gene. You need to get that straight in your head to understand the rest of the section.

Homologous chromosomes

Our DNA is stored as chromosomes in the nucleus of cells. Humans have 23 pairs of chromosomes, 46 in total — two number 1s, two number 2s, two number 3s etc. Pairs of matching chromosomes (e.g. the 1s) are called **homologous pairs**.

In a homologous pair both chromosomes are the same size and have the same genes, although they could have different alleles. Alleles coding for the same characteristic will be found at the same position (**locus**) on each chromosome in a homologous pair. This is illustrated in Figure 4.

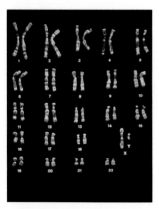

Figure 3: *A complete set of 46 chromosomes from a human male.*

Example

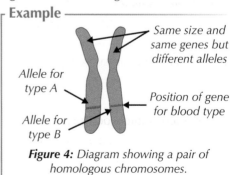

Same size and same genes but different alleles

Allele for type A

Position of gene for blood type

Allele for type B

Figure 4: *Diagram showing a pair of homologous chromosomes.*

Gene mutations

Mutations are changes in the base sequence of an organism's DNA. So, mutations can produce new alleles of genes. A gene codes for a particular protein, so if the sequence of bases in a gene changes, a non-functional or different protein could be produced.

All enzymes are proteins. If there's a mutation in a gene that codes for an enzyme, then that enzyme may not fold up properly. This may produce an active site that's the wrong shape and so a non-functional enzyme.

Tip: See pages 38-40 for a recap of enzymes and active sites. If the active site is the wrong shape, it won't be able to bind to the enzyme's substrate — so the enzyme won't work.

Example

Gene X codes for an enzyme that catalyses the conversion of A to B. A mutation in the gene may result in the formation of a non-functional enzyme. This means that the reaction can't happen.

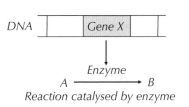

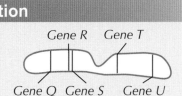

Reaction catalysed by enzyme

Tip: Not all mutations produce non-functional proteins. This is partly because the code in DNA is degenerate (see p.118) so not all base changes result in an amino acid change. Even if the amino acid changes though, it won't necessarily affect protein function.

Practice Questions — Application

Q1 The diagram shows the position of five genes on a chromosome. Draw the homologous chromosome.

Gene R   Gene T

Gene Q   Gene S   Gene U

Q2 The flow chart below illustrates how coloured pigment is produced in a certain type of flower:

White protein substrate → Enzyme A → Pink Pigment → Enzyme B → Red Pigment → Enzyme C → Purple Pigment

a) What colour would you expect the flower to be if a mutation occurred that made:

i) Enzyme A non-functional?

ii) Enzyme B non-functional?

iii) Enzyme C non-functional?

b) One plant was found to have white flowers even though enzymes A, B and C were functioning normally. Suggest a possible explanation for this.

Practice Questions — Fact Recall

Q1 What is a gene?

Q2 How many DNA bases code for one amino acid?

Q3 Name two types of non-coding DNA.

Q4 Describe how DNA helps determine our nature and development.

Q5 What is an allele?

Q6 What is the name given to the position on a chromosome that a particular allele occupies?

Q7 How are new alleles of a gene produced?

Q8 How can mutations affect enzyme activity?

- Understand the importance of meiosis in producing cells which are genetically different.

- Know that meiosis involves:

  - the formation of haploid cells.

  - genetic recombination by crossing over.

  - independent segregation of homologous chromosomes.

- Know that gametes are genetically different as a result of different combinations of maternal and paternal chromosomes.

Specification Reference 3.2.2

3. Meiosis and Genetic Variation

Most cells in the body contain exactly the same genetic information. The one major exception to this rule are the gametes — the cells involved in sexual reproduction.

Gametes and fertilisation

Gametes are the sperm cells in males and egg cells in females. They join together at fertilisation to form a zygote, which divides and develops into a new organism.

Normal body cells have the **diploid number (2n)** of chromosomes — meaning each cell contains two of each chromosome, one from the mum and one from the dad. Gametes have a **haploid (n) number** of chromosomes — there's only one copy of each chromosome.

At fertilisation, a haploid sperm fuses with a haploid egg, making a cell with the normal diploid number of chromosomes. Half these chromosomes are from the father (the sperm) and half are from the mother (the egg). The diploid cell produced by fertilisation is called a zygote.

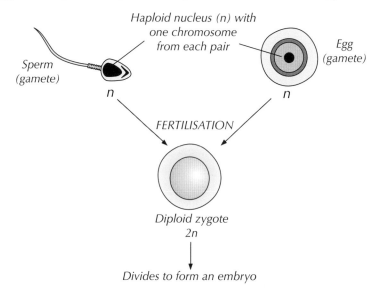

Figure 1: Diagram to show fertilisation.

A key feature of gametes is that they are genetically different — no two gametes are alike. Gametes show genetic variation because they are formed by a type of cell division called meiosis.

Meiosis

Meiosis is a type of cell division. Cells that divide by meiosis are diploid to start with, but the cells that are formed from meiosis (e.g. the gametes) are haploid — the chromosome number halves.

Without meiosis, you'd get double the number of chromosomes when the gametes fused. Not good. The process of meiosis is summarised in Figure 3 on the next page.

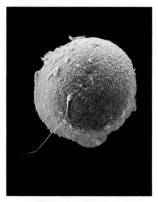

Figure 2: Electron micrograph of a sperm fertilising an egg.

Exam Tip
Meiosis is easily confused with mitosis (another type of cell division), but it's vital you know the difference for the exam. Take a look at page 146 for information on mitosis.

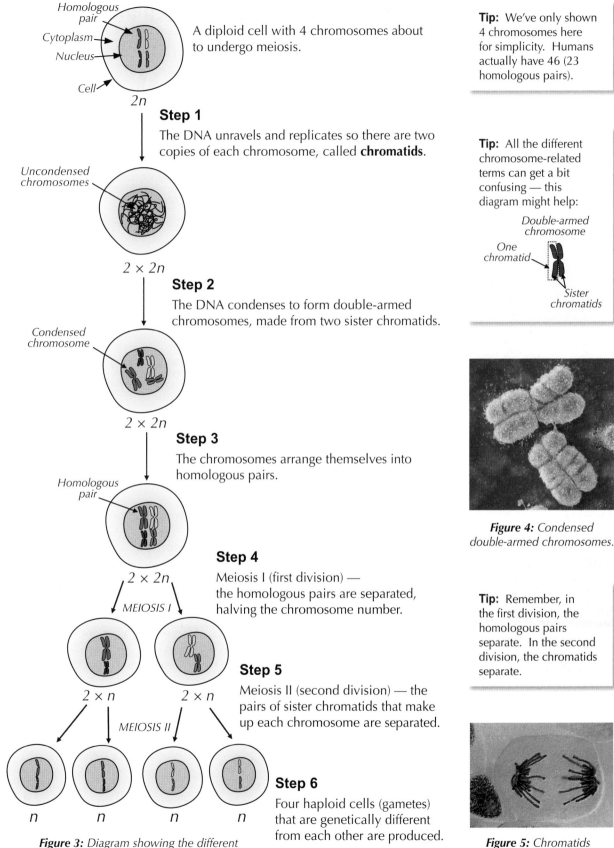

Homologous pair
Cytoplasm
Nucleus
Cell

2n

A diploid cell with 4 chromosomes about to undergo meiosis.

Tip: We've only shown 4 chromosomes here for simplicity. Humans actually have 46 (23 homologous pairs).

Step 1

The DNA unravels and replicates so there are two copies of each chromosome, called **chromatids**.

Uncondensed chromosomes

$2 \times 2n$

Tip: All the different chromosome-related terms can get a bit confusing — this diagram might help:

Double-armed chromosome
One chromatid
Sister chromatids

Step 2

The DNA condenses to form double-armed chromosomes, made from two sister chromatids.

Condensed chromosome

$2 \times 2n$

Figure 4: Condensed double-armed chromosomes.

Step 3

The chromosomes arrange themselves into homologous pairs.

Homologous pair

$2 \times 2n$

MEIOSIS I

Step 4

Meiosis I (first division) — the homologous pairs are separated, halving the chromosome number.

Tip: Remember, in the first division, the homologous pairs separate. In the second division, the chromatids separate.

$2 \times n$ $2 \times n$

MEIOSIS II

Step 5

Meiosis II (second division) — the pairs of sister chromatids that make up each chromosome are separated.

n n n n

Step 6

Four haploid cells (gametes) that are genetically different from each other are produced.

Figure 3: Diagram showing the different stages of meiosis.

Figure 5: Chromatids separating during meiosis II.

Creating genetic variation in gametes

There are two main events during meiosis that lead to genetic variation:

1. Crossing over of chromatids

During meiosis I, homologous pairs of chromosomes come together and pair up. The chromatids twist around each other and bits of chromatids swap over. The chromatids still contain the same genes but now have a different combination of alleles — see Figure 6.

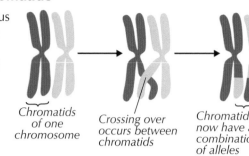

Chromatids of one chromosome   *Crossing over occurs between chromatids*   *Chromatids now have a new combination of alleles*

Figure 6: *Crossing over.*

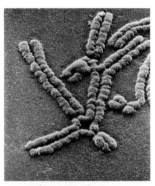

Figure 7: *Electron micrograph showing crossing over occurring in cells.*

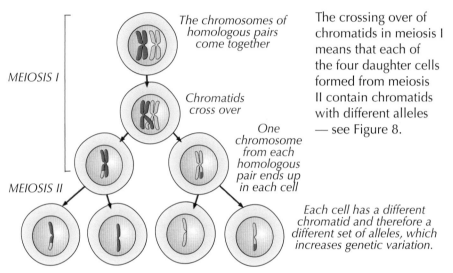

The chromosomes of homologous pairs come together

MEIOSIS I

Chromatids cross over

One chromosome from each homologous pair ends up in each cell

MEIOSIS II

The crossing over of chromatids in meiosis I means that each of the four daughter cells formed from meiosis II contain chromatids with different alleles — see Figure 8.

Each cell has a different chromatid and therefore a different set of alleles, which increases genetic variation.

Figure 8: *Crossing over in meiosis.*

2. Independent segregation of chromosomes

The four daughter cells formed from meiosis have completely different combinations of chromosomes. All your cells have a combination of chromosomes from your parents, half from your mum (called maternal chromosomes) and half from your dad (called paternal chromosomes).

When the gametes are produced, different combinations of those maternal and paternal chromosomes go into each cell. This is called independent segregation (separation) of the chromosomes — see Figure 9.

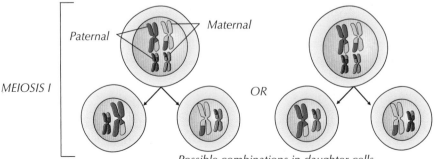

Paternal   *Maternal*

MEIOSIS I

OR

Possible combinations in daughter cells

Figure 9: *Independent segregation of chromosomes.*

Practice Questions — Application

Q1 The graph below shows the average DNA content of a group of cells that are undergoing meiosis:

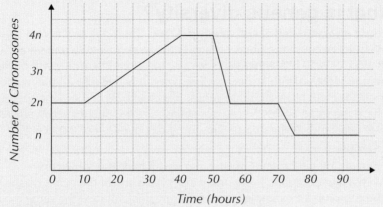

Describe what is happening:

a) between 10 hours and 40 hours.

b) between 40 hours and 50 hours.

c) between 50 and 55 hours.

d) between 70 and 75 hours.

Q2 The diagram below shows a cell which contains three pairs of homologous chromosomes and six potential gametes. Which of the gametes (A to F) could be produced from this cell by meiosis?

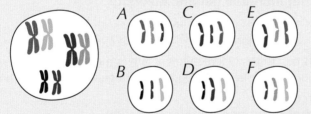

Q3 The diagram to the right shows two homologous chromosomes. The red cross marks a point at which crossing over can occur. Draw the chromosomes as they would be if crossing over occurred at this point.

Q4 For each of the following cells state what stage the cell is at in meiosis. Choose from: before meiosis I, between meiosis I and II, or after meiosis II. Give a reason for each answer.

Homologous pair

a) b) c)

Exam Tip
Examiners just love a good graph — so make sure you practice interpreting them.

Exam Tip
Make sure you know what the chromosomes look like in each stage of meiosis.

Practice Questions — Fact Recall

Q1 Are the following haploid or diploid:

a) normal body cells?   b) gametes?   c) zygotes?

Q2 Describe what happens in: a) meiosis I.   b) meiosis II.

Q3 a) What are the two main events in meiosis that lead to genetic variation?

b) Describe how each of these processes works.

Learning Objectives:

- Know that similarities and differences between organisms may be defined in terms of variation in DNA.
- Know that differences in DNA lead to genetic diversity.
- Understand the influence of the following on genetic diversity:
  - genetic bottlenecks.
  - the founder effect.
  - selection for high-yielding breeds of domesticated animals and strains of plants.
- Be able to discuss ethical issues involved in the selection of domesticated animals.

  Specification Reference 3.2.3

Tip: All members of a species have the same genes. Diversity only occurs in the form of different alleles of those genes.

Tip: The gene pool is the complete range of alleles in a population.

4. Genetic Diversity

Meiosis generates genetic diversity, but it isn't the only thing that affects it.

What is genetic diversity?

Genetic diversity is all about variety in DNA. The DNA of different species varies a lot because members of different species have different genes. The more closely related two species are, the more DNA they will have in common. DNA within a species varies very little because all the members of one species will have the same genes. But members of the same species don't all have the same alleles (version of genes). It's the differences in alleles that create genetic diversity in a species (or in a population of a species).

--- Example ---

Humans are all the same species, so we all have the same genes (with a few exceptions — women don't have any of the genes on the Y chromosome for example). We definitely don't all look the same though — and that's because of differences in our alleles.

Genetic diversity is important, because it can help a population or species to survive. It means that if the environment changes, there are likely to be some organisms with the alleles that enable them to survive the new conditions.

Factors affecting genetic diversity

The more alleles in a population, the more genetically diverse it is.

Factors that increase genetic diversity

Genetic diversity within a population is increased by:

- Mutations in the DNA — forming new alleles.
- **Gene flow**. This is where different alleles move between populations when individuals from one population migrate into another and reproduce.

Factors that decrease genetic diversity

Genetic diversity can be decreased by a number of factors including: genetic bottlenecks, the founder effect and selective breeding. There's more about these over the next few pages.

Genetic bottlenecks

A genetic bottleneck is an event that causes a big reduction in a population, e.g. when a large number of organisms within a population die before reproducing. This reduces the number of different alleles in the gene pool and so reduces genetic diversity. The survivors reproduce and a larger population is created from a few individuals — see Figure 1.

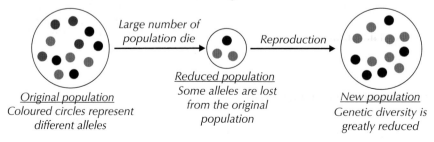

Original population
Coloured circles represent different alleles

Large number of population die

Reduced population
Some alleles are lost from the original population

Reproduction

New population
Genetic diversity is greatly reduced

Figure 1: *Diagram illustrating the effect of genetic bottlenecks.*

Example — Northern elephant seals

Northern elephant seals were hunted by humans in the late 1800s. Their original population was reduced to around 50 seals who have since produced a population of around 100 000. This new population has very little genetic diversity compared to the southern elephant seals who never suffered such a reduction in numbers.

Figure 2: *Northern elephant seals in California.*

The founder effect

The founder effect describes what happens when just a few organisms from a population start a new colony. Only a small number of organisms contribute their alleles to the gene pool, so genetic diversity is reduced — see Figure 3. There's more inbreeding in the new population, which can lead to a higher incidence of genetic disease.

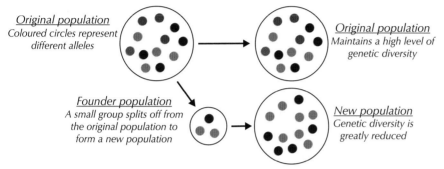

Original population
Coloured circles represent different alleles

Original population
Maintains a high level of genetic diversity

Founder population
A small group splits off from the original population to form a new population

New population
Genetic diversity is greatly reduced

Figure 3: *Diagram illustrating the founder effect.*

Tip: The founder effect is a type of genetic bottleneck.

The founder effect can occur as a result of migration leading to geographical separation or if a new colony is separated from the original population for another reason, such as religion (see below).

Example — The Amish

The Amish population of North America are all descended from a small number of Swiss who migrated there. The population shows little genetic diversity. They have remained isolated from the surrounding population due to their religious beliefs, so few new alleles have been introduced. The population suffers an unusually high incidence of certain genetic disorders.

Practice Questions — Application

The graph on the right shows how the average tail length in an isolated population of lemurs changed over a period of 8 years. The vertical bars span the difference between the longest and the shortest tail lengths.

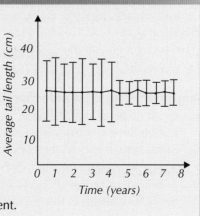

Q1 Describe what happened between years 4 and 5.

Q2 What term could be used to describe this event?

Q3 Suggest a possible cause for this event.

Figure 4: Domestic carrots (right) have been selectively bred from wild carrots (left).

Selective breeding

Changes in genetic diversity aren't just brought about by natural events like bottlenecks or migration. Selective breeding of plants and animals by humans has resulted in reduced genetic diversity in some populations. Selective breeding involves humans selecting which domesticated animals or strains of plants reproduce together in order to produce useful characteristics, e.g. a high-yield.

Example

A farmer wants a strain of corn plant that is tall and produces lots of ears, so he breeds a tall corn strain with one that produces multiple ears.

   He selects the offspring that are tallest and have most ears, and breeds them together.

   The farmer continues this until he produces a very tall strain that produces multiple ears of corn.

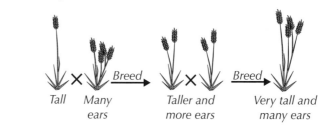

| Tall | Many ears | | Taller and more ears | | Very tall and many ears |

Selective breeding leads to a reduction in genetic diversity — once an organism with the desired characteristics (e.g. tall with multiple ears) has been produced, only that type of organism will continue being bred. So only similar organisms with similar traits and therefore similar alleles are bred together. It results in a type of genetic bottleneck as it reduces the number of alleles in the gene pool.

Arguments for and against selective breeding

You need to be able to discuss the ethical issues involved with selective breeding.

Arguments for selective breeding

- It can produce high-yielding animals and plants.
- It can be used to produce animals and plants that have increased resistance to disease. This means farmers have to use fewer drugs and pesticides.
- Animals and plants could be bred to have increased tolerance of bad conditions, e.g. drought or cold.

Arguments against selective breeding

- It can cause health problems. E.g. dairy cows are often lame and have a short life expectancy because of the extra strain making and carrying loads of milk puts on their bodies.
- It reduces genetic diversity, which results in an increased incidence of genetic disease and an increased susceptibility to new diseases because of the lack of alleles in the population.

Exam Tip
Being able to weigh up advantages and disadvantages is a crucial part of how science works — and examiners just love to test you on it.

Tip: Many dog breeds have genetic defects due to the amount of selective breeding they have undergone — e.g. bloodhounds suffer from eye and hip problems due to selective breeding.

Practice Questions — Application

A chicken farmer wants to increase his yield of eggs.

Q1 Describe how the chicken farmer could increase his yield of eggs through selective breeding.

Q2 After a few years of selective breeding the farmer manages to double his egg yield. However, some of the chickens began to show signs of an inherited disease which makes the chickens lose their feathers. Explain how the increased incidence of this disease may have been caused by selective breeding.

Practice Questions — Fact Recall

Q1 What are genetic bottlenecks and how do they affect genetic diversity?

Q2 What is the founder effect and how can it lead to an increased incidence of genetic disease?

Q3 What is selective breeding?

Q4 How does selective breeding influence genetic diversity?

Q5 Give three advantages of using selective breeding.

Q6 Give two possible disadvantages of selective breeding.

Section Summary

Make sure you know...

- The features of the double helix structure of DNA — including the structure of a nucleotide, the sugar-phosphate backbone and how polynucleotide strands are held together through specific base pairing.
- Why the structure of DNA makes it ideally suited to store genetic information — it's stable, easy to replicate and coils up tightly so it fits in the nucleus.
- How DNA is stored in eukaryotes by association with histones, and in prokaryotes by supercoiling.
- That genes are sections of DNA that code for polypeptides.
- That a sequence of three DNA bases, known as a base triplet, codes for one amino acid in a protein.
- The two main types of non-coding DNA — introns and multiple repeats.
- That, by coding for proteins (and enzymes), genes determine our nature and development.
- That alleles are different versions of the same gene and that alleles coding for the same characteristic are found at the same position (locus) on each chromosome in a homologous pair.
- That the base sequence of genes can change as a result of mutation.
- How mutations can lead to non-functional proteins/enzymes — the protein may not fold properly.
- That haploid cells contain one copy of each chromosome and diploid cells contain two copies.
- That meiosis is important for producing haploid gametes which are genetically different.
- The stages of meiosis including meiosis I and meiosis II.
- How genetic variation in gametes is generated through crossing over and independent segregation of chromosomes in meiosis.
- That genetic diversity is all about differences in DNA — and that genetic diversity within a species is caused by differences in alleles.
- How genetic bottlenecks and the founder effect reduce genetic diversity (by reducing the gene pool).
- How selective breeding reduces genetic diversity.
- The advantages and disadvantages of using selective breeding to generate new strains of organism.

1   A farmer wants to increase his yield of beef by increasing the muscle mass
        of his cows. He decides to do this using selective breeding.

   (a)   Describe how selective breeding could be used to produce cows with increased
        muscle mass.

                                                                    (2 marks)

   (b)   Discuss the advantages and disadvantages of using selective breeding in this way.

                                                                    (6 marks)

   (c)   The graph below shows how the mean muscle mass of the farmer's cows
        changed from one generation to the next. The error bars on the graph show the
        standard deviation.

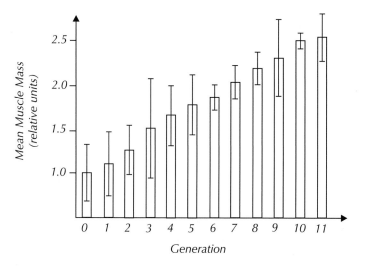

   (i)   Describe the trend shown in the graph.

                                                                    (1 mark)

   (ii)   How many generations of selective breeding did it take for the farmer to increase
        the mean muscle mass of his cows by 50%?

                                                                    (2 marks)

   (iii) By how much did the mean muscle mass of the cows increase in total?

                                                                    (1 mark)

   (iv)   Which generation has the most reliable data? Give a reason for your answer.

                                                                    (1 mark)

   (d)   Selective breeding and the founder effect both have a similar effect on
        genetic diversity. Explain why.

                                                                    (2 marks)

2   A DNA double helix is separated into two strands.
The diagram below shows a short section of one of the DNA strands:

G C A C T T G T A T G C C T A T G G

(a) (i) Write down the sequence of bases on the opposing strand.

(1 mark)

(ii) If this stretch of DNA was converted into a protein, how many amino acids would that protein contain? Explain why.

(2 marks)

(b) DNA is a polynucleotide.

What three components make up a DNA nucleotide?

(3 marks)

(c) Urea is a weak alkali. Adding urea to a solution of double-stranded DNA will severely disrupt the hydrogen bonding in the DNA.

Explain what effect this will have on the structure of the DNA.

(2 marks)

(d) Give three reasons why the structure of DNA makes it well-suited to its function.

(3 marks)

3   Cri-du-chat is a genetic disorder caused by the deletion of part of chromosome 5.

The deletion often causes the loss of the *CTNND2* gene, which is associated with brain development. This is believed to result in lower intellectual abilities in sufferers of cri-du-chat.

(a) (i) Explain why the deletion of a particular section of chromosome is likely to result in the loss of certain genes.

(1 mark)

(ii) Suggest how the loss of the *CTNND2* gene may affect a person's development, resulting in a lower intellectual ability.

(3 marks)

(b) The cri-du-chat deletion is thought to take place during the crossing over of chromatids at meiosis.

(i) Describe what happens during meiosis.

(6 marks)

(ii) Describe the process of crossing over and explain its purpose.

(2 marks)

Learning Objectives:

- Understand the role of haemoglobin in the transport of oxygen.
- Know that haemoglobin is a protein with a quaternary structure.
- Know that the haemoglobins are a group of chemically similar molecules found in many different organisms.
- Understand the loading, transport and unloading of oxygen in relation to the oxygen dissociation curve.
- Understand the effects of carbon dioxide concentration on the dissociation curve.
- Be aware that different organisms possess different types of haemoglobin with different oxygen transporting properties.
- Be able to relate differences in haemoglobin to the environment and way of life of different organisms.

Specification Reference 3.2.4

Tip: A protein with a quaternary structure just means it's made up of more than one polypeptide — see page 31 for more.

1. Variation in Haemoglobin

Many different organisms have haemoglobin in their blood to transport oxygen. But the type of haemoglobin each organism has varies depending on where they live and their way of life...

The role of haemoglobin

Human haemoglobin is found in red blood cells — its role is to carry oxygen around the body. There are many chemically similar types of haemoglobin found in many different organisms, all of which carry out the same function. As well as being found in all vertebrates, haemoglobin is found in earthworms, starfish, some insects, some plants and even in some bacteria.

Haemoglobin and oxyhaemoglobin

Haemoglobin is a large protein with a quaternary structure — it's made up of four polypeptide chains. Each chain has a haem group which contains iron and gives haemoglobin its red colour (see Figure 1). Each molecule of human haemoglobin can carry four oxygen molecules.

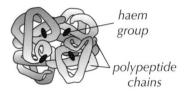

Figure 1: Human haemoglobin.

In the lungs, oxygen joins to haemoglobin in red blood cells to form **oxyhaemoglobin**. This is a reversible reaction — near the body cells, oxygen leaves oxyhaemoglobin and it turns back to haemoglobin (see Figure 2). When an oxygen molecule joins to haemoglobin it's referred to as **association** or **loading**, and when oxygen leaves oxyhaemoglobin it's referred to as **dissociation** or **unloading**.

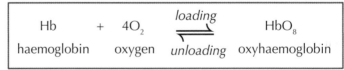

Figure 2: The formation and dissociation of oxyhaemoglobin.

Affinity for oxygen and pO_2

Affinity for oxygen means the tendency a molecule has to bind with oxygen. Haemoglobin's affinity for oxygen varies depending on the conditions it's in — one of the conditions that affects it is the **partial pressure of oxygen (pO_2)**.

pO_2 is a measure of oxygen concentration. The greater the concentration of dissolved oxygen in cells, the higher the partial pressure. As pO_2 increases, haemoglobin's affinity for oxygen also increases:

- Oxygen loads onto haemoglobin to form oxyhaemoglobin where there's a high pO_2.
- Oxyhaemoglobin unloads its oxygen where there's a lower pO_2.

Oxygen enters blood capillaries at the alveoli in the lungs. Alveoli have a high pO_2 so oxygen loads onto haemoglobin to form oxyhaemoglobin. When cells respire, they use up oxygen — this lowers the pO_2. Red blood cells deliver oxyhaemoglobin to respiring tissues, where it unloads its oxygen. The haemoglobin then returns to the lungs to pick up more oxygen. Figure 3 summarises this process.

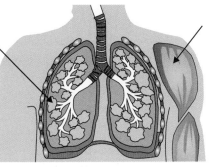

Alveoli in lungs
- *HIGH oxygen concentration*
- *HIGH pO_2*
- *HIGH affinity*
- *Oxygen LOADS*

Respiring tissue
- *LOW oxygen concentration*
- *LOW pO_2*
- *LOW affinity*
- *Oxygen UNLOADS*

Figure 3: *Oxygen loading and unloading in the body.*

Dissociation curves

An oxygen dissociation curve shows how saturated the haemoglobin is with oxygen at any given partial pressure. The affinity of haemoglobin for oxygen affects how saturated the haemoglobin is:

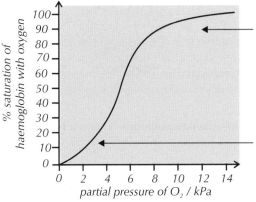

Where pO_2 is high (e.g. in the lungs), haemoglobin has a high affinity for oxygen, so it has a high saturation of oxygen.

Where pO_2 is low (e.g. in respiring tissues), haemoglobin has a low affinity for oxygen, so it has a low saturation of oxygen.

Figure 4: *Dissociation curve for adult haemoglobin.*

Weirdly, the saturation of haemoglobin can also affect the affinity — this is why the graph is 'S-shaped' and not a straight line.

When haemoglobin combines with the first O_2 molecule, its shape alters in a way that makes it easier for other molecules to join too. But as the haemoglobin starts to become saturated, it gets harder for more oxygen molecules to join. As a result, the curve has a steep bit in the middle where it's really easy for oxygen molecules to join, and shallow bits at each end where it's harder — see Figure 5. When the curve is steep, a small change in pO_2 causes a big change in the amount of oxygen carried by the haemoglobin.

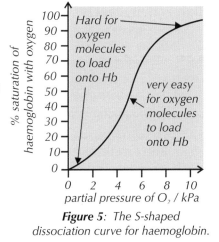

Figure 5: *The S-shaped dissociation curve for haemoglobin.*

Carbon dioxide concentration

The **partial pressure of carbon dioxide (pCO$_2$)** is a measure of the concentration of CO_2 in a cell. To complicate matters, pCO$_2$ also affects oxygen unloading. Haemoglobin gives up its oxygen more readily at a higher pCO$_2$. It's a cunning way of getting more O$_2$ to cells during activity.

When cells respire they produce carbon dioxide, which raises the pCO$_2$. This increases the rate of oxygen unloading — the dissociation curve 'shifts' right. The saturation of blood with oxygen is lower for a given pO$_2$, meaning that more oxygen is being released — see Figure 6. This is called the **Bohr effect**.

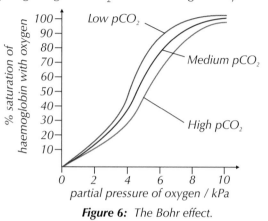

Figure 6: *The Bohr effect.*

Different types of haemoglobin

Different organisms have different types of haemoglobin with different oxygen transporting capacities — it depends on things like where they live, how active they are and their size.

Low oxygen environments

Organisms that live in environments with a low concentration of oxygen have haemoglobin with a higher affinity for oxygen than human haemoglobin. This is because there isn't much oxygen available, so the haemoglobin has to be very good at loading any available oxygen. The dissociation curve of their haemoglobin is to the left of ours.

┌ **Example** ─────────────────

A lugworm lives in burrows beneath sand where there's a low oxygen concentration. Its haemoglobin has to be able to pick up as much oxygen as possible — it has a high affinity for oxygen.

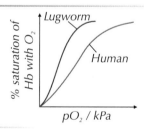

High activity levels

Organisms that are very active and have a high oxygen demand have haemoglobin with a lower affinity for oxygen than human haemoglobin. This is because they need their haemoglobin to easily unload oxygen, so that it's available for them to use. The dissociation curve of their haemoglobin is to the right of the human one.

┌ **Example** ─────────────────

A hawk has a high respiratory rate and lives where there's plenty of oxygen. Its haemoglobin has to be able to unload oxygen quickly in order to meet the high oxygen demand — it has a low affinity for oxygen.

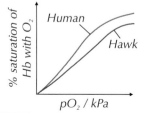

Size

Small mammals tend to have a higher surface area to volume ratio than larger mammals. This means they lose heat quickly, so they have a high metabolic rate to help them keep warm — which means they have a high oxygen demand. Mammals that are smaller than humans have haemoglobin with a lower affinity for oxygen than human haemoglobin, because they need their haemoglobin to easily unload oxygen to meet their high oxygen demand. The dissociation curve of their haemoglobin is to the right of the human one.

Tip: See page 157 for more on surface area to volume ratios.

Tip: Metabolic rate is the rate at which energy is used. A higher metabolic rate leads to a higher respiration rate. This in turn leads to a higher oxygen demand.

> **Example**
>
> A rat has a higher surface area to volume ratio than a human. Its haemoglobin needs to unload oxygen easily to meet the greater oxygen demand — it has a lower affinity for oxygen.
>
>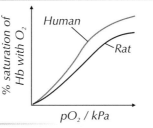

Practice Questions — Application

Q1 The graph to the right shows two oxygen dissociation curves for the same man. One curve was produced based on blood tests when he was watching television and the other was produced based on blood tests immediately after a bike ride.

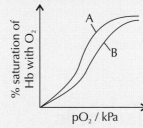

a) Which curve was produced after the bike ride? Explain your answer.

b) What name is given to the effect shown on the graph?

Tip: To help you answer Q1 a), think of the difference in respiration rates between the two activities.

Q2 The table below gives descriptions of three similarly sized animals. The graph shows each animal's dissociation curve. Match each animal to its dissociation curve and give reasons for your choices.

Animal	Description
Badger	Lives in an underground sett
Bush dog	Lives above ground, fairly active
Brown-throated sloth	Lives above ground, very sedentary

Exam Tip
In the exam you could be asked to interpret dissociation curves from animals you've never even heard of — don't let that throw you. Examiners want to make sure you really know your stuff by applying your knowledge to new situations.

Practice Questions — Fact Recall

Q1 Where is haemoglobin found in humans?

Q2 Describe what is meant by haemoglobin 'loading' and 'unloading' oxygen.

Q3 What does oxygen load onto haemoglobin to form?

Q4 Where in the body would you find cells with a high pO_2? Explain your answer.

Q5 What is shown on an oxygen dissociation curve?

- Know the fundamental differences between plant cells and animal cells.

- Know the structure of a palisade cell from a leaf as seen with an optical microscope.

- Know the appearance, ultrastructure and function of chloroplasts.

- Be able to apply knowledge of the appearance, ultrastructure and function of eukaryotic cells to explain adaptations of plant cells.

Specification Reference 3.2.4

Tip: When looking at plant cells down a microscope, you need to cut a very thin section of the tissue so that light can pass through the cells and the detail doesn't get obscured by the cells underneath.

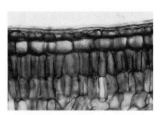

Figure 1: *Light micrograph of palisade cells in a holly leaf.*

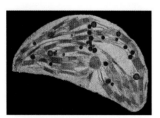

Figure 2: *Transmission electron micrograph (TEM) of a chloroplast.*

2. Variation in Plant and Animal Cells

Plant and animal cells are both types of eukaryotic cells. They have many similarities and differences that you need to know about.

Animal cells

Way, way back in Unit 1 Section 3 you learnt about animal cell structure and organelles. Well, you need to know about their structure for this section too so you can see how plant cell structure differs. Most animal cells have the following parts — make sure you know them all:

Plasma membrane — holds the cell together and controls what goes in and out.

Mitochondria — where most of the reactions for respiration take place. Respiration releases energy that the cell needs to work.

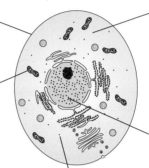

Cytoplasm — gel-like substance where most of the chemical reactions happen. It contains enzymes (see page 38) that control these chemical reactions.

Nucleus — contains genetic material that controls the activities of the cell.

Ribosomes — where proteins are made in the cell.

Plant cells

Plant cells usually have all the bits that animal cells have, plus a few extra things that animal cells don't have. For example, a **palisade cell** is a type of cell found in leaves, which absorbs light for photosynthesis. You need to know what a palisade cell looks like under an optical (light) microscope.

Rigid cell wall — made of cellulose. It supports and strengthens the cell.

Permanent vacuole — contains cell sap, a weak solution of sugar and salts.

Chloroplasts (see below) — where photosynthesis occurs, which makes food for the plant. They contain a green substance called chlorophyll.

Chloroplasts

Chloroplasts are surrounded by a double membrane, and also have membranes inside called thylakoid membranes. These membranes are stacked up in the chloroplast to form grana. Grana are linked together by lamellae — thin, flat pieces of thylakoid membrane. Some parts of photosynthesis happen in the grana, and other parts happen in the stroma (a thick fluid found in chloroplasts).

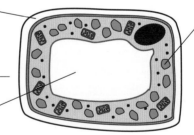

Figure 3: *Cross-section of a chloroplast.*

Variation in plant cells

In the exam, you might get a question where you need to apply your knowledge of the organelles in a plant cell to explain why it's particularly suited to its function. Here are some tips:

- Think about where the cell's located in the plant — e.g. if it's exposed to light, then it'll have lots of chloroplasts to maximise photosynthesis.

- Think about what the cell needs to do its job — e.g. if the cell uses a lot of energy, it'll need lots of mitochondria. If it makes a lot of proteins, it'll need a lot of ribosomes.

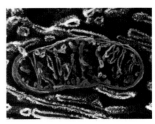

Figure 3: *Coloured scanning electron micrograph (SEM) of a single mitochondrion.*

Examples

A palisade cell (right) has lots of chloroplasts to absorb light. It also has a large vacuole to push the chloroplasts to the edge of the cell, so they're nearer to the light, and a thin cell wall to increase the diffusion of CO_2 into the cell.

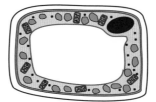

A root hair cell (left) absorbs water from the soil. Part of the cell is elongated to increase its surface area, which increases the rate of absorption. The cell has a large vacuole so that it can hold as much water as possible. The roots of a plant aren't exposed to light so they don't contain any chloroplasts.

Tip: Cells become specialised to carry out different functions by differentiation — see page 151.

Tip: Don't just look for which organelles a cell has — look for which they don't have as well. For example, a root hair cell <u>doesn't</u> have any chloroplasts, so you know it's <u>not</u> involved in photosynthesis.

Practice Questions — Application

Q1 Phloem tissue is made up of two main types of cell — sieve cells and companion cells. Sieve cells transport sugars around the plant but they have very few organelles. The companion cells' function is to support the sieve cells and provide them with the substances they need to survive.

Companion cells have more mitochondria and ribosomes than many other types of plant cell. Suggest how this adaptation makes companion cells suited to their function.

Practice Questions — Fact Recall

Q1 Label the organelles (A-H) shown on the plant cell below.

Q2 Where do most chemical reactions take place in a cell?

Q3 Give three ways in which plant cells differ from animal cells.

Q4 a) Describe the structure of a chloroplast.

b) Name two places in a chloroplast where photosynthesis occurs.

Q5 A cell's function is to make proteins. Which organelle would you expect to find a lot of in this cell?

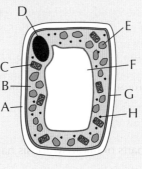

- Know the basic structure and functions of cellulose, starch and glycogen.

- Be able to relate the structure of starch, glycogen and cellulose to their functions in animals and plants.

- Know the structure of β-glucose as:

- Understand that cellulose is formed by the linking of β-glucose molecules by glycosidic bonds in condensation reactions.

- Know the appearance, ultrastructure and function of cell walls.

Specification Reference 3.2.4

Exam Tip
If you're asked to show a condensation reaction, don't forget to put the water molecule in as a product.

Figure 3: *Coloured scanning electron micrograph (SEM) of cellulose microfibrils in a plant cell wall.*

3. Variation in Carbohydrates

Plant and animal cells both use and store carbohydrates. But they use different types of carbohydrates and (you guessed it) you need to know how they vary.

Polysaccharides

Polysaccharides are made from lots of monosaccharides (sugars) joined together (see page 34). You need to know about the relationship between the structure and function of three polysaccharides — cellulose, starch and glycogen.

Cellulose

Cellulose is the major component of cell walls in plants. It's made of long, unbranched chains of beta-glucose.

Beta-glucose

Glucose is a monosaccharide with two forms — α and β. β-glucose is basically the same as α-glucose (see page 34), but the OH and H on the right are swapped around — see Figure 1.

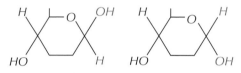

Figure 1: *β-glucose molecule (left) and α-glucose molecule (right).*

Condensation reactions

When monosaccharides join, a molecule of water is released. This is called a **condensation reaction**. The bonds that join monosaccharides together are called **glycosidic bonds**.

Cellulose is formed when beta-glucose is linked by condensation:

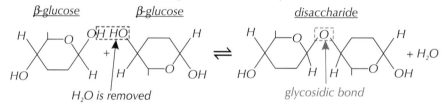

The second β-glucose molecule in this condensation reaction has been flipped upside down. This lines the two OH groups up so the glycosidic bond is straight.

Structure of cellulose

The bonds between the sugars are straight, so the cellulose chains are straight. The cellulose chains are linked together by **hydrogen bonds** to form strong fibres called **microfibrils** — see Figure 2. The strong fibres mean cellulose provides structural support for cells (e.g. in plant cell walls).

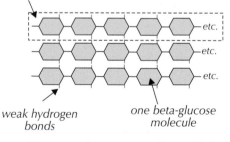

Figure 2: *The structure of microfibril.*

Starch

Starch is the main energy storage material in plants. Cells get energy from glucose, and plants store excess glucose as starch (when a plant needs more glucose for energy it breaks down starch to release the glucose). Starch is insoluble in water so it doesn't cause water to enter cells by osmosis, which would make them swell (see p. 63). This makes it good for storage. Starch is a mixture of two polysaccharides of alpha-glucose — amylose and amylopectin:

Tip: You can test for the presence of starch using the iodine test (see page 37).

Amylose

Amylose is a long, unbranched chain of α-glucose. The angles of the glycosidic bonds are different between two α-glucose molecules than they are between two β-glucose molecules. This gives amylose a coiled structure, almost like a cylinder. This makes it compact, so it's really good for storage because you can fit more in to a small space.

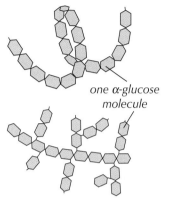

one α-glucose molecule

Exam Tip
Always specify whether you're talking about α-glucose or β-glucose — you won't get a mark for only saying glucose.

Amylopectin

Amylopectin is a long, branched chain of α-glucose. Its side branches allow the enzymes that break down the molecule to get at the glycosidic bonds easily. This means that the glucose can be released quickly.

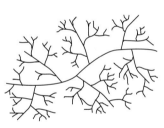

Figure 4: The structures of amylose (top) and amylopectin (bottom).

Glycogen

Glycogen is the main energy storage material in animals. Animal cells get energy from glucose too, but animals store excess glucose as glycogen — another polysaccharide of alpha-glucose. Its structure is very similar to amylopectin, except that it has loads more side branches coming off it — see Figure 5. Loads of branches means that stored glucose can be released quickly, which is important for energy release in animals. It's also a very compact molecule, so it's good for storage.

Tip: Starch and glycogen are also formed by condensation reactions.

Figure 5: The structure of glycogen.

Practice Questions — Fact Recall

Q1 What is the main energy storage material in:
  a) plants,
  b) animals?
Q2 Draw a β-glucose molecule.
Q3 What type of bond joins two β-glucose molecules together?
Q4 a) Which carbohydrate is the major component of plant cell walls?
  b) Describe the structure of this carbohydrate, and explain how its structure makes it suited to its function in cell walls.
Q5 Sketch and label a diagram of a microfibril.
Q6 a) Is starch soluble or insoluble?
  b) Use your answer to a) to describe why starch is good for storage.

Q7 a) Name the structures shown below:

A   B

b) Explain an advantage of structure A that makes it suitable for energy storage.

Q8 Describe the structure of glycogen and explain how its structure makes it suited to its function.

Section Summary

Make sure you know...

- That haemoglobin's role is to transport oxygen around the body.
- That haemoglobin is a large protein with a quaternary structure.
- That there are chemically similar versions of haemoglobin found in many different organisms.
- That affinity for oxygen means the tendency a molecule has to bind with oxygen.
- That oxygen 'loading' refers to oxygen binding to haemoglobin and oxygen 'unloading' refers to oxygen being released from haemoglobin.
- That as partial pressure of oxygen (pO_2) increases, haemoglobin's affinity for oxygen increases.
- That a dissociation curve shows how saturated haemoglobin is at any given partial pressure.
- That an increase in carbon dioxide concentration (pCO_2) increases the rate of oxygen unloading and the dissociation curve shifts right — this is called the Bohr effect.
- That organisms living in environments with a low oxygen concentration have haemoglobin with a high affinity for oxygen, so that it can load more oxygen.
- That active organisms with a high oxygen demand have haemoglobin with a low affinity for oxygen, so that it can unload more oxygen.
- That mammals with a high surface area to volume ratio have a high metabolic rate and a high oxygen demand, so have haemoglobin with a lower affinity for oxygen than the haemoglobin of larger mammals.
- That both plant and animal cells contain a plasma membrane, a nucleus, cytoplasm, mitochondria and ribosomes.
- That plant cells, but not animal cells, contain a cell wall, permanent vacuole and chloroplasts.
- That chloroplasts have a double membrane, thykaloid membranes, grana and stroma, and that photosynthesis happens in the grana and stroma.
- That plant cells have adaptations to suit their function in relation to the structures they contain.
- That the structure of β-glucose is:

- That cellulose is formed by glycosidic bonds forming between β-glucose molecules in condensation reactions.
- That cellulose is the main component of plant cell walls and is made long, unbranched chains of β-glucose.
- That starch is the main energy storage material in plants and is made from amylose and amylopectin.
- That glycogen is the main energy storage in animals and is made from long, branched chains of α-glucose.

1 Cats, pumas and foxes were used in a study to investigate haemoglobin's affinity for oxygen. For each type of animal, blood was taken from a sample that lived at sea level and a sample that lived at high altitude. The pO_2 at which each animal's haemoglobin was 50% saturated was recorded. The results are shown below.

Animal	Sea Level (pO_2 / kPa)	High Altitude (pO_2 / kPa)
Cat	3.9	3.0
Puma	4.8	4.1
Fox	3.5	2.5

(a) Describe the structure of haemoglobin.

(2 marks)

(b) There is less oxygen at high altitudes than at sea level.

Use evidence from the table to support this statement.

(3 marks)

(c) The dissociation curves for the three mammals at sea level are shown on the right.
Match each mammal to its dissociation curve, A, B or C.

(1 mark)

(d) Describe and explain what happens to an oxygen dissociation curve as the saturation level of haemoglobin is approaching 100%.

(3 marks)

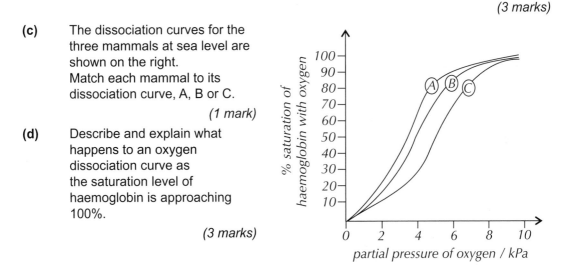

(e) Mammals with a larger surface area to volume ratio tend to have a higher rate of respiration than mammals with a smaller surface area to volume ratio.

Assuming activity levels are similar for all three mammals, suggest which mammal has the largest surface area to volume ratio. Explain your answer.

(4 marks)

(f) The study was extended to investigate the effect of pCO_2 on haemoglobin's affinity for oxygen. To do this a fox was put in a high pCO_2 atmosphere. Describe and explain how this would have changed the fox's haemoglobin dissociation curve.

(3 marks)

2   Photosynthesis is the process by which plants synthesise glucose
from carbon dioxide and water using light as an energy source.

   (a)   Name the plant cell organelle where photosynthesis occurs and describe the internal
structures of this organelle.

(5 marks)

   (b)   Glucose is a product of photosynthesis. It is stored as starch in a plant.
Amylose is one of the polysaccharides that forms starch.

      (i)   Name the other polysaccharide present in starch molecules.

(1 mark)

      (ii) Describe the structure of amylose and explain how its structure
makes it suited to its function.

(3 marks)

3   Cellulose is a polysaccharide.

   (a)   The diagram below shows cellulose chains linked together to form a microfibril.

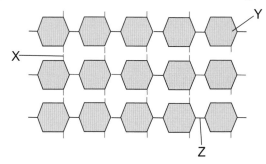

      (i)   Name the parts of the diagram labelled X, Y and Z.

(3 marks)

      (ii) Describe one feature of a microfibril that makes it suited to its function.

(2 marks)

   (b)   Starch is also a polysaccharide.
Describe three ways in which cellulose differs from starch.

(3 marks)

   (c)   The diagram below shows a glucose molecule that makes up cellulose.

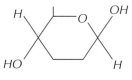

      (i)   Draw the reaction to show how two molecules of glucose link together to form
cellulose.

(3 marks)

      (ii) What name is given to this type of reaction?

(1 mark)

1. DNA Replication

Cells inside you are dividing all the time (see page 146). For cells to divide, DNA has to copy itself, so that each new cell has the full amount of DNA.

How is DNA replicated?

DNA is replicated in three main stages:

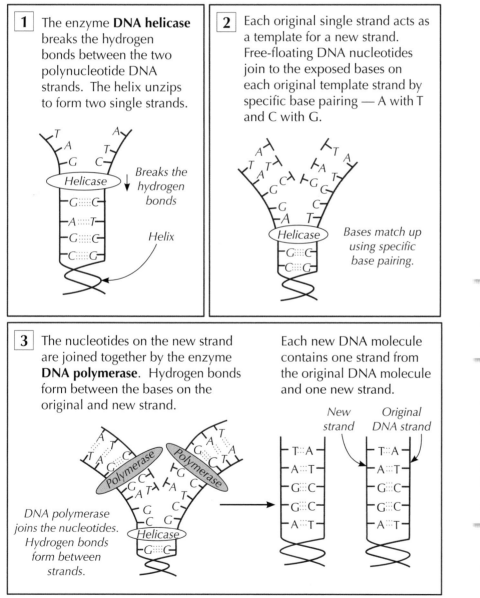

1 The enzyme **DNA helicase** breaks the hydrogen bonds between the two polynucleotide DNA strands. The helix unzips to form two single strands.

Breaks the hydrogen bonds

Helix

2 Each original single strand acts as a template for a new strand. Free-floating DNA nucleotides join to the exposed bases on each original template strand by specific base pairing — A with T and C with G.

Bases match up using specific base pairing.

3 The nucleotides on the new strand are joined together by the enzyme **DNA polymerase**. Hydrogen bonds form between the bases on the original and new strand.

Each new DNA molecule contains one strand from the original DNA molecule and one new strand.

New strand   *Original DNA strand*

DNA polymerase joins the nucleotides. Hydrogen bonds form between strands.

This type of copying is called **semi-conservative replication** because half of the new DNA molecules are from the original piece of DNA.

Learning Objectives:

- Understand the semi-conservative replication of DNA in terms of:
  - the breaking of hydrogen bonds between polynucleotide strands,
  - the attraction of new DNA nucleotides to exposed bases,
  - base pairing,
  - the role of DNA helicase and of DNA polymerase.
- Be able to analyse, interpret and evaluate data from early experiments on the role and importance of DNA.

  Specification Reference 3.2.5

Tip: See p. 115 for more on DNA structure.

Tip: Make sure you don't get the role of the two enzymes confused. DNA **h**elicase breaks **h**ydrogen bonds. DNA **p**olymerase joins the nucleotides together to form a **p**olymer.

Tip: DNA replication isn't a perfect process — during replication mutations can occur.

Q1 The diagram on the right shows a molecule of DNA. Draw the original and replicated strands after semi-conservative replication.

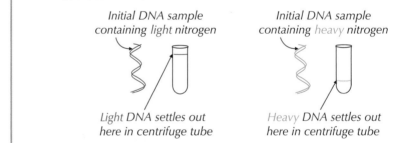

Interpreting early experiments on DNA

In the exam you might have to interpret experimental evidence that shows the role and importance of DNA. Here are some examples of the early experiments that were carried out.

┌ **Examples** ─────────────────────────────

Evidence for the semi-conservative replication of DNA

Meselson and Stahl showed DNA replicated using the semi-conservative method. Their experiment used two isotopes of nitrogen (DNA contains nitrogen) — heavy nitrogen (^{15}N) and light nitrogen (^{14}N).

1. Two samples of bacteria were grown — one in a nutrient broth containing light nitrogen, and one in a broth with heavy nitrogen. As the bacteria reproduced, they took up nitrogen from the broth to help make nucleotides for new DNA. So the nitrogen gradually became part of the bacteria's DNA.

2. A sample of DNA was taken from each batch of bacteria, and spun in a centrifuge. The DNA from the heavy nitrogen bacteria settled lower down the centrifuge tube than the DNA from the light nitrogen bacteria — because it's heavier.

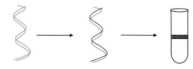

Initial DNA sample containing light nitrogen   *Initial DNA sample containing heavy nitrogen*

Light DNA settles out here in centrifuge tube   *Heavy DNA settles out here in centrifuge tube*

3. Then the bacteria grown in the heavy nitrogen broth were taken out and put in a broth containing only light nitrogen. The bacteria were left for one round of DNA replication, and then another DNA sample was taken out and spun in the centrifuge.

4. The DNA sample settled out in the middle of where the light nitrogen DNA settled out and where the heavy nitrogen DNA settled out. This was because the new bacterial DNA molecules contained one strand of the old DNA containing heavy nitrogen and one strand of new DNA containing light nitrogen. This meant that the new bacterial DNA had replicated semi-conservatively in the light nitrogen.

Figure 1: Liquid growth medium or broth before bacteria are added.

Heavy nitrogen bacteria replicates in light nitrogen broth   *DNA with combination of heavy original strands and light new strands settled out here*

Evidence of hereditary molecules

Scientists carried out an experiment with mice and the bacteria causing pneumonia (*S. pneumoniae*) to show there's a hereditary molecule (genetic material). They used two strains of *S. pneumoniae* — a disease-causing strain (D) and a non-disease-causing strain (N). Here's what happened:

1. Mice injected with strain D died and with strain N survived.
2. The strain D bacteria were then killed.
   The killed D strain was injected into mice — they survived.
3. The killed D strain and live N strain were injected together — they died.

This showed that killed D strain had passed on an inheritance molecule to the live N strain, making it capable of causing disease.

Evidence that DNA is the genetic material

Scientists were unsure if the hereditary molecule was DNA, RNA or protein. They investigated it by treating the killed D strain with protease (destroys protein), RNase (destroys RNA) or DNase (destroys DNA) and then injecting it along with live N strain into mice. The strains that had been treated with DNase didn't kill the mice, so DNA was shown to be the hereditary molecule.

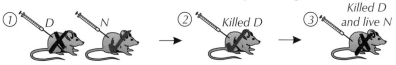

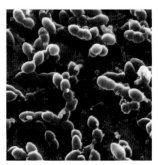

Figure 2: S. pneumoniae *bacteria were used to show there's a hereditary molecule.*

Exam Tip
You don't need to learn these experiments for the exam — they just show the types of experiments that could come up.

Exam Tip
You might get an unknown experiment in the exam and be asked questions about it. Don't let this throw you — just make sure you read the experiment method carefully and use your knowledge to answer the question.

Practice Question — Application

Q1 When viruses infect bacteria they inject their genetic material into the cell. Scientists labelled the DNA of some viruses with radioactive phosphate, ^{32}P, and the protein of some more viruses with radioactive sulfur, ^{35}S. They then let the viruses infect some bacteria. Here are the results:

Radioactive label	Where the label was found in the bacteria sample
^{32}P	Inside the bacteria
^{35}S	Outside the bacteria

Explain how this experiment shows that DNA is the genetic material.

Practice Questions — Fact Recall

Q1 Name the two enzymes involved in DNA replication.

Q2 Describe the first stage of DNA replication, in which two strands of DNA are separated.

Q3 Describe the second stage of DNA replication, where a single strand of DNA acts as a template.

Q4 DNA is copied by semi-conservative replication. What is meant by this?

- Understand that DNA is replicated during interphase.

- Understand that mitosis is part of the cell cycle.

- Know that mitosis increases cell number for growth and tissue repair.

- Understand that during mitosis the parent cell divides to produce two daughter cells, each containing an exact copy of the DNA of the parent cell.

- Be able to name and explain the events that occur during each stage of mitosis.

- Be able to recognise the stages of mitosis from drawings and photographs.

Specification Reference 3.2.5

2. The Cell Cycle and Mitosis

We need new cells for growth and to replace damaged tissue, so our body cells need to be able to make more of themselves. They do this during the cell cycle...

The cell cycle

The cell cycle is the process that all body cells from multicellular organisms use to grow and divide. The cell cycle starts when a cell has been produced by cell division and ends with the cell dividing to produce two identical cells. The cell cycle (see Figure 1) consists of a period of cell growth and DNA replication, called **interphase**, and a period of cell division, called **mitosis**. Interphase (cell growth) is subdivided into three separate growth stages. These are called G_1, S and G_2.

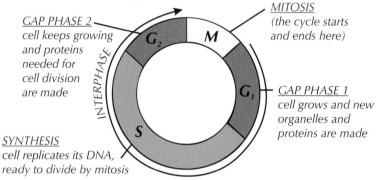

Figure 1: Stages of the cell cycle.

Interphase

During interphase the cell carries out normal functions, but also prepares to divide. The cell's DNA is unravelled and replicated, to double its genetic content. The organelles are also replicated so it has spare ones, and its ATP content is increased (ATP provides the energy needed for cell division).

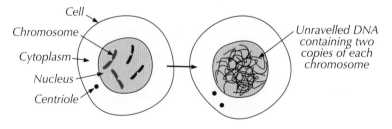

Figure 2: Interphase in bluebell cells.

Mitosis

There are two types of cell division — mitosis and meiosis (see p. 122 for more on meiosis). Mitosis is the form of cell division that occurs during the cell cycle. In mitosis a parent cell divides to produce two genetically identical daughter cells (they contain an exact copy of the DNA of the parent cell). Mitosis is needed for the growth of multicellular organisms (like us) and for repairing damaged tissues. How else do you think you get from being a baby to being a big, strapping teenager — it's because the cells in our bodies grow and divide.

Mitosis is really one continuous process, but it's described as a series of division stages — prophase, metaphase, anaphase and telophase (see the next page).

The structure of chromosomes in mitosis

Before we go into the detail of mitosis, you need to know more about the structure of chromosomes. As mitosis begins, the chromosomes are made of two strands joined in the middle by a **centromere**. The separate strands are called **chromatids**. Two strands on the same chromosome are called **sister chromatids**. There are two strands because each chromosome has already made an identical copy of itself during interphase. When mitosis is over, the chromatids end up as one-strand chromosomes in the new daughter cells.

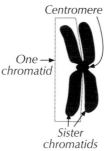

Centromere

One chromatid

Sister chromatids

Tip: You could remember the order of the phases in mitosis (**p**rophase, **m**etaphase, **a**naphase, **t**elophase) by using, 'purple mice are tasty'.

1. Prophase

The chromosomes condense, getting shorter and fatter. Tiny bundles of protein called centrioles start moving to opposite ends of the cell, forming a network of protein fibres across it called the spindle. The nuclear envelope (the membrane around the nucleus) breaks down and chromosomes lie free in the cytoplasm.

Centrioles move to opposite ends of the cell

Nuclear membrane starts to break down

Centromere

***Figure 3**: Prophase in bluebell cells.*

2. Metaphase

The chromosomes (each with two chromatids) line up along the middle of the cell and become attached to the spindle by their centromere.

Spindle fibres

Centromeres on spindle equator

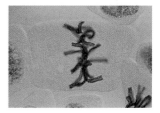

***Figure 4**: Metaphase in bluebell cells.*

3. Anaphase

The centromeres divide, separating each pair of sister chromatids. The spindles contract, pulling chromatids to opposite ends of the cell, centromere first.

Sister chromatids moving to opposite ends of the cell

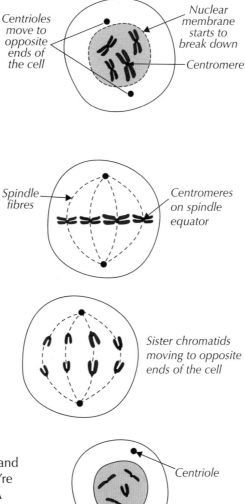

***Figure 5**: Anaphase in bluebell cells.*

4. Telophase

The chromatids reach the opposite poles on the spindle. They uncoil and become long and thin again. They're now called chromosomes again. A nuclear envelope forms around each group of chromosomes, so there are now two nuclei. The cytoplasm divides and there are now two daughter cells that are genetically identical to the original cell and to each other. Mitosis is finished and each daughter cell starts the interphase part of the cell cycle to get ready for the next round of mitosis.

Centriole

Cytoplasm beginning to divide

***Figure 6**: Telophase in bluebell cells.*

Practice Questions — Application

Q1 The photo on the right shows
    mitosis in onion cells.

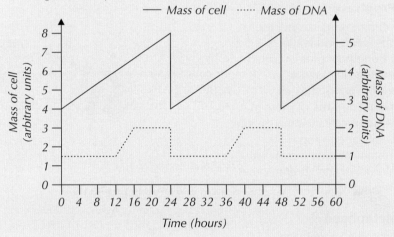

a) Which cell (A-C) is
   undergoing the following:

   i) metaphase,

   ii) prophase?

b) Describe the stage of mitosis shown by cell A.

Q2 The graph below shows changes in the mass of a cell and its DNA
    during the cell cycle.

a) During which hours does synthesis take place? Explain your
   answer.

b) At which hours does mitosis take place? Explain your answer.

c) Describe what is happening within the cell between
   0 and 24 hours.

d) i) How many cell divisions are shown on the graph?
       Explain your answer.

   ii) At what time will the next cell division take place?

Practice Questions — Fact Recall

Q1 What is the cell cycle?

Q2 How many cells are produced during mitosis?

Q3 In mitosis, a parent cell divides to produce genetically different
    daughter cells. True or False?

Q4 Why is mitosis needed?

Q5 Describe what happens during prophase.

Q6 During which stage of mitosis do chromosomes line up along
    the centre of a cell?

Q7 During which stage of mitosis are chromatids are pulled to opposite
    poles of the cell?

Q8 Describe what happens during telophase.

3. Cancer

Normally there are checks and controls within a cell that make sure the cell cycle happens just the way it should. This is important because disruptions to the cell cycle can lead to cancer...

What is cancer?

Cell growth and cell division are controlled by genes. Normally, when cells have divided enough times to make enough new cells, they stop. But if there's a mutation in a gene that controls cell division, the cells can grow out of control. The cells keep on dividing to make more and more cells, which form a **tumour**. Cancer is a tumour that invades surrounding tissue.

Cancer treatments

Some treatments for cancer are designed to disrupt the cell cycle. These treatments don't distinguish tumour cells from normal cells though — they also kill normal body cells that are dividing. However, tumour cells divide much more frequently than normal cells, so the treatments are more likely to kill tumour cells.

┌─ Examples ─────────────────────────────────

Some cell cycle targets of cancer treatments include:

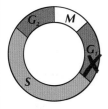

G_1 (cell growth and protein production)

Some chemical drugs (chemotherapy) prevent the synthesis of enzymes needed for DNA replication. If these aren't produced, the cell is unable to enter the synthesis phase (S), disrupting the cell cycle and forcing the cell to kill itself.

S phase (DNA replication)

Radiation and some drugs damage DNA. When the cell gets to S phase it checks for damaged DNA and if any is detected it kills itself, preventing further tumour growth.

Because cancer treatments kill normal cells too, certain steps are taken to reduce the impact on normal body cells.

┌─ Examples ─────────────────────────────────

Repeated treatments are given with periods of non-treatment (breaks) in between. A large dose could kill all the tumour but also so many normal cells that the patient could die. Repeated treatments with breaks allows the body to recover and produce new cells. The treatment is repeated as any tumour cells not killed by the treatment will keep dividing and growing during the breaks too. The break period is kept short so the body can recover but the cancer can't grow back to the same size as before.

A chunk of tumour is often removed first using surgery. This removes a lot of tumour cells and increases the access of any left to nutrients and oxygen, which triggers them to enter the cell cycle, making them more susceptible to treatment.

Learning Objective:

- Be able to apply your understanding of the cell cycle to cancer and its treatment.

Specification Reference 3.2.5

Tip: Mutations are changes in the base sequence of an organism's DNA (see p. 121).

Tip: Rapidly dividing cells, like hair cells and cells that line the gut, are often affected by cancer treatments. This can cause side effects like hair loss.

Tip: Cancer is basically uncontrolled cell division.

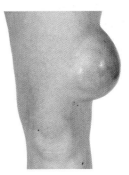

Figure 1: Cancer of the knee — the tumour is sticking out of the leg.

Practice Questions — Application

Tip: Don't let the tricky names of the drugs throw you when answering Q1 here. Just apply your knowledge to the information given in the question.

Q1 Methotrexate and vincristine are drugs used to treat cancer. Methotrexate blocks the formation of nucleotides within cells and vincristine prevents the formation of spindle fibres within the nuclei of cells. Which stage of the cell cycle is disrupted by:

a) methotrexate,

b) vincristine?

Q2 The graph below shows the number of healthy cells and cancer cells in a cancer patient, during their course of chemotherapy. Each session of chemotherapy lasts for a few days and is followed by a break period.

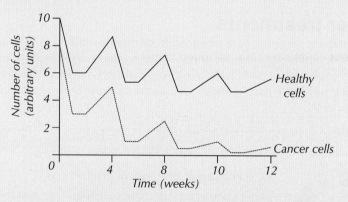

a) How many sessions of chemotherapy did the patient go through?

b) Chemotherapy stops the cell cycle at the G_1 stage. Explain why, during each session of chemotherapy, the number of cancer cells decreases by a greater amount than the number of healthy cells.

c) i) How long is each break period between the sessions of chemotherapy?

   ii) Explain why the break period is kept short.

d) Explain why the patient can't receive a large dose of chemotherapy all at once.

Q3 If the DNA in a normal cell is damaged, a protein call ATM causes the cell cycle to stop. A mutation in the gene for ATM can cause cancer, such as breast cancer. Explain how.

Practice Questions — Fact Recall

Q1 Describe the difference in the number of times a normal body cell divides compared to a cancer cell.

Q2 What is cancer?

Q3 Describe one example of how a cancer treatment targets a part of the cell cycle.

Q4 Explain why part of a tumour is often removed prior to treatment with chemotherapy.

4. Cell Differentiation and Organisation

There are loads of different types of cell in your body, which are grouped together to make up tissues, organs and organ systems.

Differentiation

Multicellular organisms are made up from many different cell types, e.g. nerve cells, muscle cells, white blood cells. All these cell types are **specialised** — they're designed to carry out specific functions (see the examples below). The structure of each specialised cell type is adapted to suit its particular job. The process of becoming specialised is called differentiation.

┌─ **Examples** ──────────────────────

Squamous epithelium cells are found in many places. They're thin, with not much cytoplasm. In the lungs they line the alveoli and are thin to allow gases to pass through them easily.

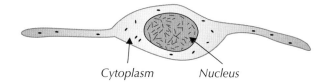

Cytoplasm   *Nucleus*

Palisade mesophyll cells in leaves are where photosynthesis occurs. They contain many chloroplasts, so they can absorb as much sunlight as possible. The walls are thin, so carbon dioxide can easily enter.

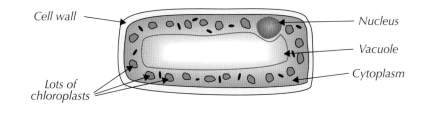

Cell wall   *Nucleus*
                Vacuole
                Cytoplasm
Lots of chloroplasts

Practice Question — Application

Q1 The diagrams below show a red blood cell and a root hair cell.

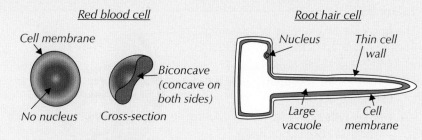

Red blood cell
Cell membrane
No nucleus   Cross-section
Biconcave (concave on both sides)

Root hair cell
Nucleus   Thin cell wall
Large vacuole   Cell membrane

Explain one way in which:

a) The red blood cell is adapted for transporting oxygen around the body.

b) The root cell is adapted for absorbing water from the soil.

Learning Objectives:

- Understand that the cells of multicellular organisms may differentiate and become adapted for specific functions.

- Know that:
    - tissues are aggregates of similar cells,
    - organs are aggregates of tissues performing specific physiological functions,
    - organs are organised into organ systems.

Specification Reference 3.2.6

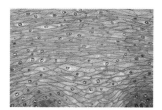

***Figure 1**: Squamous epithelial cells lining the oesophagus.*

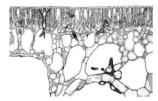

***Figure 2**: The band of green cells at the top of this water lily leaf are palisade mesophyll cells.*

Exam Tip
You could get asked how any type of cell is adapted for its function. All you need to do is look at each feature of the cell and think about how it helps the cell to do its job.

Tissues

Similar cells are grouped together into **tissues**.

---Examples---

Squamous epithelium tissue is a single layer of flat cells lining a surface. Squamous epithelium tissue is found in many places including the alveoli in the lungs.

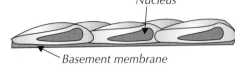

Nucleus

Basement membrane

Phloem tissue transports sugars around the plant. It's arranged in tubes and is made up of sieve cells, companion cells, and some ordinary plant cells. Each sieve cell has end walls with holes in them, so that sap can move easily through them. These end walls are called sieve plates.

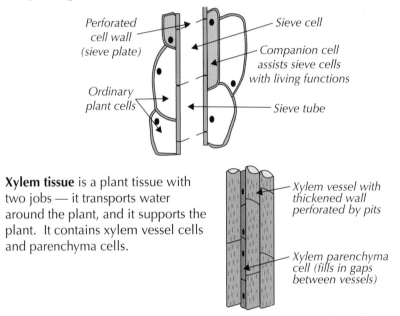

Perforated cell wall (sieve plate)

Sieve cell

Companion cell assists sieve cells with living functions

Ordinary plant cells

Sieve tube

Tip: Tissues aren't always made up of one type of cell. Some tissues include different types of cell working together. For example, blood is a tissue made up of red blood cells and white blood cells.

Xylem tissue is a plant tissue with two jobs — it transports water around the plant, and it supports the plant. It contains xylem vessel cells and parenchyma cells.

Xylem vessel with thickened wall perforated by pits

Xylem parenchyma cell (fills in gaps between vessels)

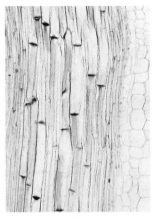

Figure 3: *Phloem vessels in a Cucurbita plant. The sieve cells are stained blue and the sieve plates are dark green.*

Organs

An organ is a group of different tissues that work together to perform a particular function.

---Examples---

The **lungs** are an example of an animal organ. They're made up of the following tissues:

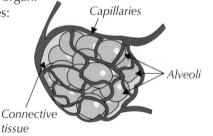

Capillaries

Alveoli

Connective tissue

- Squamous epithelium tissue — surrounds the alveoli (where gas exchange occurs).

- Fibrous connective tissue — forms a continuous mesh around the lungs and contains fibres that help to force the air back out of the lungs when exhaling.

- Blood vessels — capillaries surround the alveoli.

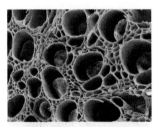

Figure 4: *Xylem tissue in a rootlet. The xylem vessels are brown and the parenchyma cells green.*

Exam Tip
Remember, the important bit of the definition of an organ is that it's made up of different tissues.

The **leaf** is an example of a plant organ. It's made up of the following tissues:

- Lower epidermis — contains stomata (pores) to let air in and out for gas exchange.
- Spongy mesophyll — full of spaces to let gases circulate.
- Palisade mesophyll — most photosynthesis occurs here.
- Xylem — carries water to the leaf.
- Phloem — carries sugars away from the leaf.
- Upper epidermis — covered in a waterproof waxy cuticle to reduce water loss.

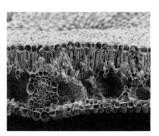

Figure 5: *The cross section of a taro leaf. The palisade mesophyll is bright green, the spongy mesophyll yellow, and the xylem and phloem are grey.*

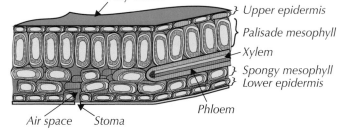

Organ systems

Organs work together to form organ systems — each system has a particular function.

Exam Tip
Make sure you know the definition of tissues, organs and organ systems really well. You could be asked to apply your knowledge to lots of different examples in the exam — and it's easy marks if you've got the definitions straight in your head.

Examples

The **circulatory system** allows the transport of gases and other substances around the body. It includes:

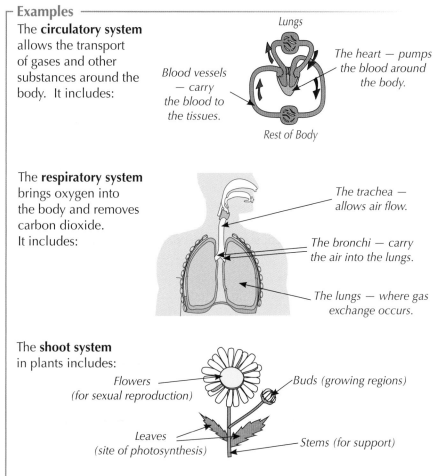

The **respiratory system** brings oxygen into the body and removes carbon dioxide. It includes:

Tip: There's more information about the respiratory system in Unit 1 Section 4 and the circulatory system in Unit 1 Section 5.

The **shoot system** in plants includes:

Figure 6: *The flower, bud, stems and leaves of a shoot system.*

Q1 What is a specialised cell?

Q2 What is the name given to the process by which cells become specialised?

Q3 Give an example of a specialised cell.

Q4 Explain the difference between a tissue and an organ.

Q5 What is an organ system?

Q6 Give an example of an organ system and explain why it is classed as an organ system.

Section Summary

Make sure you know:

- The process of semi-conservative replication — the hydrogen bonds between polynucleotide strands are broken, free nucleotides join to the exposed bases by base pairing, and the nucleotides are joined together to form a DNA molecule with one new strand and one original strand.

- The function of DNA helicase (it breaks hydrogen bonds between polynucleotide strands) and DNA polymerase (it joins nucleotides together to form a new polynucleotide strand).

- How to analyse, interpret and evaluate experimental data relating to the role and importance of DNA.

- The stages of the cell cycle — interphase (gap phase 1, synthesis, and gap phase 2) and mitosis.

- That DNA replication takes place during interphase (synthesis) of the cell cycle.

- That two new cells are produced by mitosis for growth and tissue repair, each containing an exact copy of the parent cell's DNA.

- The stages of mitosis — prophase (chromosomes condense, the spindle forms and the nuclear envelope breaks down), metaphase (chromosomes line up along the centre of the cell and attach to the spindle), anaphase (the spindle contracts, pulling chromatids to opposite poles of the cell) and telophase (the cytoplasm divides, forming two new cells).

- How to recognise the stages of mitosis from drawings and photographs.

- That cancer is a tumour which invades surrounding tissue and is caused by uncontrolled cell division.

- That some cancer treatments disrupt the cell cycle.

- That the cells of multicellular organisms are specialised (adapted for a specific function) and that the process of becoming specialised is called differentiation.

- That tissues are similar cells grouped together.

- That an organ is a group of different tissues that work together to perform a particular function.

- That organs work together to form organ systems, and that each system has a particular function.

Exam-style Questions

1 A team of scientists has been investigating the interphase stage of the cell cycle.

(a) (i) During which stage of interphase does DNA replication occur?

(1 mark)

(ii) Describe how the amount of DNA in a cell changes during interphase and explain why.

(2 marks)

(iii) Describe the process of semi-conservative DNA replication.

(6 marks)

(b) The team analysed a sample of dividing cells using a flow cytometer (a machine that sorts cells). A graph was produced of the amount of DNA against the number of cells with that amount of DNA. The graph is shown below.

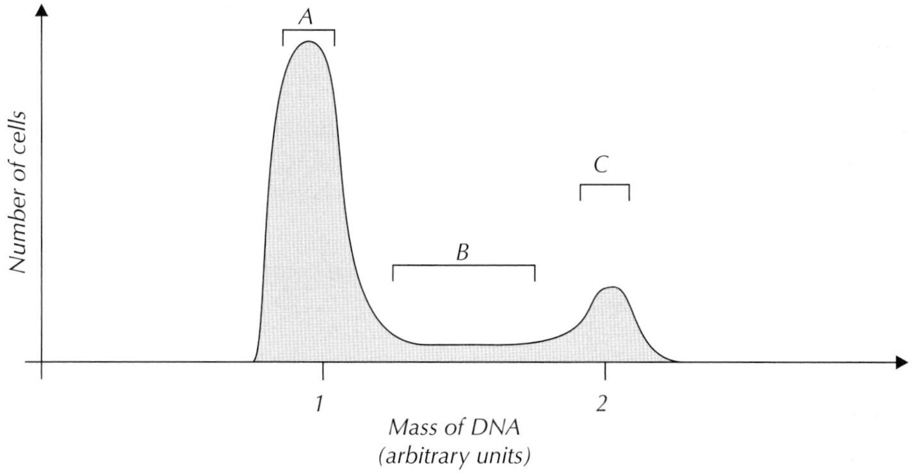

Three stages of interphase are shown by the labels A, B and C on the graph. Name each phase and explain your answers.

(3 marks)

(c) Suggest why there are more cells in phase A than in stage C.

(1 mark)

2 The cell cycle contains two gap phases — G_1 and G_2.

(a) Describe what happens to the cell during each of these stages.

(2 marks)

A cancer treatment targets the G_1 stage.

(b) Describe the effect of the cancer treatment on the cell.

(2 marks)

(c) Cancer cells are more susceptible than healthy cells to cancer treatments which affect the cell cycle. Explain why.

(1 mark)

3 Proteins control all the different stages of the cell cycle. An experiment was conducted on the effect of protein X on mitosis in one species of yeast cells. At intervals the activity of the protein was measured and a microscope was used to determine the percentage of dividing yeast cells. The results are shown on the graph below.

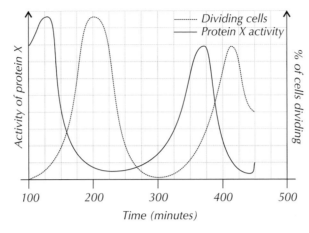

(a) Describe the trend shown on the graph.

(1 mark)

(b) A scientist uses the data shown in the graph to conclude there is a causal relationship between protein X activity and cell division in all species of yeast. Do you agree with his conclusion? Explain your answer.

(2 marks)

(c) Suggest a control experiment that could have been carried out and explain its purpose.

(2 marks)

(d) Give an advantage and disadvantage of measuring the percentage of dividing cells using a microscope.

(2 marks)

4 The diagram below shows an eye.

The iris, which controls how much light enters the eye.

The cornea, which refracts light into the eye. It's made up of five layers of cells, the outermost being the epithelium.

The retina, which is made up of light-sensitive cells called rods and cones.

(a) Is the eye a tissue or an organ?
Use evidence from the diagram to explain your answer.

(2 marks)

(b) In normal cells there is a protein called Rb that stops the cell from leaving the G_1 phase of the cell cycle unless the cell needs to divide. A mutation in the gene for Rb can cause retinoblastoma — an eye cancer. Explain why.

(3 marks)

1. Size and Surface Area

Every organism has substances it needs to take in and others it needs to get rid of in order to survive. An organism's size and surface area affect how quickly this is done.

Exchange of substances with the environment

Every organism, whatever its size, needs to exchange things with its environment. Cells need to take in oxygen (for aerobic respiration) and nutrients. They also need to excrete waste products like carbon dioxide and urea. Most organisms need to stay at roughly the same temperature, so heat needs to be exchanged too.

Surface area : volume ratio

An organism's surface area : volume ratio affects how quickly substances are exchanged. But before going into the effects of surface area : volume ratios, you need to understand a bit more about them. Smaller organisms have higher surface area : volume ratios than larger organisms, as shown in the example below.

--- **Example** ---

A mouse has a bigger surface area relative to its volume than a hippo. This can be hard to imagine, but you can prove it mathematically.

Imagine these animals as cubes...

The mouse could be represented by a cube measuring 1 cm × 1 cm × 1 cm.

Its volume is: $1 \times 1 \times 1 = 1 \text{ cm}^3$

Its surface area is: $6 \times 1 \times 1 = 6 \text{ cm}^2$

So the mouse has a surface area : volume ratio of <u>6 : 1</u>.

1 cm   1 cm
1 cm
"cube mouse"

Compare this to a cube hippo measuring 2 cm × 4 cm × 4 cm.

Its volume is: $2 \times 4 \times 4 = 32 \text{ cm}^3$

Its surface area is:

$2 \times 4 \times 4 = 32 \text{ cm}^2$
(top and bottom surfaces of cube)

$+ \ 4 \times 2 \times 4 = 32 \text{ cm}^2$
(four sides of the cube)

Total surface area = 64 cm^2

4 cm
4 cm
2 cm
"cube hippo"

So the hippo has a surface area : volume ratio of 64 : 32 or <u>2 : 1</u>.

The cube mouse's surface area is six times its volume, but the cube hippo's surface area is only twice its volume. Smaller animals have a bigger surface area compared to their volume.

Learning Objectives:

- Understand the relationship between the size of an organism or structure and surface area to volume ratio.

- Know that over large distances, efficient supply of materials is provided by mass transport.

- Be able to explain the significance of the relationship between size and surface area to volume ratio for the exchange of substances and heat.

- Know that changes to body shape and the development of systems in larger animals are adaptations. These adaptations facilitate exchange as the surface area : volume ratio reduces.

Specification Reference 3.2.7

Figure 1: *A hippo (top) has a small surface area:volume ratio. A mouse (bottom) has a large surface area:volume ratio.*

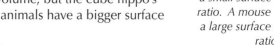

Q1 Below are three blocks of different sizes (not drawn to scale).

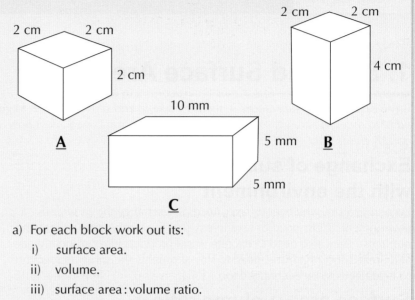

a) For each block work out its:
   i)   surface area.
   ii)   volume.
   iii) surface area : volume ratio.
b) Which block has the greatest surface area : volume ratio?

Figure 2: A bacterium — an example of a single-celled organism.

Exchange organs and mass transport systems

An organism needs to supply every one of its cells with substances like glucose and oxygen (for respiration). It also needs to remove waste products from every cell to avoid damaging itself. Different sized organisms do this in different ways:

Single-celled organisms

In single-celled organisms, these substances can **diffuse** directly into (or out of) the cell across the cell surface membrane. The diffusion rate is quick because of the small distances the substances have to travel (see p. 62).

Multicellular organisms

In multicellular organisms, diffusion across the outer membrane is too slow, for two reasons:

1. Some cells are deep within the body — there's a big distance between them and the outside environment.

2. Larger animals have a low surface area to volume ratio — it's difficult to exchange enough substances to supply a large volume of animal through a relatively small outer surface.

So rather than using straightforward diffusion to absorb and excrete substances, multicellular organisms need specialised **exchange organs** (like lungs — see p. 75).

They also need an efficient system to carry substances to and from their individual cells — this is **mass transport**. In mammals, 'mass transport' normally refers to the circulatory system, which uses blood to carry glucose and oxygen around the body. It also carries hormones, antibodies and waste like CO_2.

Heat exchange

As well as creating waste products that need to be transported away, the metabolic activity inside cells creates heat. Staying at the right temperature is difficult, and it's pretty heavily influenced by your size and shape...

Body size

The rate of heat loss from an organism depends on its surface area. As you saw on page 157, if an organism has a large volume, e.g. a hippo, its surface area is relatively small. This makes it harder for it to lose heat from its body. If an organism is small, e.g. a mouse, its relative surface area is large, so heat is lost more easily.

Body shape

Animals with a compact shape have a small surface area relative to their volume — minimising heat loss from their surface. Animals with a less compact shape (those that are a bit gangly or have sticky outy bits) have a larger surface area relative to their volume — this increases heat loss from their surface.

Adaptations for heat exchange

Whether an animal is compact or not depends on the temperature of its environment — the animal's body shape is **adapted** to suit its environment.

Tip: Imagine you're feeling really cold in bed. You might curl up into a ball to keep warm. Doing this makes you more compact and reduces the surface area you have exposed to the environment (so reduces your surface area : volume ratio). The reverse is true when you're too hot — you spread as wide as you can to increase the surface area you have exposed (and increase your surface area : volume ratio).

Exam Tip
Make sure you write about surface area : volume ratio in the exam and not just surface area.

Examples

Arctic fox

Body temperature — 37 °C
Average outside temperature — 0 °C

The Arctic fox has small ears and a round head to reduce its surface area : volume ratio and heat loss.

African bat-eared fox

Body temperature — 37 °C
Average outside temperature — 25 °C

The African bat-eared fox has large ears and a more pointed nose to increase its surface area : volume ratio and heat loss.

European fox

Body temperature — 37 °C
Average outside temperature — 12 °C

The European fox is intermediate between the two, matching the temperature of its environment.

Practice Questions — Application

Q1 An Emperor penguin is much larger than an Adélie penguin.

   a) Which penguin would you expect to have the larger surface area : volume ratio?

   b) Which penguin would you expect to find in the coldest regions? Explain your answer.

Q2 An Adélie penguin has a compact shape with short wings and legs. A Rockhopper penguin is less compact with longer wings and legs. Assuming the two penguins are roughly the same size, explain which one you would expect to live in the colder regions.

Figure 3: *A squirrel eats high energy foods to fuel its high metabolic rate.*

Figure 4: *A woodland jumping mouse hibernates to keep warm.*

Figure 5: *An elephant's large, flat ears help it keep cool.*

Behavioural and other physiological adaptations for heat exchange

Not all organisms have a body size or shape to suit their climate — some have other adaptations to aid exchange instead...

- Animals with a high surface area : volume ratio tend to lose more water as it evaporates from their surface. This is a problem particularly for animals living in hot regions where water evaporates quickly. Some small desert mammals have kidney structure adaptations so that they produce less urine to compensate.

- Smaller animals living in colder regions often have a much higher metabolic rate to compensate for their high surface area : volume ratio — this helps to keep them warm by creating more heat. To do this they need to eat large amounts of high energy foods such as seeds and nuts.

- Smaller mammals may have thick layers of fur or hibernate when the weather gets really cold.

- Larger organisms living in hot regions, such as elephants and hippos, find it hard to keep cool as their heat loss is relatively slow. Elephants have developed large flat ears which increase their surface area, allowing them to lose more heat. Hippos spend much of the day in the water — a behavioural adaptation to help them lose heat.

Practice Questions — Application

Q1 In snowy, winter months small animals such as mice and voles live in underground tunnels. Suggest why they have developed this behaviour.

Q2 In winter some birds 'fluff' their feathers to trap more warm air close to their body. Would you expect this physiological adaptation to be more common among small or large birds? Explain your answer.

Q3 Some large desert animals, such as coyotes, sleep during the day and are only active at night. Suggest why they have this behaviour.

Practice Questions — Fact Recall

Q1 a) Name two substances an animal needs to take in from its environment.

   b) Name two substances an animal needs to release into its environment.

Q2 Do most large animals have a higher or lower surface area : volume ratio than small animals?

Q3 Give two reasons why diffusion is too slow in multicellular organisms for them to absorb and excrete substances this way.

Q4 What is meant by a 'mass transport' system?

Q5 Will the rate of heat loss at a given temperature be greater for an animal with a high or low surface area : volume ratio?

Q6 Explain how an animal's shape can help to control its temperature.

Q7 Other than body size or shape, give two adaptations a small animal may have to survive in a cold environment.

Q8 Other than body size or shape, give two adaptations a large animal might have to survive in a hot environment.

2. Gas Exchange

Organisms are constantly exchanging gases with their environment. In large organisms that's not always easy, so many plants, animals and insects have adaptations to aid gas exchange.

Gas exchange surfaces

Gas exchange occurs over a **gas exchange surface** — a boundary between the outside environment and the internal environment of an organism. Most gas exchange surfaces have two things in common that increase the rate of diffusion:

1. They have a large surface area.
2. They're thin (often just one layer of epithelial cells) — this provides a short diffusion pathway across the gas exchange surface.

The organism also maintains a steep concentration gradient of gases across the exchange surface, which increases the rate of diffusion.

Gas exchange in single-celled organisms

Single-celled organisms absorb and release gases by diffusion through their outer surface. They have a relatively large surface area, a thin surface and a short diffusion pathway (oxygen can take part in biochemical reactions as soon as it diffuses into the cell) — so there's no need for a gas exchange system.

Gas exchange in fish

There's a lower concentration of oxygen in water than in air. So fish have special adaptations to get enough of it. In a fish, the gas exchange surface is the gills.

Structure of gills

Water, containing oxygen, enters the fish through its mouth and passes out through the gills. Each gill is made of lots of thin plates called **gill filaments**, which give a big surface area for exchange of gases (and so increase the rate of diffusion). The gill filaments are covered in lots of tiny structures called **lamellae**, which increase the surface area even more — see Figure 1. The lamellae have lots of blood capillaries and a thin surface layer of cells to speed up diffusion, between the water and the blood.

Learning Objectives:

- Be able to explain the adaptations of gas exchange surfaces using knowledge of diffusion.

- Understand gas exchange in the following places:
  - across the body surface of a single-celled organism,
  - across the gills of a fish (gill lamellae and filaments including the counter-current principle),
  - in the leaves of dicotyledonous plants (mesophyll and stomata),
  - in the tracheal system of an insect (tracheae and spiracles).

- Know the structural and functional compromises between efficient gas exchange and water loss, in terrestrial insects and xerophytic plants.

Specification Reference 3.2.7

Tip: You might've thought the slits on the side of a fish's head were its gills, but in fact the actual gills are inside the fish. Those slits just let out water that has flowed over the gills.

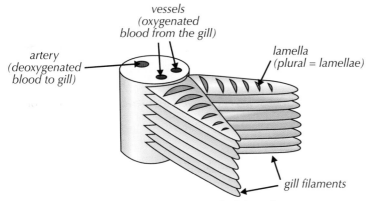

Figure 1: A section of a fish's gill.

vessels (oxygenated blood from the gill)

artery (deoxygenated blood to gill)

lamella (plural = lamellae)

gill filaments

Figure 2: The gills inside a mackerel.

The counter-current system

In the gills of a fish, blood flows through the lamellae in one direction and water flows over in the opposite direction — see Figure 3. This is called a counter-current system. The counter-current system means that the water with a relatively high oxygen concentration always flows next to blood with a lower concentration of oxygen. This in turn means that a steep concentration gradient is maintained between the water and the blood — so as much oxygen as possible diffuses from the water into the blood.

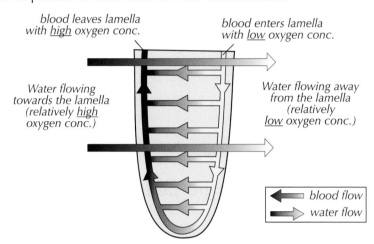

blood leaves lamella with <u>high</u> oxygen conc.

blood enters lamella with <u>low</u> oxygen conc.

Water flowing towards the lamella (relatively <u>high</u> oxygen conc.)

Water flowing away from the lamella (relatively <u>low</u> oxygen conc.)

← blood flow
→ water flow

Figure 3: *The counter-current system across a lamella.*

Gas exchange in dicotyledonous plants

Plants need CO_2 for photosynthesis, which produces O_2 as a waste gas. They need O_2 for respiration, which produces CO_2 as a waste gas. The main gas exchange surface is the surface of the **mesophyll cells** in the leaf. They're well adapted for their function — they have a large surface area.

The mesophyll cells are inside the leaf. Gases move in and out through special pores in the epidermis called **stomata** (singular = stoma). The stomata can open to allow exchange of gases, and close if the plant is losing too much water. **Guard cells** control the opening and closing of stomata.

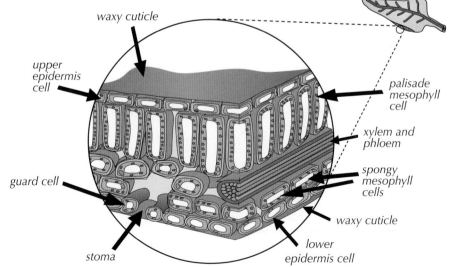

waxy cuticle

upper epidermis cell

palisade mesophyll cell

xylem and phloem

spongy mesophyll cells

guard cell

waxy cuticle

stoma

lower epidermis cell

Figure 4: *Structure of a dicotyledonous plant leaf.*

Gas exchange in insects

Terrestrial insects have microscopic air-filled pipes called **tracheae** which they use for gas exchange. Air moves into the tracheae through pores on the surface called **spiracles**. Oxygen travels down the concentration gradient towards the cells. Carbon dioxide from the cells moves down its own concentration gradient towards the spiracles to be released into the atmosphere. The tracheae branch off into smaller **tracheoles** which have thin, permeable walls and go to individual cells. This means that oxygen diffuses directly into the respiring cells — the insect's circulatory system doesn't transport O_2. Insects use rhythmic abdominal movements to move air in and out of the spiracles.

Tip: Terrestrial insects are just insects that live on land.

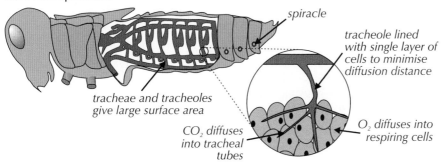

Figure 6: Gas exchange across the tracheal system of an insect.

Figure 5: A spiracle on the surface of a garden tiger moth caterpillar.

Control of water loss

Exchanging gases tends to make you lose water — there's a sort of trade-off between the two. Luckily for plants and insects though, they've evolved adaptations to minimise water loss without reducing gas exchange too much.

If insects are losing too much water, they close their spiracles using muscles. They also have a waterproof, waxy cuticle all over their body and tiny hairs around their spiracles, both of which reduce evaporation.

Plants' stomata are usually kept open during the day to allow gaseous exchange. Water enters the guard cells, making them turgid, which opens the stomatal pore. If the plant starts to get dehydrated, the guard cells lose water and become flaccid, which closes the pore.

Tip: Being <u>turgid</u> means the guard cells become swollen/plump. Being <u>flaccid</u> means they become limp.

Some plants are specially adapted for life in warm, dry or windy habitats, where water loss is a problem. These plants are called **xerophytes**. Examples of xerophytic adaptations include:

- Stomata sunk in pits to trap water vapour, reducing evaporation by lowering the diffusion gradient.

- Curled leaves with the stomata inside, protecting them from wind and so reducing water loss.

- A layer of 'hairs' on the epidermis to trap water vapour round the stomata, reducing the diffusion gradient.

- A reduced number of stomata, so there are fewer places for water to escape.

- Waxy, waterproof cuticles on leaves and stems to reduce evaporation.

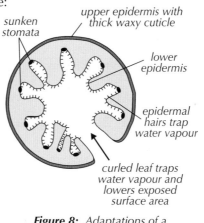

Figure 8: Adaptations of a xerophytic plant.

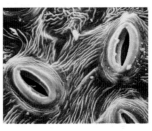

Figure 7: Open stomata on the epidermis of a leaf.

Tip: See p. 171 for more on water loss in plants.

Q1 The photographs below show sections of leaves from two different plants.

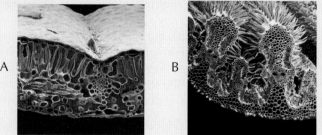

A   B

Which leaf belongs to a xerophyte? Explain your answer.

Q2 In polluted water the dissolved oxygen concentration is lower than it is in clean water. Explain how this would affect gas exchange across the gills of a fish.

Q3 The graph on the right shows how the relative oxygen concentrations of blood and water change with distance along a lamella.

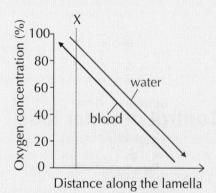

a) What happens to the oxygen concentration of blood as it moves along the lamella?

b) What happens to the oxygen concentration of water as it moves along the lamella?

c) What is the oxygen concentration of the blood at distance X on the graph?

d) Use evidence from the graph to explain why the oxygen concentration of the blood increases straight after point X.

Practice Questions — Fact Recall

Q1 Give two things that all gas exchange surfaces have in common.

Q2 Explain why single-celled organisms don't need a gas exchange system.

Q3 Describe the structure of fish gills.

Q4 Describe how the 'counter-current' system in fish aids gas exchange.

Q5 What is the main gas exchange surface for a dicotyledonous plant?

Q6 Where do gases move in and out of a leaf?

Q7 How does air get into an insect's tracheae?

Q8 Describe how carbon dioxide moves out of an insect's cells into the atmosphere.

Q9 What is a xerophyte?

Q10 Give three adaptations that xerophytic plants have to reduce water loss.

3. The Circulatory System

The mammalian circulatory system is a mass transport system — it carries raw materials, as well as waste products, around the body of the mammal.

Function of the circulatory system

Multicellular organisms, like mammals, have a low surface area to volume ratio (see p. 157), so they need a specialised transport system to carry raw materials from specialised exchange organs to their body cells — this is the circulatory system.

Structure of the circulatory system

The circulatory system is made up of the heart and blood vessels. The heart pumps blood through blood vessels (**arteries**, **arterioles**, **veins** and **capillaries**) to reach different parts of the body. You need to know the names of all the blood vessels entering and leaving the heart, liver and kidneys. These are shown in Figures 1 and 2.

Learning Objectives:

- Understand the general pattern of blood circulation in a mammal. Know the names of the coronary arteries and of blood vessels entering and leaving the heart, liver and kidneys.

- Know the structure of arteries, arterioles and veins in relation to their function.

- Know the structure of capillaries and their importance in metabolic exchange.

- Understand the formation of tissue fluid and its return to the circulatory system.

Specification Reference 3.2.7

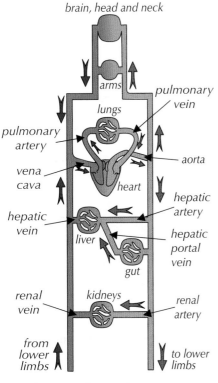

Figure 1: The circulatory system.

Vessel	Carries blood from...	Carries blood to...
Pulmonary artery	heart	lungs
Pulmonary vein	lungs	heart
Aorta	heart	body
Vena cava	body	heart
Hepatic artery	body	liver
Hepatic vein	liver	vena cava
Hepatic portal vein	gut	liver
Renal artery	body	kidneys
Renal vein	kidneys	vena cava

Figure 2: Blood vessels in a mammalian circulatory system.

Tip: Blood always flows from a higher pressure to a lower pressure in the circulatory system. The vena cava is the final blood vessel that takes the blood back to the heart from the body, so it has the lowest pressure.

Tip: The gut is another name for the digestive tract or a part of it, e.g. the intestines.

Blood transports respiratory gases, products of digestion, metabolic wastes and hormones round the body. There are two circuits. One circuit takes blood from the heart to the lungs, then back to the heart. The other loop takes blood around the rest of the body. The heart has its own blood supply — the left and right **coronary arteries** — see Figure 3.

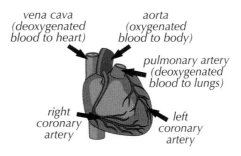

vena cava
(deoxygenated blood to heart)

aorta
(oxygenated blood to body)

pulmonary artery
(deoxygenated blood to lungs)

right coronary artery

left coronary artery

Figure 3: Blood vessels of the heart.

Tip: When you're looking at a diagram of a heart, imagine it's in the body of someone standing opposite you, so the left and right sides are opposite to your left and right.

Arteries, arterioles and veins

Arteries, arterioles and veins have different characteristics, and you need to know why...

Arteries

Tip: Arteries are the 'way art' (way out) of the heart, and veins are the 'vey in' (way in).

Arteries carry blood from the heart to the rest of the body. Their walls are thick and muscular and have elastic tissue to cope with the high pressure produced by the heartbeat. The inner lining (called the **endothelium**) is folded, allowing the artery to stretch — this also helps it to cope with high pressure. All arteries carry oxygenated blood except for the pulmonary arteries, which take deoxygenated blood to the lungs.

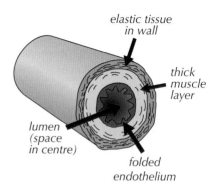

elastic tissue in wall

thick muscle layer

lumen (space in centre)

folded endothelium

Exam Tip
An artery stretches to cope with high pressure and then recoils under low pressure — you won't get marks for writing that it contracts and relaxes, or expands.

Arterioles

Arteries divide into smaller vessels called arterioles. These form a network throughout the body. Blood is directed to different areas of demand in the body by muscles inside the arterioles, which contract to restrict the blood flow or relax to allow full blood flow.

mainly circular muscle

Tip: The pressure decreases along a blood vessel due to friction.

Veins

Veins take blood back to the heart under low pressure. They have a wider lumen than equivalent arteries, with very little elastic or muscle tissue. Veins contain **valves** to stop the blood flowing backwards (see page 91). Blood flow through the veins is helped by contraction of the body muscles surrounding them. All veins carry deoxygenated blood (because oxygen has been used up by body cells), except for the pulmonary veins, which carry oxygenated blood to the heart from the lungs.

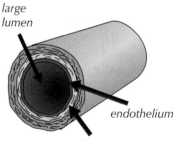

large lumen

endothelium

thin muscle wall

Exam Tip
Don't get the endothelium mixed up with the epidermis or endodermis in the exam.

Practice Question — Application

Q1 The graph on the right shows the relative increase in blood pressure in different blood vessels of a mammal's circulatory system.

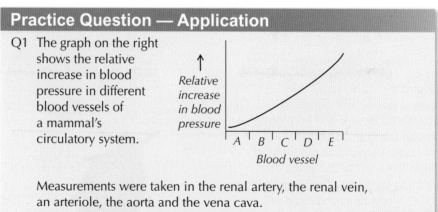

Relative increase in blood pressure

A B C D E
Blood vessel

Measurements were taken in the renal artery, the renal vein, an arteriole, the aorta and the vena cava.

Suggest which letter represents each blood vessel. Explain your choices.

Capillaries

Arterioles branch into capillaries, which are the smallest of the blood vessels. Substances (e.g. glucose and oxygen) are exchanged between cells and capillaries, so they're adapted for efficient diffusion. Capillaries are always found very near cells in exchange tissues (e.g. alveoli in the lungs), so there's a short diffusion pathway. Their walls are only one cell thick, which also shortens the diffusion pathway. There are a large number of capillaries, to increase surface area for exchange. Networks of capillaries in tissue are called **capillary beds**.

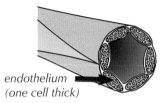

endothelium
(one cell thick)

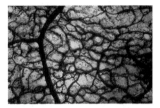

Figure 4: *Light micrograph of capillaries.*

Tip: Capillaries connect arterioles and veins together at capillary beds.

Tissue fluid

Tissue fluid is the fluid that surrounds cells in tissues. It's made from substances that leave the blood, e.g. oxygen, water and nutrients (like glucose and amino acids). Cells take in oxygen and nutrients from the tissue fluid, and release metabolic waste into it.

Substances move out of blood capillaries, into the tissue fluid, by pressure filtration. At the start of the capillary bed, nearest the arterioles, the pressure inside the capillaries is greater than the pressure in the tissue fluid. This difference in pressure forces fluid out of the capillaries and into the spaces around the cells, forming tissue fluid. As fluid leaves, the pressure reduces in the capillaries — so the pressure is much lower at the end of the capillary bed that's nearest to the veins. Due to the fluid loss, the water potential at the end of the capillaries nearest the veins is lower than the water potential in the tissue fluid — so some water re-enters the capillaries from the tissue fluid at the vein end by osmosis (see p. 63 for more on osmosis).

Unlike blood, tissue fluid doesn't contain red blood cells or big proteins, because they're too large to be pushed out through the capillary walls. Any excess tissue fluid is drained into the **lymphatic system** (a network of tubes that acts a bit like a drain), which transports this excess fluid from the tissues and dumps it back into the circulatory system.

Tip: Pressure is highest at the start of a capillary bed nearest the arterioles — this is caused by the left ventricle contracting and sending the blood out of the heart, through the arteries and arterioles, at high pressure.

Exam Tip
Don't write in the exam that tissue fluid doesn't contain _any_ proteins — it still contains some, just not big ones.

Tip: Blood plasma is just the liquid that carries everything in the blood.

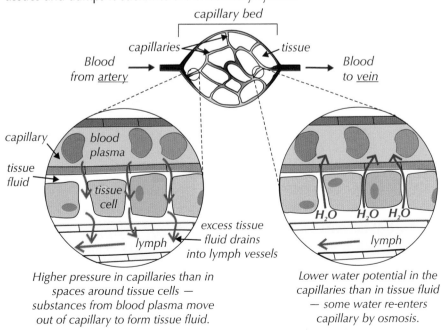

Higher pressure in capillaries than in spaces around tissue cells — substances from blood plasma move out of capillary to form tissue fluid.

Lower water potential in the capillaries than in tissue fluid — some water re-enters capillary by osmosis.

Figure 5: *The movement of fluid between capillaries, tissue fluid and lymph.*

Practice Questions — Application

Tip: Hydrostatic pressure is the pressure exerted by a liquid.

Q1 A scientist recorded the hydrostatic pressure of blood and tissue fluid at two points along a capillary bed. The results are shown in the table below.

	Pressure at Point A (kPa)	Pressure at Point B (kPa)
Blood	2	3.5
Tissue fluid	4	2

  a) The direction of fluid movement between blood and tissue fluid changes along the capillary.

  i) Where does fluid move from and to at point B?

  ii) What does the fluid contain at point B?

  b) Suggest where on the capillary bed you would find:

  i) point A   ii) point B

Tip: For Q2, think about how the concentration of protein in the blood affects the water potential of the capillary.

Q2 Albumin is a protein found in the blood. Hypoalbuminemia is a condition where the level of albumin in the blood is very low. It causes an increase in tissue fluid, which can lead to swelling. Explain how hypoalbuminemia causes an increase in tissue fluid.

Practice Questions — Fact Recall

Q1 Why do mammals need a mass transport system?

Q2 Name the two blood vessels that carry blood into the heart.

Q3 Which blood vessel carries deoxygenated blood to the lungs?

Q4 What is the function of the hepatic portal vein?

Q5 Which blood vessel carries blood to the kidneys?

Q6 Which vessels supply the heart tissue with blood?

Q7 Name the blood vessels A - D shown below. (The diagrams are not drawn to scale).

Tip: To distinguish between different types of blood vessels, you need to think about how thick the walls need to be for each types and how much muscle there will be in the walls, etc.

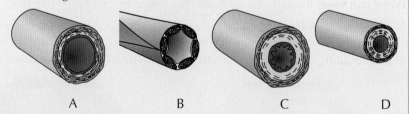

A   B   C   D

Q8 Describe the structure of an artery.

Q9 What is an arteriole?

Q10 a) Name the blood vessels that have valves in them.

  b) What is the function of these valves?

Q11 Give two ways in which capillaries are adapted for efficient diffusion.

Q12 What is tissue fluid?

Q13 a) Explain the movement of fluid at the artery end of a capillary bed.

  b) Explain the movement of water at the vein end of a capillary bed.

4. Water Transport in Plants

Learning Objectives:

- Know the structure of a dicotyledonous root in relation to the pathway of water from root hairs through the cortex and endodermis to the xylem.

- Understand the apoplast and symplast pathways through plant roots.

- Understand the roles of root pressure and cohesion-tension in moving water through the xylem.

- Understand what transpiration is and the effects of light, temperature, humidity and wind on it.

Specification Reference 3.2.7

Plants are pretty clever when it comes to transporting water. They can take it up from their roots to their leaves against the force of gravity. Let's see how they manage that...

How does water enter a plant?

Water has to get from the soil, through the root and into the **xylem** — the system of vessels that transports water throughout the plant. The bit of the root that absorbs water is covered in **root hairs**. These increase the root's surface area, speeding up water uptake. Once it's absorbed, the water has to get through the **cortex**, including the **endodermis**, before it can reach the xylem — see Figure 1.

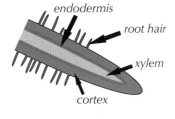

Figure 1:   Cross-section of a root.

Water always moves from areas of higher water potential to areas of lower water potential — it goes down a **water potential gradient**. The soil around roots generally has a high water potential (i.e. there's lots of water there) and leaves have a lower water potential (because water constantly evaporates from them). This creates a water potential gradient that keeps water moving through the plant in the right direction, from roots to leaves — see Figure 2.

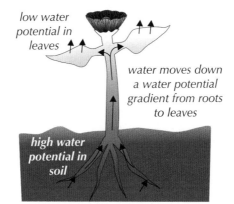

Figure 2:   Water potential gradient up a plant.

Tip: Water moves into a root hair cell by osmosis. There's more about osmosis and water potential on page 63.

Water transport through the root

Water can travel through the roots into the xylem by two different paths.

1. The symplast pathway

The symplast pathway goes through the cytoplasm. The cytoplasm of neighbouring cells connect through **plasmodesmata** (small channels in the cell walls).

Figure 3:   Root hairs on a cress root.

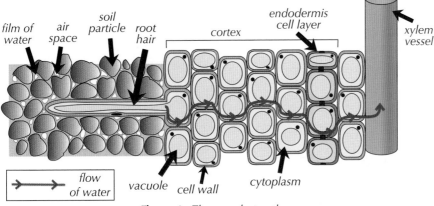

Figure 4: The symplast pathway.

2. The apoplast pathway

The apoplast pathway goes through the cell walls. The walls are very absorbent and water can simply diffuse through them, as well as passing through the spaces between them.

When water in the apoplast pathway gets to the endodermis cells though, its path is blocked by a waxy strip in the cell walls, called the **Casparian strip**. Now the water has to take the symplast pathway. This is useful, because it means the water has to go through a cell membrane. Cell membranes are able to control whether or not substances in the water get through (see p.57). Once past this barrier, the water moves into the xylem.

Tip: Both pathways are used, but the main one is the apoplast pathway because it provides the least resistance.

Exam Tip
Don't write that the endodermis blocks the apoplast pathway — it's the Casparian strip that blocks it.

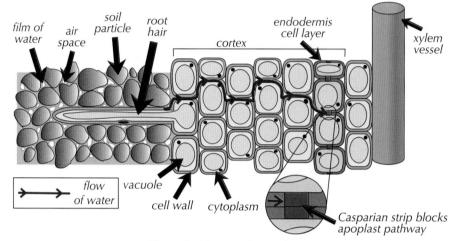

Figure 5: The apoplast pathway.

Water movement up a plant

Water moves up a plant against the force of gravity. It can move up a plant in two ways:

Cohesion and tension

Cohesion and tension help water move up plants, from roots to leaves, against the force of gravity.

1. Water evaporates from the leaves at the 'top' of the xylem.
2. This creates tension (suction), which pulls more water into the leaf.
3. Water molecules are cohesive (they stick together) so when some are pulled into the leaf others follow. This means the whole column of water in the xylem, from the leaves down to the roots, moves upwards.
4. Water then enters the stem through the roots.

Tip: This is known as the 'cohesion-tension theory'.

Tip: Water movement up a plant increases as the transpiration rate increases — see page 171.

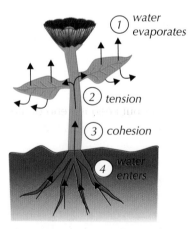

Figure 6: Water movement up a plant.

Root pressure

Root pressure also helps move the water upwards. When water is transported into the xylem in the roots, it creates a pressure and shoves water already in the xylem further upwards. This pressure is weak, and couldn't move water to the top of bigger plants by itself. But it helps, especially in young, small plants where the leaves are still developing.

Transpiration

Transpiration is the **evaporation** of water from a plant's surface, especially the leaves. Water evaporates from the moist cell walls and accumulates in the spaces between cells in the leaf. When the stomata open, it moves out of the leaf down the water potential gradient (there's more water inside the leaf than in the air outside).

Factors affecting transpiration rate

There are four main factors that affect transpiration rate.

1. **Light** — the lighter it is the faster the transpiration rate. This is because the stomata open when it gets light. When it's dark the stomata are usually closed, so there's little transpiration.

2. **Temperature** — the higher the temperature the faster the transpiration rate. Warmer water molecules have more energy so they evaporate from the cells inside the leaf faster. This increases the water potential gradient between the inside and outside of the leaf, making water diffuse out of the leaf faster.

3. **Humidity** — the lower the humidity, the faster the transpiration rate. If the air around the plant is dry, the water potential gradient between the leaf and the air is increased, which increases transpiration.

4. **Wind** — the windier it is, the faster the transpiration rate. Lots of air movement blows away water molecules from around the stomata. This increases the water potential gradient, which increases the rate of transpiration.

Measuring transpiration — potometers

A potometer is a special piece of apparatus used to estimate transpiration rates. It actually measures water uptake by a plant, but it's assumed that water uptake by the plant is directly related to water loss by the leaves. Here's what you'd do:

1. Cut a shoot underwater to prevent air from entering the xylem. Cut it at a slant to increase the surface area available for water uptake.

2. Assemble the potometer in water and insert the shoot under water, so no air can enter.

3. Remove the apparatus from the water but keep the end of the capillary tube submerged in a beaker of water.

4. Check that the apparatus is watertight and airtight.

5. Dry the leaves, allow time for the shoot to acclimatise and then shut the tap.

6. Remove the end of the capillary tube from the beaker of water until one air bubble has formed, then put the end of the tube back into the water.

7. Record the starting position of the air bubble, then record the distance moved by the bubble per unit time, e.g. per minute.

8. Repeat the experiment to increase the reliability of the results (see p. 3).

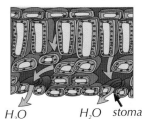

H_2O H_2O stoma

Figure 7: *Cross-section of a leaf showing how water moves out during transpiration.*

Tip: Transpiration's really a side effect of photosynthesis — the plant needs to open its stomata to let in CO_2 so that it can produce glucose, but this also lets water out.

Tip: Transpiration rate isn't exactly the same as water uptake by a plant — some water is used for photosynthesis and to support the plant, and some water is produced during respiration.

Tip: You can test the effect of different factors on transpiration rate, e.g. by using a fan to increase air movement or a lamp to increase light etc.

Tip: If you want to compare water loss from different types of plant, you need to measure the surface area of the leaves because it will vary with type of plant.

Exam Tip
To work out the rate of water uptake in cm^3 per minute, you need to measure the distance moved by the bubble per unit time <u>and</u> the diameter of the capillary tube.

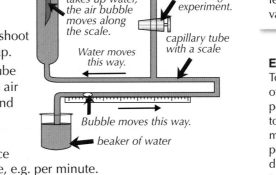

reservoir of water used to return bubble to start for repeats

As the plant takes up water, the air bubble moves along the scale.

Tap is shut off during experiment.

Water moves this way.

capillary tube with a scale

Bubble moves this way.

beaker of water

Practice Questions — Application

A potometer was used to test the effect of temperature on transpiration rate. The test was repeated 3 times. The results are shown in the table.

Temperature (°C)	Distance moved by the bubble in 10 minutes (mm)		
	Test 1	Test 2	Test 3
10	15	12	14
20	19	16	19
30	25	22	23

Q1   a)   Calculate the mean result for each temperature.

      b)   Plot a graph of the mean results and use it to estimate the distance the bubble would move in ten minutes at 25 °C.

Q2   Describe and explain the results of the experiment.

Practice Questions — Fact Recall

Q1   Describe the pathway of water from the soil into the xylem.

Q2   Describe how water moves through the symplast and apoplast pathways.

Q3   Describe and explain two ways in which water can move up a plant.

Q4   Explain how wind affects transpiration rate.

Section Summary

Make sure you know...

- That smaller organisms have a higher surface area : volume ratio than larger organisms.
- That mass transport is used to transport materials over a long-distance.
- That a high surface area : volume ratio increases the rate of substance and heat exchange.
- That some organisms have adaptations which can help in the exchange of substances (e.g. the development of mass transport systems) and in the exchange of heat (e.g. changes to body shape, behavioural and physiological adaptations).
- How gas exchange surfaces are adapted to increase the rate of diffusion — they're thin and have a large surface area.
- How gas exchange occurs in single-celled organisms (across the body surface), fish (across gill filaments and lamellae using the counter-current system), the leaves of dicotyledonous plants (across the surface of mesophyll cells) and insects (in the tracheal system).
- The adaptations that terrestrial insects and xerophytic plants have to control water loss.
- The general pattern of blood circulation in a mammal — heart to arteries to arterioles to capillaries to veins and back to the heart again.
- The names of the coronary arteries, and the blood vessels leading to and from the liver, kidneys and heart.
- The structure of arteries, arterioles and veins in relation to their function.
- The structure of capillaries and how it relates to their function of exchanging substances.
- How tissue fluid is formed and how it returns to the circulatory system.
- The structure of a dicotyledonous plant root and how water passes from the root to the xylem.
- The symplast pathway (via the cytoplasm of cells) and the apoplast pathway (via the cell walls).
- How cohesion and tension, and root pressure move water up the xylem.
- What transpiration is and how it's affected by light, temperature, humidity and wind.
- How a potometer is used to measure transpiration rate.

Exam-style Questions

1 (a) The gills of a fish are adapted for efficient gas exchange.

    (i) Explain how lamellae aid efficient gas exchange.

(2 marks)

    (ii) Explain the advantage to fish of having a counter-current system.

(2 marks)

(b) (i) Insects have a tracheal system for exchanging gases with the environment.
Explain how oxygen gets into an insect's respiring cells.

(3 marks)

    (ii) Water is lost as a result of gas exchange.
What features do insects have to reduce unwanted water loss?

(2 marks)

(c) *E.coli* is a single-celled organism.
Explain why *E.coli* doesn't have a gas exchange system.

(3 marks)

2 The bar graph shows the relative surface area : volume ratios
for three different animals.

(a) (i) Describe the trend shown by the graph.

(1 mark)

(ii) Which of the animals from the graph would
lose heat the fastest? Explain your answer.

(1 mark)

(iii) Rhinos live in hot regions and spend a lot of
time in muddy pools.
Using the information in the graph, suggest
why it might be beneficial for them to do this.

(3 marks)

Surface area : volume ratio — rat, wolf, rhino — Animal

(b) The photographs below show wolves from two different climates.

A

B
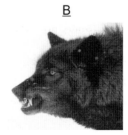

Explain which wolf is most suited to living in a hot climate.

(3 marks)

3 (a) The diagram below shows the passage of water through part of a plant's root.

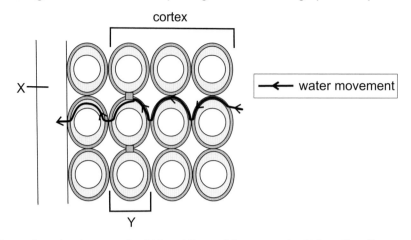

(i) Name the structure marked X and the cell layer marked Y on the diagram.

(2 marks)

(ii) Describe and explain the movement of the water in the diagram above.

(3 marks)

(b) Explain how water moves up the plant by cohesion and tension.

(4 marks)

(c) Would the speed at which water moves up the plant be faster or slower on humid days? Explain your answer.

(2 marks)

(d) Explain, in terms of light and temperature, why a plant's transpiration rate increases during the summer.

(6 marks)

4 The diagram shows part of the circulatory system of a mammal. The arrows show the direction of blood flow.

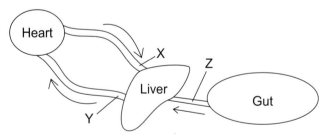

(a) Name the vessels marked X, Y and Z on the diagram.

(3 marks)

(b) Which vessel on the diagram transports blood at the highest pressure? Explain your answer.

(2 marks)

(c) The liver is surrounded by a capillary bed. Explain how the liver cells get the substances they need (e.g. oxygen and glucose) from the blood.

(3 marks)

1. Classification Basics

Scientists group organisms together to make them easier to study.

Classification systems

Classification is the act of arranging organisms into groups based on their similarities and differences. The science of classification is known as **taxonomy**. Taxonomy makes it easier for scientists to identify organisms and to study them.

There are a few different classification systems in use. In the most common system, there are seven levels of groups (called taxonomic groups) which are used to classify organisms. These seven groups are organised into a hierarchy — a system where smaller groups are contained within larger groups. Organisms can only belong to one group at each level in the taxonomic hierarchy — there's no overlap.

Similar organisms are first sorted into large groups called kingdoms, e.g. all animals are in the animal kingdom (Animalia). Similar organisms from that kingdom are then arranged into a smaller group called a phylum. Similar organisms from each phylum are then grouped into a class, and so on down the seven levels of the hierarchy. This is illustrated in Figure 1.

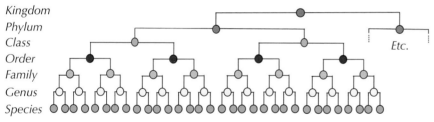

Kingdom
Phylum
Class
Order
Family
Genus
Species

Etc.

Figure 1: *A diagram illustrating the seven taxonomic groups used in classification.*

Example — the classification of humans

Kingdom = *Animalia*, Phylum = *Chordata*, Class = *Mammalia*,
Order = *Primates*, Family = *Hominidae*, Genus = *Homo*, Species = *sapiens*.

As you move down the hierarchy, there are more groups at each level but fewer organisms in each group. The hierarchy ends with **species** — the groups that contain only one type of organism (e.g. humans). A species is a group of similar organisms able to reproduce to give fertile offspring.

Example

If a female horse breeds with a male horse of the same species their offspring will be fertile. But if a female horse breeds with a male donkey their offspring (known as a mule) will be infertile. Because horses and donkeys can't reproduce to give fertile offspring, they're classified as separate species.

Scientists constantly update classification systems because of discoveries about new species and new evidence about known organisms (e.g. DNA sequence data — see page 178).

Phylogenetics

Phylogenetics is the study of the evolutionary history of groups of organisms. It tells us who's related to whom and how closely related they are. All organisms have evolved from shared common ancestors (relatives). Closely related species diverged away from each other most recently.

Tip: 'Diverged' just means 'evolved to become a different species'.

Figure 2: Orangutans, chimps and gorillas are all closely related.

Example

Members of the Hominidae family (great apes and humans) evolved from a common ancestor. First orangutans diverged from this common ancestor. Next gorillas diverged, then humans, closely followed by bonobos and chimpanzees.

This is illustrated on the phylogenetic tree below...

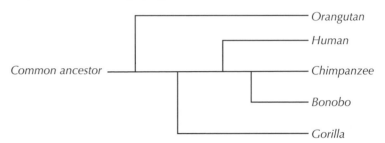

Humans and chimpanzees are closely related, as they diverged very recently. You can see this because their branches are close together. Humans and orangutans are more distantly related, as they diverged longer ago, so their branches are further apart.

Phylogenetics is closely linked to classification because the grouping of organisms needs to reflect their evolutionary relationships. E.g. members of one genus must be more closely related to each other than they are to organisms of a different genus, etc. As a result, evolutionary relationships are often used to classify organisms.

Problems with classification

Scientists can have problems when using the definition of a species on the previous page to decide which species an organism belongs to or if it's a new, distinct species. This is because you can't always see their reproductive behaviour (you can't always tell if different organisms can reproduce to give fertile offspring). Here are some of the reasons why:

- They're extinct, so obviously you can't study their reproductive behaviour.
- They reproduce asexually — they never reproduce together even if they belong to the same species, e.g. bacteria.
- There are practical and ethical issues involved — you can't see if some organisms reproduce successfully in the wild (due to geography) and you can't study them in a lab (because it's unethical), e.g. humans and chimps are classed as separate species but no one's ever tried mating them.

Tip: See pages 178-179 for more on how scientists compare the DNA of different organisms.

Because of these problems some organisms are classified as one species or another using other techniques. Scientists can now compare the DNA of organisms to see how related they are, e.g. the more DNA they have in common the more closely related they are. But there's no strict cut-off to say how much shared DNA can be used to define a species. E.g. only about 6% of human DNA differs from chimpanzee DNA but we are separate species.

Naming species

Species are given a scientific name to distinguish them from similar organisms. This is a two-word name in Latin. The first word is the genus name and the second word is the species name.

Examples

Humans are *Homo sapiens* — The genus is *Homo* and the species is *sapiens*.
Dogs are *Canis familiaris* — The genus is *Canis* and the species is *familiaris*.
Cats are *Felis catus* — The genus is *Felis* and the species is *catus*.

Giving organisms a scientific name enables scientists to communicate about organisms in a standard way that minimises confusion.

Example

Americans call a type of bird cockatoos and Australians call them flaming galahs, but it's the same bird. If the correct scientific name is used — *Eolophus roseicapillus* — there's no confusion.

Tip: In Latin names the genus is often shortened to the first letter. E.g. *E. coli* is short for *Escherichia coli* — *Escherichia* is the genus and *coli* is the species.

Exam Tip
The plural of genus is genera. You'll see this sometimes in exams.

Practice Questions — Application

The diagram below shows a simplified phylogenetic tree for the phylum Chordata:

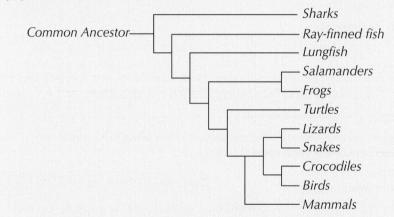

Tip: It might surprise you that some species are closely related — but just because you can't see a similarity in their features doesn't mean the phylogenetic tree is wrong.

Q1 Which group was first to diverge from the common ancestor?

Q2 Are frogs more closely related to salamanders or turtles?

Q3 To which other group are:
  a) birds most closely related?
  b) snakes most closely related?

Practice Questions — Fact Recall

Q1 What is taxonomy?

Q2 The list below shows the seven levels of the taxonomic hierarchy. Complete the list by filling in the blanks:

> Kingdom   ?   Class   Order   ?   ?   Species

Q3 How would you define a species?

Q4 What major problem do scientists face when trying to classify a new species and how are these problems being overcome?

- Know that genetic comparisons can be made between different species by direct examination of their DNA or of the proteins encoded by this DNA.

- Know that comparison of DNA base sequences is used to elucidate relationships between organisms and that these comparisons have led to new classification systems in plants.

- Know that similarities in DNA may be determined by DNA hybridisation.

- Know that comparisons of amino acid sequences in specific proteins can be used to elucidate relationships between organisms.

- Know that immunological comparisons may be used to compare variations in specific proteins.

- Be able to interpret data relating to similarities and differences in base sequences and in amino acid sequences to suggest relationships between different organisms.

Specification Reference 3.2.9

Tip: See pages 115-117 for more on DNA.

2. Classification Using DNA or Proteins

The original systems for classifying organisms were based on features that could be seen, e.g. how an organism looked or behaved. Today, we use DNA and proteins to help us classify organisms more accurately...

How are species classified using DNA or proteins?

Species can be classified into different groups in the taxonomic hierarchy (see p. 175) based on similarities and differences in their genes. This can be done by comparing their DNA sequence or by looking at their proteins (which are coded for by their DNA). Organisms that are more closely related will have more similar DNA and proteins than distantly related organisms. E.g. humans are more closely related to chimps than to mice, so the DNA and proteins in humans are more similar to those in chimps than those in mice.

Comparing DNA

DNA similarity can be measured by looking at the sequence of bases or by DNA hybridisation:

1. DNA sequencing

The DNA of organisms can be directly compared by looking at the order of the bases (As, Ts, Gs and Cs) in each. Closely related species will have a higher percentage of similarity in their DNA base order, e.g. humans and chimps share around 94%, humans and mice share about 85%.

┌─ **Example 1** ─────────────────────────

The table below shows the % similarity of DNA using DNA sequence analysis between several species of bacteria.

Species A and B have a higher percentage of DNA in common with each other than they do with either species C or D. This means that A and B are more closely related to each other than they are to either C or D.

	Species A	Species B	Species C	Species D
Species A	100%	86%	42%	44%
Species B	86%	100%	51%	53%
Species C	42%	51%	100%	91%
Species D	44%	53%	91%	100%

┌─ **Example 2** ─────────────────────────

The diagram below shows the DNA sequence for gene X in three different species...

Species A: ATTGTCTGATTGGTGCTAGTCGTCGATGCTAGGATCG

Species B: ATTGTATGATTGGTGCTAGTCGGCGATGCTAGGATCG

Species C: ATTGATTGAAAGGAGCTACTCGTAGATATAAGGAGGT

There are 13 differences between the base sequences in species A and C, but only 2 differences between the base sequences in species A and B. This suggests that species A and B are more closely related than A and C.

DNA sequence comparison has led to new classification systems for plants, e.g. the classification system for flowering plants is based almost entirely on similarities between DNA sequences.

2. DNA hybridisation

DNA hybridisation is used to see how similar DNA is without sequencing it. Here's how it's done:

- DNA from two different species is collected, separated into single strands and mixed together.

- Where the base sequences of the DNA are the same on both strands, hydrogen bonds form between the base pairs by specific base pairing. The more DNA bases that hybridise (bond) together, the more alike the DNA is.

- The DNA is then heated to separate the strands again. Similar DNA will have more hydrogen bonds holding the two strands together, so a higher melting temperature (i.e. more energy) will be needed to separate the strands.

Tip: Organisms that are closely related will also have more similar mitochondrial DNA (mtDNA). Most organisms only inherit mtDNA from their mother — this allows scientists to trace their female ancestors. (Male ancestors can be traced by comparing DNA sequences on the Y chromosome.)

Tip: There's more on specific base pairing on page 116.

Tip: The melting temperature is the temperature at which the two strands of DNA separate.

Example

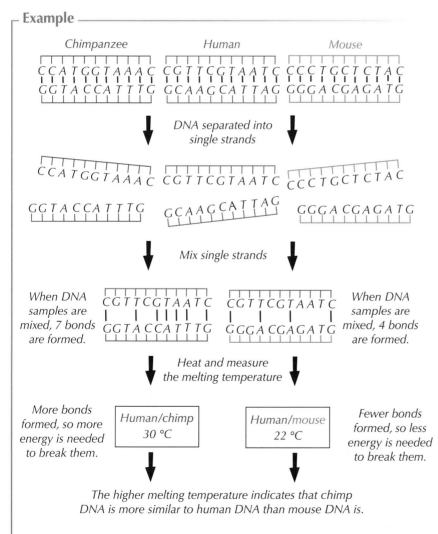

Figure 1: *A DNA hybridisation machine being used in the lab.*

When DNA samples are mixed, 7 bonds are formed.

When DNA samples are mixed, 4 bonds are formed.

More bonds formed, so more energy is needed to break them.

Human/chimp 30 °C

Human/mouse 22 °C

Fewer bonds formed, so less energy is needed to break them.

The higher melting temperature indicates that chimp DNA is more similar to human DNA than mouse DNA is.

Figure 2: *Diagram showing how the process of DNA hybridisation works.*

Exam Tip
In an exam, you won't necessarily have all this information — you might just be given the number of bonds formed or the melting temperatures in a table. Just remember that more bonds = higher melting temperature = more similar DNA sequences.

Q1 The graph below illustrates the sequence of a small stretch of DNA in 3 different species:

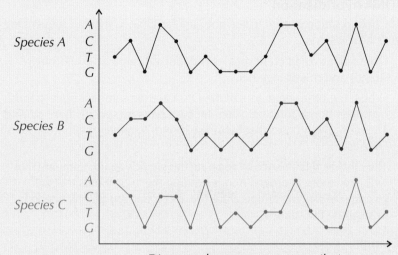

Distance along gene sequence (bp)

Tip: The distance along the gene sequence on the diagram is given as 'bp' — base pairs.

a) Using the graph, write down the base sequence for this stretch of DNA in each of the three species.

b) In how many places do the base sequences of species A and B differ?

c) In how many places do the base sequences of species A and C differ?

d) Is species A more closely related to species B or species C? Explain your answer.

e) To which of the two species is species C most closely related? Explain your answer.

Q2 The table below shows the melting temperatures of hybridised DNA when a small section of DNA from the following species was mixed:

Species A	Species B	Melting temperature (°C)
Human	Orangutan	64
Human	Spider monkey	62
Human	Guinea pig	58
Human	Dandelion plant	?

a) Explain how this data has been collected.

b) On the basis of this data, to which other organisms are humans most closely related? Explain your answer.

c) Would you expect the melting temperature of human:dandelion hybrid DNA to be higher or lower than that for human:guinea pig hybrid DNA? Why?

Comparing proteins

Similar organisms will have similar proteins in their cells.
Proteins can be compared in two ways:

Tip: See page 118 for more information on how DNA codes for proteins.

1. Comparing amino acid sequences

Proteins are made of amino acids. The sequence of amino acids in a protein is coded for by the base sequence in DNA. Related organisms have similar DNA sequences and so similar amino acid sequences in their proteins.

Example

The diagram below shows the amino acid sequences of a certain protein from three different species.

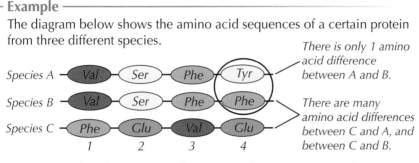

There is only 1 amino acid difference between A and B.

There are many amino acid differences between C and A, and between C and B.

Tip: 'Val', 'Ser', 'Phe' and 'Glu' are short for the names of the amino acids.

You can see that the amino acid sequences from species A and B are very similar. The sequence from species C is very different to any of the other sequences. This suggests that species A and B are more closely related.

2. Immunological comparisons

Immunological comparison involves using antibodies to determine how similar two proteins are. Antibodies bind to proteins in a specific manner — so similar proteins will bind the same antibodies.

Tip: See pages 12-13 for more on antibodies binding to proteins.

Example

If antibodies to a human version of a protein are added to isolated samples from some other species, any protein that's like the human version will also be recognised (bound) by that antibody. So here, the chimp protein is more similar to the human one than the mouse protein.

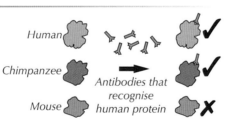

Antibodies that recognise human protein

Tip: Proteins that bind antibodies will often form a precipitate (solid mass) in solution. The more antibodies the protein binds, the more precipitate will form — so the amount of precipitate can be used to determine how similar two proteins are.

Practice Questions — Application

Q1 The amino acid sequence of the insulin protein was determined for humans, horses and chickens. When this was done, it was found that horse insulin was more similar to human insulin than chicken insulin. What does this tell you?

Q2 Antibodies against a protein from species X were fluorescently labelled and mixed with cells from three other species. Any unbound antibody was then washed away and the level of remaining fluorescence was recorded. Use the results table above to determine which species is most closely related to species X. Explain your choice.

Species	Relative fluorescence after washing
A	0.2
B	10.5
C	2.1

Tip: Antibodies are often linked to a fluorescent protein (e.g. GFP). This allows the antibodies to be detected once they have bound to a protein.

Learning Objectives:
- Know that courtship behaviour is a necessary precursor to successful mating.
- Understand the role of courtship in species recognition.

Specification Reference 3.2.9

3. Classification Using Courtship Behaviour

Similar species don't only look similar — they also behave in a similar way. This means that behaviour can also be used to help classify species. Courtship behaviour can be particularly useful when classifying species.

What is courtship behaviour?

Courtship behaviour is carried out by organisms to attract a mate of the right species. It can be fairly simple or quite complex.

--- Examples ---

Simple Courtship behaviours:

- Releasing a chemical — e.g. male bumble bees produce chemicals called pheromones to attract female bumble bees to their territory.
- Using sound — e.g. male red deer make a roaring noise to attract a mate.
- Visual displays — e.g. the great tit will attract a mate by puffing out it's chest to show off it's black stripe.

Complex Courtship behaviours:

- Dancing — e.g. blue-footed boobies perform a complex dance which involves lifting up their feet to show off the blue colour (see Figure 1).
- Building — e.g. bowerbirds construct bowers (shelters) made of leaves, twigs, flowers, shells, stones and whatever else the male can find (see Figure 2).

Figure 1: *The dance of the blue-footed booby.*

Courtship behaviours can be performed by either the male or the female or may sometimes involve both sexes.

Using courtship behaviour to classify species

Courtship behaviour is species specific — only members of the same species will do and respond to that courtship behaviour. This prevents interbreeding and so makes reproduction more successful (as mating with the wrong species won't produce fertile offspring).

Figure 2: *A male bowerbird constructing a bower.*

--- Examples ---

- Fireflies give off pulses of light. The pattern of flashes is specific to each species.
- Crickets make sounds that are similar to Morse code, the code being different for different species.
- Male peacocks show off their colourful tails. This tail pattern is only found in peacocks (see Figure 3).
- Male butterflies use chemicals to attract females. Only those of the correct species respond.

Because of this specificity, courtship behaviour can be used to classify organisms. The more closely related species are, the more similar their courtship behaviour.

Figure 3: *A male peacock displaying his tail feathers.*

Practice Questions — Application

Male fireflies give off pulses of light to attract females. To investigate this, 10 fireflies were caught and the pattern of light pulses that they used was observed. The table below shows the results:

Firefly	Pattern of pulses produced
1	xx-xx-xx-xx
2	xxx-x-xxx-x-xxx
3	x-xx-xxx-x-xx-xxx
4	xxx-xxx-xxx
5	x-x-x-x-x-x
6	xx-xx-xx-xx
7	x-xx-x-xx-x-xx
8	xx-xx-xx-xx
9	xxx-xxx-xxx
10	x-xx-xxx-x-xx-xxx

Key:
x = flash of light
- = no light

Exam Tip
Whatever the topic, examiners love data-interpretation questions. Get used to seeing data presented in lots of different ways.

Q1 Fireflies 4 and 9 both produced the same pattern of light pulses. What does this suggest about fireflies 4 and 9?

Q2 How many different species of firefly were caught in total?

Q3 Are fireflies 1 and 3 likely to be closely related or distantly related? Explain your answer.

Q4 Firefly 2 was later found to belong to a family of fireflies that all start their display with three pulses of light. Are any of the other fireflies likely to belong to the same family?

Section Summary

Make sure you know...

- What taxonomy is (the science of classification) and why it's important (it makes it easier to identify and study organisms).
- The seven taxonomic groups — kingdom, phylum, class, order, family, genus and species.
- That classification systems consist of a hierarchy — larger groups are divided into smaller groups, and there is no overlap between groups.
- That a species is defined as a group of similar organisms able to reproduce to give fertile offspring.
- That phylogenetics is the study of the evolutionary history of groups of organisms.
- Why defining species can be difficult — you can't always test the reproductive behaviour of two different organisms.
- How species can be classified using DNA (through DNA sequencing and DNA hybridisation) and that DNA sequencing has led to new classification systems in plants.
- How species can be classified using proteins — by comparing amino acid sequences and through immunological comparisons.
- How to interpret data on DNA or protein similarities and use this to suggest relationships between different organisms.
- That courtship behaviour is carried out to attract a mate of the right species.
- That courtship behaviour is species specific, so it can be used to help classify organisms.

Exam-style Questions

1   A group of scientists are studying field mice.
They discover what they think may be a new species.

(a)   What is the definition of a species?

(1 mark)

(b)   The new field mice are rare and nocturnal.
Suggest how this may make classifying them difficult.

(1 mark)

(c)   After confirming that the mouse was in fact a new species, the scientists
decided to name it *Mus insignis* for "uncommon mouse".
To what genus does this mouse belong?

(1 mark)

(d)   The mouse is classified using a hierarchy consisting of seven groups.
The largest group is a kingdom.

    (i) Give the names of the other six groups in the hierarchy in the correct order.

(2 marks)

    (ii) Explain how classification using a hierarchy works.

(2 marks)

2   The RuBisCo gene is found in all plants.

When a new species of plant is being classified, this gene is often compared with
the gene in other species to determine evolutionary relatedness.

(a)   Describe how DNA hybridisation can be used to compare the DNA sequences
of two different plant species.

(5 marks)

(b)   Suggest another way in which DNA from two different organisms can be compared.

(1 mark)

(c)   Why is the RuBisCo gene useful for determining relationships
between plant species?

(1 mark)

(d)   Evolutionary relationships could also be determined by comparing the
RuBisCo protein itself. Describe one way in which proteins from two different
organisms could be used to determine evolutionary relationships.

(2 marks)

3 Songbirds use elaborate songs to attract a mate.
This is a type of courtship behaviour.

(a) Explain one way in which courtship behaviour makes organisms more likely to mate successfully.

(2 marks)

The graphs below illustrate a mating song from three different songbirds.
The arrows on the graphs show the beginnings of each phrase. Each phrase is made up of a series of notes and is repeated multiple times to make a song:

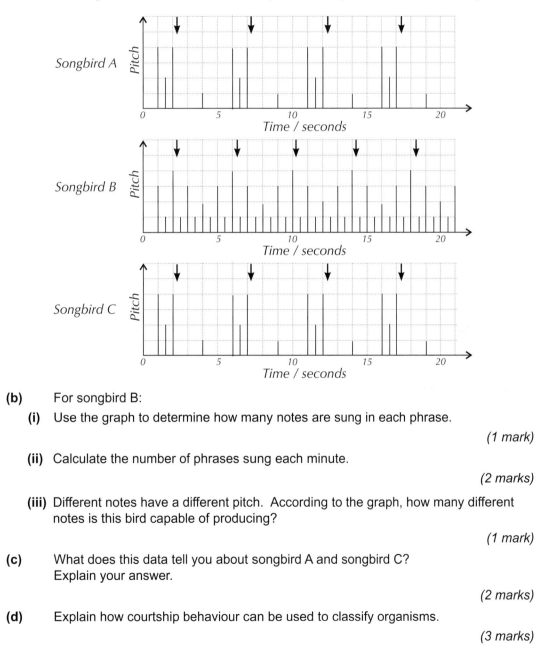

(b) For songbird B:

(i) Use the graph to determine how many notes are sung in each phrase.

(1 mark)

(ii) Calculate the number of phrases sung each minute.

(2 marks)

(iii) Different notes have a different pitch. According to the graph, how many different notes is this bird capable of producing?

(1 mark)

(c) What does this data tell you about songbird A and songbird C?
Explain your answer.

(2 marks)

(d) Explain how courtship behaviour can be used to classify organisms.

(3 marks)

Learning Objectives:

- Know that antibiotics may be used to treat bacterial disease.

- Understand that one way in which antibiotics function is by preventing the formation of bacterial cell walls, resulting in osmotic lysis.

Specification Reference 3.2.10

Tip: Bacteria are prokaryotic cells — see page 70 for more on what organelles they have and what they do.

1. Antibiotics

Most people will develop a bacterial infection at some point in their lives, and most of these infections will be treated fairly easily with antibiotics.

Antibiotic action

Antibiotics are used to treat bacterial diseases. They are chemicals that either kill or inhibit the growth of bacteria. Different types of antibiotics kill or inhibit the growth of bacteria in different ways. Some prevent growing bacterial cells from forming the bacterial cell wall, which usually gives the cell structure and support (see p. 70). This can lead to **osmotic lysis**.

How osmotic lysis works

- The antibiotics inhibit enzymes that are needed to make the chemical bonds in the cell wall.

- This prevents the cell from growing properly and weakens the cell wall.

- Water moves into the cell by osmosis.

- This causes the cell contents to expand, increasing the pressure on the cell wall.

- The weakened cell wall can't withstand the increase in pressure and bursts (lyses) — see Figure 1.

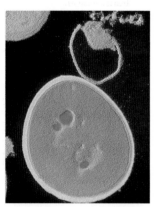

Figure 2: An electron micrograph of an intact Staphylococcus aureus *bacterium (bottom) and one undergoing lysis (top).*

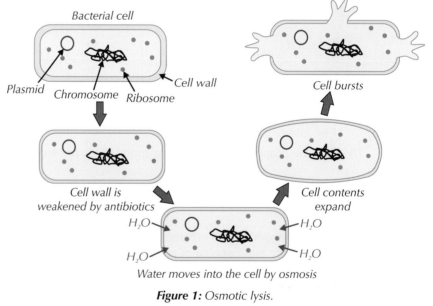

Figure 1: Osmotic lysis.

Tip: Antibiotics don't always kill bacteria by osmotic lysis — for example, some can inhibit protein synthesis. But you only need to know how osmotic lysis works for the exam.

Practice Questions — Fact Recall

Q1 What are antibiotics?

Q2 What are antibiotics used for?

Q3 Describe how antibiotics can cause cell death via osmotic lysis.

2. Antibiotic Resistance

Unfortunately for us, disease-causing bacteria are withstanding our attempts to wipe them out by developing antibiotic resistance. Worse still, they're also passing the resistance around to their family and friends.

Learning Objectives:

- Know that DNA is the genetic material in bacteria as well as in most other organisms.
- Know that mutations are changes in DNA and result in different characteristics.
- Understand that mutations in bacteria may result in resistance to antibiotics.
- Understand that resistance to antibiotics may be passed to subsequent generations by vertical gene transmission.
- Understand that resistance may also be passed from one species to another when DNA is transferred during conjugation. This is horizontal gene transmission.

Specification Reference 3.2.10

Mutations and antibiotic resistance

The genetic material in bacteria is the same as in most other organisms — DNA. The DNA of an organism contains genes that carry the instructions for different proteins. These proteins determine the organism's characteristics.

Mutations are changes in the base sequence of an organism's DNA. If a mutation occurs in the DNA of a gene it could change the protein and cause a different characteristic. Some mutations in bacterial DNA mean that the bacteria are not affected by a particular antibiotic any more — they've developed **antibiotic resistance**.

Example: Methicillin

Methicillin is an antibiotic that inhibits an enzyme involved in cell wall formation (see previous page). Some bacteria have developed resistance to methicillin, e.g. **MRSA** (methicillin-resistant *Staphylococcus aureus*).

Usually, resistance to methicillin occurs because the gene for the target enzyme of methicillin has mutated. The mutated gene produces an altered enzyme that methicillin no longer recognises, and so can't inhibit. This means the bacterial cell can form a normal cell wall and is unaffected by osmotic lysis — see Figure 1.

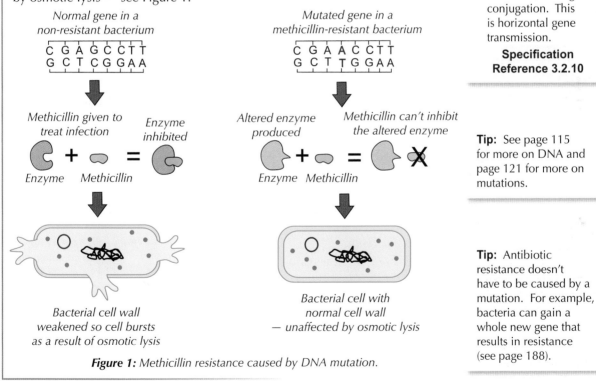

Figure 1: Methicillin resistance caused by DNA mutation.

Tip: See page 115 for more on DNA and page 121 for more on mutations.

Tip: Antibiotic resistance doesn't have to be caused by a mutation. For example, bacteria can gain a whole new gene that results in resistance (see page 188).

How is resistance passed on?

One single resistant bacterium isn't enough to cause disease or infection — so the resistant gene must be passed on to other bacteria. There are two ways this happens: **vertical gene transmission** and **horizontal gene transmission**.

Vertical gene transmission

Vertical gene transmission is where genes are passed on during reproduction. Bacteria reproduce asexually — in other words, a single parent cell divides to produce two genetically identical daughter cells. Each daughter cell is a clone (exact copy) of the parent cell — this means it has an exact copy of the parent cell's genes, including any that give it antibiotic resistance.

Genes for antibiotic resistance can be found in the bacterial chromosome or in plasmids. The chromosome and any plasmids are passed on to the daughter cells during reproduction. So antibiotic resistance is passed on from generation to generation — see Figure 2.

Tip: Plasmids are small rings of DNA found in bacterial cells — see page 70 for more.

Tip: Remember — bacterium is singular, bacteria is plural.

Tip: Remember the vertical shape of the vertical transmission diagram — resistance goes <u>down</u>.

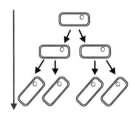

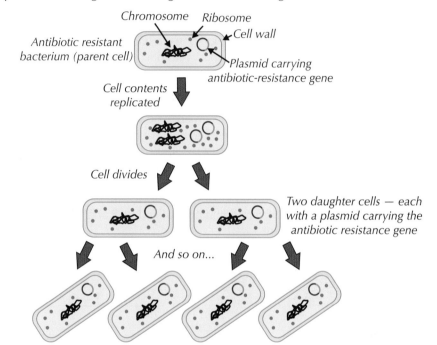

Figure 2: Antibiotic resistance being passed on by vertical gene transmission.

Horizontal gene transmission

Genes for resistance can also be passed on horizontally. This happens when two bacteria join together and a copy of a plasmid is passed from one cell to the other — this process is called **conjugation** (see Figure 3).

Tip: It can be helpful to think of conjugation as a bit like bacterial sex (just make sure you use the term conjugation in the exam).

Tip: Genes are only transferred in one direction (i.e. they can't be passed from the recipient cell back to the donor).

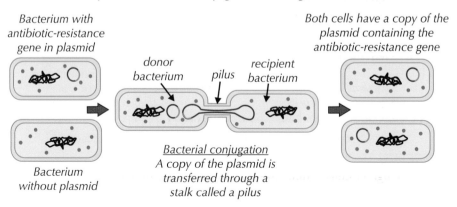

Figure 3: Antibiotic resistance being passed on by horizontal gene transmission.

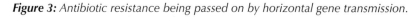

Plasmids can be passed on to a member of the same species or a totally different species. The plasmid can then be passed on vertically too, leading to even more bacteria acquiring resistance — see Figure 4.

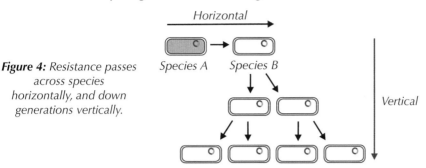

Figure 4: *Resistance passes across species horizontally, and down generations vertically.*

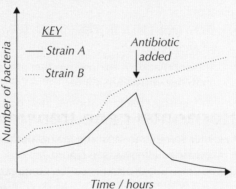

Figure 5: *An electron micrograph of* Escherichia coli *bacteria conjugating.*

Practice Questions — Application

Q1 Some strains of *Enterococcus faecalis* carry a gene, *vanA*, that makes them resistant to the antibiotic vancomycin.

In 2002, a vancomycin-resistant strain of *Staphylococcus aureus* was isolated from a patient. Vancomycin-resistant *E. faecalis*, carrying the *vanA* gene, was isolated from the same patient.

a) Describe how the *S. aureus* strain gained the *vanA* gene.

b) Describe how subsequent generations of *S. aureus* would obtain the *vanA* gene.

Q2 The graph below shows the effect of adding an antibiotic to two growing strains of a bacterial species.

DNA analysis of gene X revealed the following base sequences:
Strain A: ATTCGC,
Strain B: ATACGC.

a) Describe the results shown in the graph.

b) Which bacterial strain appears to be resistant to the antibiotic?

c) Suggest a possible explanation for these results.

Practice Questions — Fact Recall

Q1 What is the genetic material in bacteria?

Q2 What is a mutation?

Q3 Describe how a mutation in bacterial DNA can lead to antibiotic resistance.

Q4 A bacterium passes a gene for antibiotic resistance on to its daughter cells. Name this type of gene transmission.

Q5 a) What is meant by the term 'conjugation'?

b) What type of gene transmission uses conjugation?

▪ Be able to apply the
concepts of adaptation
and selection to
antibiotic resistance
and other examples.
**Specification
Reference 3.2.10**

Tip: Variation in a
population's
characteristics is caused
by gene mutations. So
adaptations are caused
by gene mutations.

Tip: An allele is just
a different version of a
gene, e.g. one with a
mutation (see page 120).

Exam Tip
Make sure you
remember this example
for the exam.

Tip: Bacteria can also
receive new antibiotic-
resistance genes
via horizontal gene
transmission — but
adaptations in other
organisms only arise
through mutations that
cause new alleles.

Tip: The gene for
antibiotic resistance
is passed on to the
offspring by vertical
gene transmission
(see page 188).

3. Evolution of Antibiotic Resistance

*You can pretty much watch antibiotic resistance evolve by growing bacteria in
the presence of an antibiotic. In the end, only bacteria that are resistant will
survive and grow — this is an example of evolution by natural selection.*

Natural selection

An **adaptation** is a characteristic that increases an organism's chance of
survival, e.g antibiotic resistance. Adaptations can become more common in
a population because of natural selection. Here's how natural selection works:

▪ Individuals within a population show variation in their characteristics.

▪ Predation, disease and competition create a struggle for survival.

▪ Individuals with better adaptations are more likely to survive, reproduce
and pass on the alleles that cause the adaptations to their offspring.

▪ Over time, the number of individuals with the advantageous adaptations
increases.

▪ Over generations this leads to evolution as the favourable adaptations
become more common in the population.

EXAMPLE: Evolution of antibiotic resistance by natural selection

Here's how populations of antibiotic-resistant bacteria evolve by natural
selection:

▪ Some individuals in a population have alleles that give them resistance to
an antibiotic.

▪ The population is exposed to that antibiotic, killing bacteria without the
antibiotic resistance allele.

▪ The resistant bacteria survive and reproduce without competition, passing
on the allele that gives antibiotic resistance to their offspring.

▪ After some time most organisms in the population will carry the antibiotic
resistance allele — see Figure 1.

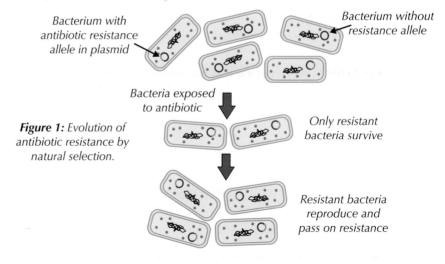

*Bacterium with
antibiotic resistance
allele in plasmid*

*Bacterium without
resistance allele*

*Bacteria exposed
to antibiotic*

*Only resistant
bacteria survive*

***Figure 1:** Evolution of
antibiotic resistance by
natural selection.*

*Resistant bacteria
reproduce and
pass on resistance*

Natural selection in other organisms

Natural selection happens in all populations — not just in bacterial populations. There are loads of examples, but they all follow the same basic principle — the organism has a characteristic that makes it more likely to survive, reproduce and pass on the alleles for the better characteristic.

In your exam you might be asked to explain why certain characteristics are common (or have increased). To do this you should identify why the adaptations (characteristics) are useful and explain how they've become more common due to natural selection. Here are some examples of the kinds of characteristics that can help organisms to survive:

Exam Tip
No matter what example you get given in the exam, the important thing to remember is that all adaptations help organisms to <u>survive</u>, <u>reproduce</u> and <u>pass on</u> their alleles.

Adaptations that could increase chance of survival	How the adaptations could increase survival
Streamlined body, camouflage, larger paws for running quicker, etc.	They help to escape from predators.
Streamlined body, camouflage, larger paws for running quicker, larger claws, etc.	They help to catch prey/get food.
Shorter/longer hairs, large ears, increased water storage capacity, etc.	They make the animal more suited to the climate.

Example

In 1810 a herd of caribou were taken from the Arctic to an area with a warmer climate. In 1810 the average fur length was 3.5 cm.
In 1960 it was 2.1 cm. This change can be explained by natural selection:

- There is variation in fur length in the population of caribou.

- Caribou with shorter fur will be better adapted to the warmer climate as they'll be less likely to overheat. These caribou will be more likely to survive and reproduce.

- The alleles for shorter fur length will be more likely to be passed on to the next generation, and so the population will gradually get shorter and shorter fur.

Practice Questions — Application

Q1 There are many different species of rat snake, all found in different habitats and with slightly different colourings. The black rat snake lives in wooded habitats and has a dark, brown-black colouring (see Figure 2). Describe how natural selection could explain the evolution of a rat snake with black colouring in a wooded habitat.

Q2 DDT is a chemical insecticide that was first used to kill malaria-carrying mosquitos around the time of WWII. In the 1950s, DDT-resistant mosquitos began to appear in areas of widespread DDT use. Describe how DDT-resistance became widespread in some mosquito populations.

Practice Questions — Fact Recall

Q1 What is an adaptation?

Q2 Describe how populations of antibiotic-resistant bacteria evolve by natural selection.

Figure 2: A black rat snake climbing up a tree.

Learning Objective:

- Understand the problems associated with antibiotic resistance in terms of the difficulty of treating tuberculosis and MRSA.

Specification Reference 3.2.10

4. Treating Antibiotic-Resistant Infections

Diseases caused by bacteria are treated using antibiotics. Because bacteria are becoming resistant to different antibiotics through natural selection it's becoming more and more difficult to treat some bacterial infections, such as tuberculosis (TB) and methicillin-resistant Staphylococcus aureus *(MRSA).*

MRSA

Tip: *S. aureus* and MRSA are different strains of the same bacterial species. There are several different strains classified as MRSA.

Staphylococcus aureus is a bacteria that causes a range of illnesses from minor skin infections to life-threatening diseases such as meningitis and septicaemia. Methicillin-resistant *Staphylococcus aureus* (MRSA) is a strain of the *S. aureus* bacterium that has evolved to be resistant to a number of commonly used antibiotics, including methicillin.

The major problem with MRSA is that some strains are resistant to nearly all the antibiotics that are available. Also, it can take a long time for clinicians to determine which antibiotics, if any, will kill the strain each individual is infected with. During this time the patient may become very ill and even die. Drug companies are trying to develop alternative ways of treating MRSA to try to combat the emergence of resistance.

Health authorities and hospitals are trying to find ways to reduce the spread of MRSA. For example, patients diagnosed with MRSA and other multidrug-resistant bacterial infections are often isolated from other patients. Investigations into how infections are spread have led to changes in hygiene practices and sterilisation procedures in hospitals — for example, the introduction of antiseptic gels for hand washing, see page 196.

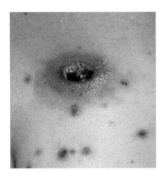

Figure 1: *Skin abscess caused by methicillin-resistant* Staphylococcus aureus *(MRSA).*

Tuberculosis

Tip: TB is caused by the bacteria *Mycobacterium tuberculosis*. There's more about TB on page 81.

Tuberculosis (TB) is a lung disease caused by bacteria. TB was once a major killer in the UK, but the number of people dying from TB decreased with the development of specific antibiotics that killed the bacterium. Also the number of people catching TB dropped due to a vaccine (see p. 16).

More recently though, some populations of TB bacteria have evolved resistance to the most effective antibiotics. Natural selection has led to populations that are resistant to a range of different antibiotics — the populations (strains) are multidrug-resistant.

To try to combat the emergence of resistance, TB treatment now involves taking a combination of different antibiotics for about 6 months. TB is becoming harder to treat as multidrug-resistant strains are evolving quicker than drug companies can develop new antibiotics.

Practice Questions — Fact Recall

Q1 a) What does MRSA stand for?   b) What illnesses can MRSA cause?

Q2 Describe the clinical problems associated with treating cases of MRSA infection.

Q3 What is TB?

Q4 Why did the number of patients dying from TB decrease in the UK?

Q5 Describe the recent problems regarding the treatment of TB and the current solutions.

5. Evaluating Antibiotic Resistance Data

Learning Objective:
- Be able to evaluate methodology, evidence and data relating to antibiotic resistance.
  Specification Reference 3.2.10

We need to study antibiotic resistance for many reasons — to see what antibiotics a sample of bacteria is resistant to, to discover why bacteria are resistant, to see if resistance is increasing, and so on. And just like with any other study, it's important that other scientists check that the methodology is sound and that any data supports the conclusions made.

It's very possible that you could get some data in the exam and be asked to check that the data is reliable and the conclusions are valid. The data could come from an experiment, like the one below:

Tip: Scientists check each other's work using a process called peer review — see page 2 for more.

Example

A clinician needs to find out which antibiotics will treat a patient's infection. They spread a sample of bacteria taken from the patient onto an agar plate. Then they place paper discs soaked with different concentrations of each antibiotic onto the plate. A negative control of a paper disc soaked in sterile water is added to the plate also. The bacteria are then allowed to grow (forming a 'lawn'). The clinician then measures the areas of growth inhibition after a set period of time. The results are shown in Figure 1.

Anywhere bacteria can't grow can be seen as a clear patch in the lawn of bacteria. This is called an inhibition zone. The size of the inhibition zone tells you how well an antibiotic works. The larger the zone, the more the bacteria were inhibited from growing.

Figure 2: *Culture plates testing the resistance of two strains of* Staphylococcus aureus. *You can see the clear inhibition zones where the antibiotic has stopped the bacteria from growing.*

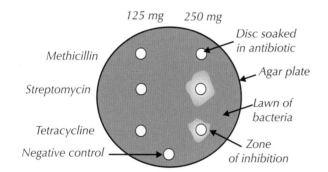

Figure 1: *Antibiotic resistance experiment results.*

Tip: The lowest concentration of antibiotic that inhibits bacterial growth is called the minimum inhibitory concentration (MIC).

You might be asked to describe the data...

Make sure you're precise about what the data shows — use exact amounts. E.g. A 250 mg dose of streptomycin inhibited growth the most. A 250 mg dose of tetracycline inhibited growth a small amount. The bacteria appear to be resistant to methicillin up to 250 mg.

...or evaluate the methodology

The experiment included a negative control, which is good. The bacteria grew around this disc, which shows the paper disc or sterilised water alone doesn't kill the bacteria.

The experiment only looked at two different concentrations of each antibiotic, so we don't know if it's resistant to methicillin or just resistant up to 250 mg.

Exam Tip
Examiners love asking about controls, so make sure you can spot them and explain why they're used (see pages 3-4).

You could also get data from a study into antibiotic resistance. It's still the same idea though — you could have to answer questions on the methods, evidence, data and any conclusions drawn. Here's an example that looks at the link between antibiotic use and antibiotic resistance:

Tip: It's not unusual for scientists to pull together data from different studies to look for links, or to increase the amount of overall data.

Example

Study 1 — MRSA on death certificates

This study investigated the number of death certificates mentioning MRSA in the UK between 1994 and 1997. The data was collected from UK death certificates issued between these dates. The results are shown in Figure 3.

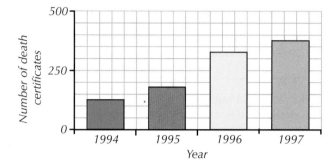

Figure 3: Study 1 results — graph to show the number of death certificates mentioning MRSA between 1994 and 1997.

Tip: The larger the sample size, the more reliable the results usually are — a sample size of 1.4 million suggests these results are pretty reliable.

Study 2 — Antibiotic prescriptions

This study counted the number of antibiotic prescriptions given out from 1994 to 1997. The information was gathered from a sample population covering 211 practices across the UK, which look after 1.4 million people. The results are shown in Figure 4.

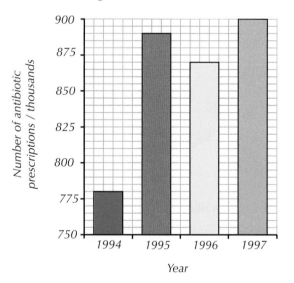

Figure 4: Study 2 results — graph to show the number of antibiotic prescriptions issued to a sample of the UK population between 1994 and 1997.

You might be asked to describe the data...

Study 1 shows that the number of death certificates mentioning MRSA increased between 1994 and 1997. Study 2 shows that generally the number of antibiotic prescriptions given increased between 1994 and 1997.

Exam Tip
If you're asked to describe the data, the level of detail you give should be suitable for the number of marks the question is worth — i.e. lots of marks means lots of detail.

...or draw conclusions...

If you're given two graphs you might be asked to see what conclusions you can draw using the graphs combined. These graphs show that the increase in the number of antibiotic prescriptions shows a positive correlation with an increase in the number of death certificates mentioning MRSA.

...or evaluate the evidence...

E.g. Dr Bottril said, 'This data proves that the increase in antibiotic prescriptions caused an increase in antibiotic resistance'. Does the data support this conclusion? No, there's a link between the number of prescriptions and MRSA being mentioned on death certificates, but that's all. Also, study 1 only looked at MRSA — not all forms of antibiotic resistance.

...or evaluate the methodology

The time period is relatively short — only 4 years. This trend may not continue, e.g. data for the next four years may show prescriptions rising further whilst resistant bacteria levels fall.

The number of death certificates mentioning MRSA increased but this doesn't necessarily mean the number of MRSA infections increased. The number of MRSA infections each year may have stayed the same, showing no increasing trend (just more people are dying from MRSA or the method for identifying and reporting MRSA has improved).

Study 2 includes all forms of antibiotic — prescriptions for methicillin may not have increased.

Tip: Don't jump to conclusions when analysing data. A correlation (link) does not mean cause — see page 5 for more.

Exam Tip
If you get an exam question that involves looking at two studies together, make sure you think about the positives and negatives of both of them, not just one.

Tip: Because of evidence like this, scientists are relatively confident that increased antibiotic usage is linked to rising levels of antibiotic resistance. Decision makers have used this scientific knowledge to set guidelines on the appropriate use of antibiotics — see the next page.

Practice Questions — Application

Q1 The graph below shows the percentage of antibacterial resistance in *E. coli* samples isolated from blood cultures in country X in 2009 and 2010.

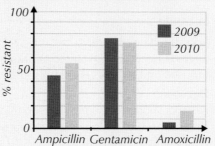

a) What percentage of samples were resistant to amoxicillin in 2009?

b) A doctor concluded that resistance is no longer a concern in country X as resistance has stabilised. Do the results agree with his conclusion? Explain your answer.

Q2 Turbidity is a measure of the cloudiness of a liquid. The more bacteria in a liquid, the cloudier it will be. A scientist measured the turbidity of some samples of bacteria over time to see how an antibiotic affected growth. The results are shown on the right. The antibiotic (diluted in sterile water) was added at 4 hours.

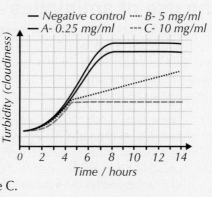

a) Suggest what the negative control might be and explain why it's used.

b) Describe and explain what has happened to Sample C.

- Be able to discuss the ways in which society uses scientific knowledge relating to antibiotic resistance to inform decision-making.
- Be able to discuss the ethical issues associated with the use of antibiotics.

Specification Reference 3.2.10

6. Making Decisions About Antibiotic Resistance

When new scientific information about antibiotics and antibiotic resistance has been validated by scientists, society can use this information to make informed decisions.

Using scientific knowledge to make decisions

Bacteria will develop antibiotic resistance by natural selection — it's nature. But scientific research has shown that certain things can be done to slow down the natural process. People working in the public health sector, together with patients, have to be made aware of recent scientific findings so that they can act upon them.

Here are two examples:

--- Example 1 ---

Scientific Knowledge:
Using an antiseptic gel to wash hands can help to reduce the spread of infectious diseases by person-to-person contact (especially in hospitals).

Decision:
Health workers should reduce spread by washing their hands with antiseptic gel (placed at all hand basins, and elsewhere in hospitals) before and after visiting each patient on a ward.

--- Example 2 ---

Scientific knowledge:
Bacteria become resistant to antibiotics more quickly when antibiotics are misused and patients don't finish the course.

Decision:
Doctors should only prescribe antibiotics when absolutely necessary. Patients have to be told the importance of finishing all the antibiotics even if they start to feel better.

Ethical issues surrounding the use of antibiotics

People are very concerned about the spread of antibiotic-resistant bacteria. Limiting the use of antibiotics is one way of helping to slow down the emergence of resistance, but this raises some ethical issues.

Here are some examples:

--- Examples ---

- Some people believe that antibiotics should only be used in life-threatening situations to reduce the increase of resistance. Others argue against this because people would take more time off work for illness, it could reduce people's standard of living, it could increase the incidence of disease and it could cause unnecessary suffering.

Figure 1: *An alcohol gel hand sanitiser in place in a hospital. The prominent placement of the hand gel encourages visitors and staff to use it regularly to prevent the spread of infections within hospitals.*

- A few people believe doctors shouldn't prescribe antibiotics to those suffering from dementia. They argue that they may forget to take them, increasing the chance of resistance developing. However, some people argue that all patients have the right to medication.

- Some also argue that terminally ill patients shouldn't receive antibiotics because they're going to die. But withholding antibiotics from these patients could reduce their length of survival and quality of life.

- Some people believe animals shouldn't be given antibiotics (as this may increase antibiotic resistance). Other people argue that this could cause unnecessary suffering to the animals.

Tip: It's not the scientists who make the decisions — they just provide the information for other people to make the decisions, e.g. people in the government. See page 6 for more.

Practice Questions — Application

Q1 A recent study investigated the presence of two different bacterial strains on doctors' ties and the frequency with which they washed their ties. From a sample of 40 ties at a single hospital, 20% of ties were found to carry *Staphylococcus aureus* and 2.5% MRSA. 70% of doctors had never cleaned their tie.

  a) Comment on the methodology of this study.

  b) Suggest a decision the hospital in question might make, given the scientific data presented to them above.

Q2 It has been suggested that the increase in the number of antibiotic-resistant infections of TB in England and Wales over the last 10 years is linked to increased immigration. This has led some organisations to call for the compulsory screening of all immigrants.
Suggest reasons for and against this proposal.

Exam Tip
If you get an exam question asking you to suggest a decision based on data, just think sensibly about what you would do. The most obvious suggestion is often the right one.

Section Summary

Make sure you know...

- That antibiotics are chemicals that either kill or inhibit the growth of bacteria and they're used to treat bacterial diseases.

- That antibiotics can kill bacteria by preventing the formation of the bacterial cell wall, leading to osmotic lysis.

- That DNA is the genetic material of bacteria and that it contains genes which code for proteins.

- That mutations are changes in the base sequences of DNA and that if a mutation occurs in a gene, it can alter the protein produced and lead to a different characteristic in the organism.

- That antibiotic resistance in bacteria can be caused by mutations.

- How antibiotic resistance is passed down through generations of bacteria by vertical gene transmission.

- How antibiotic resistance can be passed between bacteria of the same or different species by horizontal gene transmission and conjugation.

- The problems in treating MRSA and TB because of antibiotic resistance.

- The concepts of adaptation and natural selection — an adaptation will help an organism to survive, reproduce and pass on the allele for the adaptation to the next generation.

- How to apply the concepts of adaptation and natural selection to antibiotic resistance and other examples.

- How to evaluate the methodology, evidence and data of studies relating to antibiotic resistance.

- How new knowledge about antibiotic resistance is used by society to make decisions.

- That there are ethical issues involved in the use of antibiotics, and how to explain some of these.

Exam-style Questions

1   Species of *Streptomyces* bacteria are naturally found in soil, along with many other types of bacteria. They produce a wide range of clinically useful antibiotics including tetracycline-based antibiotics.

(a)   Tetracycline-based antibiotics work by inhibiting protein synthesis.
Give one other way that antibiotics can kill or inhibit bacterial growth.

(1 mark)

(b)   Use your knowledge of evolution by natural selection to explain how tetracycline-producing *Streptomyces* species may have become common in the population.

(3 marks)

(c)   Species of *Streptomyces* also possess tet-resistance genes that protect them from the effects of tetracycline. For example, the *tetA* genes are responsible for pumping tetracycline out of cells, thereby protecting cells from its harmful effects.

Tet-resistance genes are now found in a number of other species of bacteria, including a number of pathogens. Explain the presence of these resistant genes in other species of bacteria.

(2 marks)

(d)   Scientists investigated the link between the use of antibiotics in cattle feed and the tetracycline resistance of *E. coli* samples isolated from the cattle. The samples were grown on agar plates and then tested for resistance to tetracycline. The results are shown in the graph below.

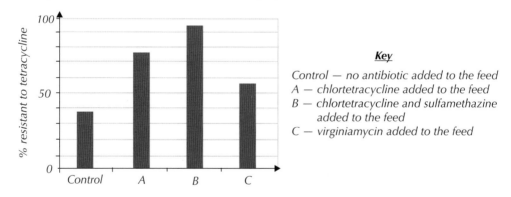

Key

Control — no antibiotic added to the feed
A — chlortetracycline added to the feed
B — chlortetracycline and sulfamethazine added to the feed
C — virginiamycin added to the feed

(i)   Suggest two factors the scientists should have considered when selecting cattle for the experiment.

(2 marks)

(ii)   Explain why the bacteria in the control sample were taken from cattle that had no antibiotics added to their feed.

(1 mark)

(iii)   What conclusions can be drawn from the results of the study?

(5 marks)

2   MRSA is a strain of the *Staphylococcus aureus* bacterium. It is often in the media in articles relating to death rates of patients in hospital.

(a)   Suggest why the media commonly refer to MRSA as a 'super bug'.

(1 mark)

(b)   Explain how a mutation might have led to the development of MRSA.

(3 marks)

(c)   Limiting the use of antibiotics could slow the spread of strains such as MRSA. Discuss the ethical issues surrounding limiting the use of antibiotics.

(6 marks)

(d)   A study was carried out in hospital wards to investigate the effect of increased cleaning on the spread of hospital-acquired infections, including MRSA. Two wards (A and B) were compared. One had an extra cleaner on duty for 6 months and the other did not. Tests were done each week to determine the aerobic colony count (number of aerobic bacteria) at places on the wards that were in frequent contact with hands. Results from 3 months of the study are shown in the graph below.

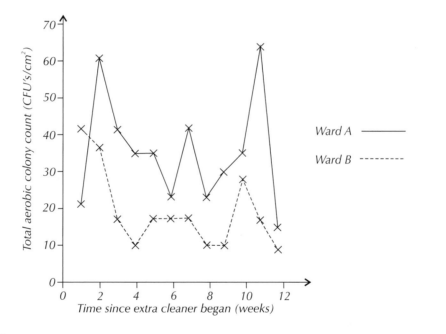

(i)   Suggest which ward had an extra cleaner during the study period. Explain your answer.

(2 marks)

(ii) By how much did the total aerobic colony count in Ward B drop over the 12 week period? Give your answer as a percentage of the original count.

(2 marks)

(iii) How might these results affect decision-making relating to the spread of antibiotic-resistant infections in hospitals?

(1 mark)

(iv) Suggest one other method, other than increased cleaning, that might reduce the presence of MRSA in hospitals.

(1 mark)

1. Investigating Species Diversity

Species diversity is important — the higher the species diversity in an ecosystem, the healthier that ecosystem is.

What is species diversity?

Species diversity is the number of different species and the abundance of each species within a community. The higher the species diversity of plants and trees in an area, the higher the species diversity of insects, animals and birds. This is because there are more habitats (places to live) and a larger and more varied food source. Diversity can be measured to help us monitor ecosystems and identify areas where it has been dramatically reduced.

Measuring diversity

The simplest way to measure diversity is just to count up the number of different species. But that doesn't take into account the population size of each species. Species that are in a community in very small numbers shouldn't be treated the same as those with bigger populations. This is where the **index of diversity** comes in.

The index of diversity is a useful way of measuring species diversity. It's calculated using an equation that takes different population sizes into account. You can calculate the index of diversity (*d*) of a community using the following formula:

Tip: An <u>ecosystem</u> consists of all the <u>living</u> (biotic) and <u>non-living</u> (abiotic) things that can be found in a certain area. The living things within an ecosystem form a <u>community</u>.

$$d = \frac{N(N-1)}{\Sigma n(n-1)}$$

Where...

N = Total number of all organisms

n = Total number of organisms in one species

Σ = 'Sum of' (i.e. added together)

The higher the number the more diverse the area is. If all the individuals are of the same species (i.e. no diversity) the diversity index is 1.

Tip: When calculating the bottom half of the equation you need to work out the $n(n-1)$ bit for each different species then add them all together.

— **Example** —

There are 3 different species of flower in this field — a red species, a white and a blue. There are 3 of the red species, 5 of the white and 3 of the blue.

There are 11 organisms altogether, so $N = 11$.

So the species diversity index of this field is:

$$d = \frac{11(11-1)}{3(3-1) + 5(5-1) + 3(3-1)} = \frac{110}{6 + 20 + 6} = 3.44$$

Calculating the index of diversity can get quite tricky. If you've got a lot of data you might find it easier to plug the numbers into a table (see example on the next page) — that way you can make sure you don't miss out any steps.

A student investigates the diversity of fish species in her local pond.
She finds 46 fish of 6 different species. To help her calculate the index of
diversity for the pond she draws the following table:

Species	n (total number of organisms in species)	$n - 1$	$n(n - 1)$
A	1	0	0
B	6	5	30
C	2	1	2
D	15	14	210
E	3	2	6
F	19	18	342
N (total number of all organisms)	46		

Tip: $n(n-1)$ just means $n \times (n-1)$.

Tip: To get the figures in the last column in the table, you multiply together the figures in the second and third columns.

She then uses the numbers from the table to calculate the diversity index:

$$d = \frac{N(N - 1)}{\sum n(n-1)} = \frac{46(46 - 1)}{0 + 30 + 2 + 210 + 6 + 342} = \frac{2070}{590} = 3.51$$

Practice Questions — Application

Q1 The table below shows the number of individuals of each species
of insect found in two ponds.

Species	Number of individuals found in Pond A	Number of individuals found in Pond B
Damselfly	3	13
Dragonfly	5	5
Stonefly	2	7
Water boatman	3	2
Crane fly	1	18
Pond skater	4	9

a) Use the data provided in the table and the formula given below to
calculate the index of diversity for:

i) Pond A

ii) Pond B

$$d = \frac{N(N - 1)}{\sum n(n-1)}$$

where N = total number of all organisms
and n = total number of organisms in one species.

b) Birds and amphibians feed on insects. Which of the two
ponds would you expect to have a higher diversity of birds and
amphibians? Explain your answer.

Exam Tip
If you've got time at
the end of the exam,
always go back over any
calculation questions
and check the answer —
it's easy to make a silly
mistake somewhere and
lose marks.

Q2 A study was conducted on the trees found in a wood and town.
The results are shown in the graph below.

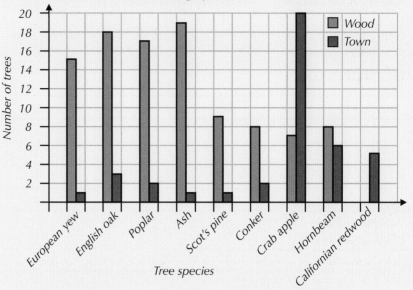

Exam Tip
Don't be thrown if you
get asked to calculate
species diversity using
data from a graph —
just read off the values
carefully.

a) Use the data in the graph and the formula provided below to
calculate the index of diversity for the tree species in:

i) the wood

ii) the town

$$d = \frac{N(N-1)}{\sum n(n-1)}$$

where N = total number of all organisms
and n = total number of organisms in one species.

Exam Tip
You can use a calculator
to help you with this
question — you'll be
allowed to take one into
the exam with you.

b) The index of diversity gives a better estimate of the diversity of
tree species than simply counting the number of species present.
Explain why, using data from the graph to support your answer.

2. Human Impacts on Biodiversity and Species Diversity

Lots of things humans do can affect the diversity of species — including cutting down forests and farming.

Learning Objectives:

- Understand the influence of deforestation and the impact of agriculture on species diversity.
- Be able to evaluate the associated benefits and risks of human activity on species diversity.

Specification Reference 3.2.11

Biodiversity

The term 'biodiversity' describes the variety of living organisms and ecosystems on Earth. Species diversity is a key part of this.

Biodiversity is important because it provides us with food, fresh water, oxygen, medicines and the raw materials we need to live. But human activities like farming and deforestation are reducing species diversity — causing biodiversity to fall as a result.

Deforestation

We cut down forests to get wood and create land for farming and settlements. Deforestation directly reduces the number of trees and sometimes the number of different tree species (see Figure 1). It also destroys habitats, so some species could lose their shelter and food source. This means that these species will die or be forced to migrate to another suitable area, further reducing diversity. The migration of organisms into increasingly smaller areas of remaining forest may temporarily increase species diversity in those areas.

> **Example**
>
> On the Indonesian island of Sulawesi, a study was conducted into the impact of rainforest deforestation on bird diversity. When a diversity index for bird species in different regions was calculated, it was found to be 25% lower in areas that had been logged than in areas of natural forest.

Exam Tip
Be specific with your terminology — you need to talk about species losing their 'food sources' rather than 'food' in the exam, otherwise you won't get the mark.

Agriculture

Farmers try to maximise the amount of food that they can produce from a given area of land. Many of the methods they use reduce species diversity. These methods include:

- Woodland clearance — this is done to increase the area of farmland. This reduces species diversity for the same reasons as deforestation.

- Hedgerow removal — this is also done to increase the area of farmland by turning lots of small fields into fewer large fields. This reduces species diversity for the same reasons as woodland clearance and deforestation.

- Pesticides — these are chemicals that kill organisms (pests) that feed on crops. This reduces diversity by directly killing the pests. Also, any species that feed on the pests will lose a food source, so their numbers could decrease too.

- Herbicides — these are chemicals that kill unwanted plants (weeds). This reduces plant diversity and could reduce the number of organisms that feed on the weeds.

- Competition — some crops may be better at competing for certain resources than other plants. E.g, in cramped conditions, wheat is better at competing for light than some weed species. The other plants can't get the resources they need to survive and die, so species diversity is reduced.

Figure 1: *Satellite images of the Amazon rainforest taken in 1985 (top) and 2000 (bottom). The light green and brown areas show where deforestation has taken place.*

Figure 2: *A monoculture field containing a single crop.*

Tip: Extinction is where a species no longer exists.

Tip: CO_2 is a greenhouse gas. When plants and trees photosynthesise they take in CO_2 from the air and store it. The cutting down and burning of trees is increasing the level of CO_2 in the atmosphere, which is contributing to global warming.

Figure 3: *Chemicals from the Madagascan periwinkle have been used to treat leukaemia.*

- Monoculture — this is when farmers grow fields containing only one type of plant (see Figure 2). A single type of plant will support fewer species, so diversity is reduced.

Example

A study carried out over several decades found that the diversity of insect species in the UK fell during years when agricultural practices were intensified and when large areas of land were given over to growing cereals. This was correlated with a fall in the diversity of birds who fed on the insects.

Benefits and risks of human activities

Deforestation and agriculture can have a huge impact on species diversity, so the benefits and risks of these activities need to be considered carefully.

Deforestation	Benefits	▪ Wood and land for homes to be built. ▪ Local areas become more developed by attracting businesses.
	Risks	▪ Diversity is reduced — species could become extinct. ▪ Less carbon dioxide is stored because there are fewer plants and trees, which contributes to climate change. ▪ Many medicines come from organisms found in rainforests (see Figure 3) — possible future discoveries may be lost. ▪ Natural beauty is lost.
Agriculture	Benefits	▪ More food can be produced. ▪ Food is cheaper to produce, so food prices are lower. ▪ Local areas become more developed by attracting businesses.
	Risks	▪ Diversity is reduced — because of monoculture, woodland and hedgerow clearance, herbicide and pesticide use. ▪ Natural beauty is lost.

Practice Questions — Fact Recall

Q1 Explain how deforestation reduces species diversity.

Q2 Many farmers clear woodland and remove hedgerows from their land. Explain:
   a) why this is done.
   b) how these practices can reduce species diversity.

Q3 Pesticides and herbicides are often sprayed over crops.
   a) What are: i) pesticides? ii) herbicides?
   b) Describe the effect of pesticides and herbicides on species diversity.

Q4 What is monoculture?

Q5 Explain why competition with crops can reduce species diversity.

Q6 Give two benefits and two risks of deforestation.

3. Species Diversity Data

Data showing the effect humans have had on species diversity can help society make decisions — but first scientists need to be able to interpret it. Funnily enough, the exam board expects you to be able to interpret it too...

Interpreting diversity data

You might have to interpret some data in the exam. Here are a couple of examples of the kind of thing you might get:

Example 1 — Loss of rainforest

Figure 1 shows the results of a study that compared the diversity in a rainforest with the diversity in a deforested area that had been cleared for agricultural use.

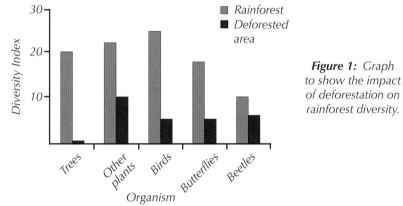

Figure 1: Graph to show the impact of deforestation on rainforest diversity.

Describe the data:

For all types of organism studied, species diversity is higher in the rainforest than in the deforested area. Deforestation has reduced the species diversity of trees the most.

Explain the data:

Many organisms can't adapt to the change in habitat and must migrate or die — reducing diversity in the area. Reduced tree diversity leads to a reduction in the diversity of all other organisms (see p. 200).

Example 2 — Herbicides

Herbicides kill unwanted plants (weeds) whilst leaving crops unharmed. The crops can then grow better because they're not competing for resources with weeds. Figure 3 shows plant diversity in an untreated field and a field treated annually with herbicide.

Figure 3: Graph to show plant diversity in a field treated with herbicide and an untreated field.

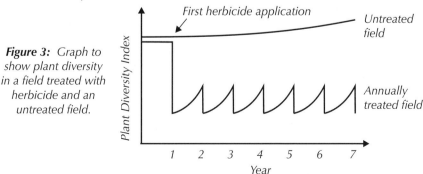

Figure 2: Deforestation in Ethiopia.

Learning Objectives:

- Be able to interpret data relating to the effects of human activity on species diversity.
- Be able to discuss the ways in which society uses science to inform the making of decisions relating to biodiversity.

Specification Reference 3.2.11

Exam Tip
An easy way to lose marks in the exam is to describe a trend when you're asked to explain it. Explain means <u>give reasons</u> for something.

Figure 4: Spraying herbicide on crops.

Describe the data:

Plant diversity in the untreated field showed a slight increase in the seven years. Plant diversity decreased a lot in the treated field when the herbicide was first applied. The diversity then recovered throughout each year, but was reduced again by each annual application of herbicide.

Explain the data:

When the herbicide was applied, the weeds were killed, reducing species diversity. In between applications, diversity increased as new weeds grew. These were then killed again by each annual application of herbicide.

Using diversity data

Society uses diversity data to make decisions. Diversity data can be used to see which species or areas are being affected by human activity. This information can then be used by society to make decisions about human activities. For example:

Scientific Finding	Decision Made
Fewer hedgerows reduces diversity.	The UK government offers farmers money to encourage them to plant hedgerows, and to cover the cost of not growing crops on these areas.
Deforestation reduces diversity.	Some governments encourage sustainable logging (a few trees are taken from lots of different areas and young trees are planted to replace them).
Human development reduces diversity.	Many governments are setting up protected areas (e.g. national parks) where human development is restricted to conserve diversity.
Some species are facing extinction.	Breeding programmes in zoos help to increase the numbers of endangered species in a safe environment before reintroducing them to the wild.

Tip: Take a look at page 6 for more on how society makes decisions based on scientific evidence.

Practice Questions — Application

Q1 The graph below shows the diversity index of bees at two sites in an area of rainforest. Deforestation occurred at one of the sites.

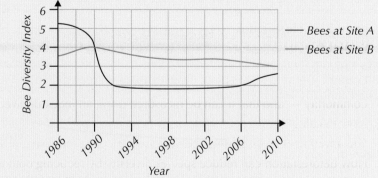

a) Describe the trend in bee diversity at Site A.

b) Which of the two sites, A or B, underwent deforestation? Explain your answer.

c) A conservation programme involving the planting of new trees was carried out at Site A. Suggest when the programme began. Give an explanation for your answer.

Tip: Bees rely on pollen and nectar from trees and plants to survive.

Q2 In the mid-1960s, some coffee plantations began growing species of coffee which needed to be planted alongside trees that would provide shade. Some of these plantations grew the coffee next to native tree species and the other half grew the coffee next to exotic tree species.

The graph below shows the changes in plant species diversity on each type of plantation as well as the average yield of coffee beans.

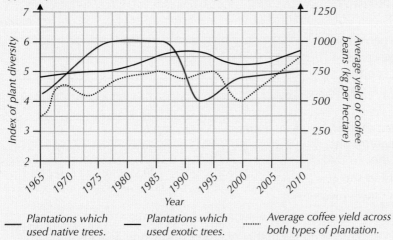

___ Plantations which used native trees.   ___ Plantations which used exotic trees.   .... Average coffee yield across both types of plantation.

a) Describe the trend in plant diversity on plantations which used native trees.

b) During the time period shown on the graph, the native trees were affected by a fungal blight but the exotic trees were not.

i) When did the fungal blight affect the native trees? Explain your answer.

ii) Give one advantage and one disadvantage of planting the native trees compared to the exotic trees.

c) This data was used to conclude that there's no correlation between plant diversity and coffee bean yield on plantations which used native trees. Is this conclusion valid? Explain your answer.

Tip: If you want to know more about drawing conclusions, take a look at page 5 in How Science Works.

Section Summary

Make sure you know:

- That species diversity is the number of different species and the abundance of each species within a community — and that it can be measured using an index of diversity.

- How to calculate an index of diversity from given data.

- The advantages of measuring species diversity using the index of diversity.

- How deforestation can reduce species diversity by reducing both the overall number of trees and the number of different tree species, as well as by removing habitats and food sources for other species.

- How agriculture can reduce species diversity through woodland clearance, pesticides, herbicides, hedgerow removal, competition and monoculture.

- The benefits and risks of human activities that affect species diversity.

- How to describe and explain trends using data on species diversity.

- How society uses science to help make decisions that may affect biodiversity.

Exam-style Questions

1   A team of students have investigated plant species diversity on two farms.

(a)   What is species diversity?

(1 mark)

(b)   The table on the right shows the number of individuals of different plant species found in a single hedgerow on each farm.

Plant Species	Farm A	Farm B
A	3	12
B	6	2
C	9	4
D	7	6
E	11	3
F	11	0

(i)   Calculate the plant diversity index for the hedgerow on each farm using the equation provided below.

$$d = \frac{N(N-1)}{\sum n(n-1)}$$

where, N = total number of all organisms and n = total number of organisms in one species.

(4 marks)

(ii)   One of the farms grows organic crops and does not use chemical herbicides. Which farm is this most likely to be? Explain your answer.

(2 marks)

(c)   Many organic farms use biological pesticides. These are organisms which prey on the pests that eat crops. The students behind the first study want to investigate the impact of biological pesticides on insect species diversity in farm hedgerows.

(i)   Suggest a control the students might use in their investigation.

(1 mark)

(ii)   Other than using a control, suggest two ways in which the students could increase the reliability of their results.

(2 marks)

(d)   The government offers grants to farmers to maintain their hedgerows.

(i)   Suggest one advantage to farmers of removing hedgerows from their land.

(1 mark)

(ii)   Suggest what impact hedgerow removal could have on insect diversity. Explain your answer.

(3 marks)

(e)   The owner of Farm B is keen to purchase woodland next to his farm and clear the area to plant crops. However he has met with opposition from local conservationists who believe the risks of this activity outweigh the benefits.

Discuss the benefits and risks of converting the woodland to farmland.

(6 marks)

2 A group of scientists issued a report on the diversity of roadside trees in urban areas. They calculated the species diversity of trees at six locations across the UK. Data included in the report is shown in the table below.

Location	Location Type	Human Population	Diversity Index of Trees	Number of Tree Species Present
A	City	500 000	12.2	13
B	City	195 000	4.6	15
C	Town	11 500	6.1	10
D	Village	1700	7.9	5
E	Hamlet	45	9.7	18
F	Town	25 400	8.2	14

(a) Calculate the mean diversity index of roadside trees in towns and cities.

(1 mark)

(b) The scientists looked at the diversity of roadside trees by counting the number of tree species present. They also calculated the diversity index of trees.

Which of these two methods is a more accurate way of analysing species diversity? Explain your answer.

(2 marks)

(c) The report stated that tree populations must have a diversity index of 20 for their population to have long term stability. It concluded that most cities in the UK do not have stable roadside tree populations.

Is their conclusion valid? Explain your answer.

(2 marks)

3 A study investigated the effect of altitude on flower diversity and the area of land under cultivation. The results are shown in the graph below.

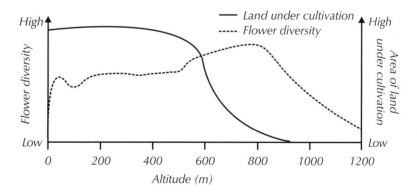

(a) Describe the trends shown by the graph.

(2 marks)

(b) Which do you think has the bigger impact on flower diversity, altitude or the area of land under cultivation? Explain your answer.

(4 marks)

Exam Help

1. Exam Structure

You'll take two exams as part of AS Level Biology. Everything you need to know about them is summarised below.

Unit 1 exam — Biology and Disease

- There are 60 marks to be had.
- It's 1 hour 15 minutes long (so you've got just over 1 minute per mark).
- There will be 5-7 short answer questions, plus two longer questions (one of which is a comprehension question — one that tests your recall and understanding of a passage of text).

Unit 2 exam — The Variety of Living Organisms

- There are 85 marks in total.
- It's 1 hour 45 minutes long (again, that's just over 1 minute per mark).
- There will be 5-7 short answer questions, plus two longer questions that test How Science Works and data interpretation skills.

2. Command Words

Command words are just the bits of a question that tell you what to do. You'll find answering exam questions much easier if you understand exactly what they mean, so here's a brief summary table of the most common ones:

Command word:	What to do:
Give / Name / State	Give a brief one or two word answer, or a short sentence.
Define	Give the meaning of a word.
What is meant by...	Give the meaning of a word or phrase.
Describe	Write about what something's like, e.g. describe the structure of fish gills.
Explain	Give reasons for something.
Suggest	Use your scientific knowledge to work out what the answer might be.
Compare	Give the similarities and differences between two things.
Evaluate	Give the arguments both for and against an issue, or the advantages and disadvantages of something. You also need to give an overall judgement.

Some questions will also ask you to answer 'using the information provided' (e.g. a graph, table or passage of text) — if so, you must refer to the information you've been given or you won't get the marks.

Exam Tip
You'll be marked on the quality of your written English (so things like spelling and grammar) and the correct use of scientific terms in both exam papers.

Tip: The unit 1 exam is worth 33.3% of your AS Level and the unit 2 exam is worth 46.7%. The other 20% comes from an internal assessment (testing your practical and investigative skills).

Exam Tip
When you're reading exam questions, underline the command words. That way you'll know exactly what type of answer to give.

Exam Tip
If you're answering a longer 'compare' or 'evaluate' question make a mental list of the similarities and differences or pros and cons first, so you know what you want your answer to include before you start writing.

3. Answering Data Questions

You'll get lots of questions about data in the exam, so you need to be a dab hand at describing the data, drawing conclusions from it and commenting on the reliability of the data. It's quite a lot to get your head around, but this will help...

Describing the data

You need to be able to describe any data you're given. The level of detail in your answer should be appropriate for the number of marks given. Loads of marks = more detail, few marks = less detail.

Example 1 — Experiment A

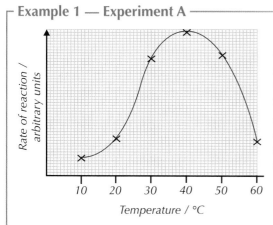

Experiment A examined the effect of temperature on the rate of an enzyme-controlled reaction. The rate of reaction for enzyme X was measured at six different temperatures. All other variables were kept constant. The results are shown in the graph on the left.

Exam Tip
It's easy to get <u>describe</u> and <u>explain</u> mixed up. If you're asked to describe the data, just state the overall pattern or trend. If you're asked to explain the data, you'll need to <u>give reasons</u> for the trend.

Describing the data (2 marks):

The data shows that the rate of reaction increases as temperature increases up to a certain point. The rate of reaction then decreases as temperature increases.

Describing the data (3 marks):

The data shows that the rate of reaction increases as temperature increases from 10 °C up to 40 °C. The rate is fastest between 20 and 30 °C. The rate of reaction then decreases rapidly as temperature increases from 40 °C to 60 °C.

Exam Tip
If you need to describe the data in detail, it's a good idea to include numbers from the graph.

Example 2 — Study B

Study B examined the effect of farm hedgerow length on the number of species in a given area. The number of species present during a single week on 12 farms was counted by placing ground-level traps. All the farms were a similar area. The traps were left out every day, at 6 am for two hours and once again at 6 pm for two hours. The results are shown in the scattergram on the right.

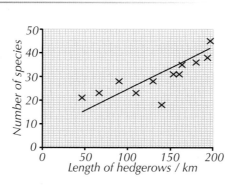

Exam Tip
You'll see data presented in all sorts of ways in the exam — scatter graphs, line graphs, bar charts, tables... Make sure you're comfortable interpreting all of them.

Describing the data (1 mark):

The data shows a positive correlation between the length of hedgerows and the number of species in the area.

Exam Tip
If a question is only worth 1 mark, don't waste time writing more than you need to.

Drawing and checking conclusions

You have to be very careful when drawing conclusions in the exam.
For results that show a correlation between the variables, remember that this doesn't prove that a change in one causes a change in the other.

Tip: See page 5 for more on correlations and causal relationships.

Example — Study B

The length of the hedgerows shows a positive correlation with the number of species in that area. But you can't conclude more hedgerows cause more species (or that fewer hedgerows cause fewer species). Other factors may have been involved, for example, the number of predators in an area may have decreased or the farmers may have used less pesticide there.

The data should always support the conclusion too. This may sound obvious but it's easy to jump to conclusions. Conclusions have to be precise — not make sweeping generalisations.

Exam Tip

Data questions are fairly common in the exams. You might be given a conclusion for the data and asked to evaluate it — this just means you have to give reasons why it is (or isn't) a valid conclusion.

Example — Experiment A

A science magazine concluded from this data that enzyme X works best at 40 °C. The data doesn't support this. The enzyme could work best at 42 °C or 47 °C but you can't tell this from the data because increases of 10 °C at a time were used. The rates of reaction at in-between temperatures weren't measured.

Commenting on reliability

Exam Tip

If you're asked to evaluate the method used in an experiment, you also need to comment on the same things mentioned here.

If the data isn't reliable for whatever reason you can't draw a valid conclusion. Here are some of the things you'll need to think about if you're asked to comment on the reliability of an experiment or study in the exam.

1. Size of the data set

For experiments, the more repeats you do, the more reliable the data. The general rule for studies is the larger the sample size, the more reliable the data is.

Example — Study B

Study B is quite small — they only used 12 farms. The trend shown by the data may not appear if you studied 50 or 100 farms, or studied them for a longer period of time.

---

2. Variables

The more variables you control, the more reliable your data is.

Example 1 — Experiment A

In Experiment A, all other variables were controlled, e.g. pH, concentrations, volumes, so the results are reliable and you can be sure the temperature is causing the change in the reaction rate.

Tip: Reliability means the results can be consistently reproduced in independent experiments. See pages 3-5 for more info.

Example 2 — Study B

In Study B you're not told if all the other variables were controlled, e.g. you don't know if all the farms had a similar type of land, similar weather, the same crops growing, etc. This means you don't know how reliable the study is — you can't be sure that the factor being investigated (hedgerows) is the only one affecting the thing being measured (number of species).

---

3. Data collection

Think about all the problems with the method and see if bias has slipped in. The less bias there is, the more reliable the data.

Example — Study B

In Study B the traps were placed on the ground, so species like birds weren't included. The traps weren't left overnight, so nocturnal animals wouldn't get counted, etc. This could have affected the results.

Tip: Bias can also come from the people collecting the data. For example, a company testing its own product might report the data in a way that makes it look better than it is.

4. Controls

Without controls, it's very difficult to draw valid conclusions.

Example — Experiment A

A negative control should have been used for experiment A containing everything from the experiment except the enzyme. This would show that the change in reaction rate was caused by the effect of temperature on the enzyme, and not anything else (e.g. the water, or something in the test tube).

Tip: There's more on control experiments and control groups on pages 3 and 4.

5. Repetition by other scientists

For theories to become accepted as 'fact' other scientists need to repeat the work (see page 2). If multiple studies or experiments come to the same conclusion, then that conclusion is more reliable.

Example — Experiment A

If a second group of scientists carried out the same experiment for enzyme X and got the same results, the results would be more reliable.

Exam Tip
You might be asked to evaluate the reliability of an experiment in the exam — or you might be asked to suggest ways to improve its reliability. Either way, keep these 5 points in mind.

Analysing the data

Sometimes it's easier to compare data by making a few calculations first, e.g. converting raw data into ratios or percentages.

Example

Three UK hospitals have been trying out three different methods to control the spread of chest infections. A study investigated the number of people suffering from chest infections in those hospitals over a three month period. The table on the right shows the results.

Hospital	Number of cases per 6000 patients		
	Jan	Feb	March
1	60	65	78
2	14	24	55
3	93	96	110

If you just look at the number of cases in the last month (March) then the method of hospital 3 appears to have worked least well, as they have the highest number of infections. But if you look at the percentage increase in infections you get a different picture:

Hospital 1: $\dfrac{(78 - 60)}{60} \times 100 = \dfrac{18}{60} \times 100 = 30\%$

Hospital 2: $\dfrac{(55 - 14)}{14} \times 100 = \dfrac{41}{14} \times 100 = 293\%$

Hospital 3: $\dfrac{(110 - 93)}{93} \times 100 = \dfrac{17}{93} \times 100 = 18\%$

So hospital 3 has the lowest percentage increase, suggesting their method of control is working the best.

Tip: Remember, ratios and percentages are used so you can <u>compare</u> different sets of data fairly.

Standard deviation (SD)

Standard deviation is a measure of the spread of values about the mean. The smaller the SD the closer all the values are to the mean. SDs can be shown on a graph using error bars. The ends of the bars show one SD above and one SD below the mean. Standard deviation can show how reliable the data is — the lower the standard deviation the more reliable it is. For example, data set 1 on the right has a smaller SD than data set 2, so it's more reliable.

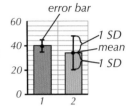

4. Graph Skills

You should be a dab hand at all things to do with graphs by now, but if you aren't don't worry — here are some tips to help.

Reading values off graphs

If there's a key pay close attention to it — you'll be throwing away easy marks if you don't. If the graph has more than one vertical axis make sure you read off the correct one. Also, always put the units on your answer.

Calculating the gradient of a graph

A little trickier is calculating the gradient of the graph:

$$\text{Gradient} = \frac{\text{Change in Y}}{\text{Change in X}} \qquad \text{Units} = \frac{Y}{X}$$

┌─ **Example** ─────────────────────────

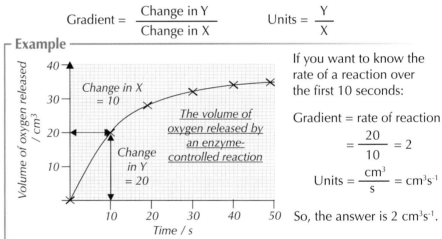

If you want to know the rate of a reaction over the first 10 seconds:

Gradient = rate of reaction

$$= \frac{20}{10} = 2$$

$$\text{Units} = \frac{cm^3}{s} = cm^3s^{-1}$$

So, the answer is 2 cm³s⁻¹.

Drawing graphs

Here are a few rules:

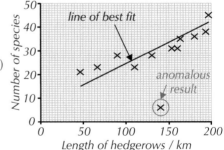

- The dependent variable should go on the y-axis (the vertical axis) and the independent on the x-axis (the horizontal axis).

- Always label the axes and include the units.

- If you need to draw a line (or curve) of best fit on a scatter graph, don't just join the points up. Instead, draw the line through or as near to as many points as possible, ignoring any anomalous results.

- To estimate what a result outside the range that you studied might be, just extend the line of best fit then read off the data.

Answers

Unit 1

Section 1: Disease and Immunity

1. Disease
Page 9 — Application Questions
Q1 0.8
Q2 8 g × 4 = **32 g** so they have a lower risk.
Q3 There's a correlation between the relative risk of CHD and alcohol consumption. The relative risk decreases from 1.0 when no alcohol is drunk to a minimum of 0.8 around 25 g of alcohol a day. The risk then begins to increase with increasing consumption, but is still lower than the risk of non-drinkers for alcohol consumption of between 25 g and 80 g of alcohol a day. After drinking more than 80 g of alcohol a day, the relative risk increases steadily up to around 1.6 for 150 g of alcohol a day.
Q4 Drinking between 0 and 80 g of alcohol a day is correlated with a reduced risk of CHD relative to non-drinkers. There's a positive correlation between drinking more alcohol and an increased risk of CHD for people who drink more than 80 g per day.
You need to be really specific when drawing conclusions. The last bit that says 'for people who drink more than 80 g per day' is absolutely essential — the statement wouldn't be true if you left that bit out.

Page 9 — Fact Recall Questions
Q1 Any three from, e.g. a poor diet / smoking / lack of exercise / excessive alcohol intake.
Q2 E.g. smoking — mouth cancer / throat cancer / lung cancer.
Excessive exposure to sunlight — skin cancer.
Excessive alcohol intake — liver cancer.

2. Pathogens
Page 11 — Fact Recall Questions
Q1 An organism that causes disease.
Q2 Pathogens are trapped by mucus lining the lung epithelium. The cilia on these cells beat, moving the mucus up to the mouth so it can be removed.
Q3 Pathogens can enter the body through cuts in the skin and through the digestive system if you eat or drink food containing pathogens.
Q4 By producing toxins and by cell damage.

3. The Immune Response
Page 13 — Application Questions
Q1 With fewer T-cells, fewer pathogens are killed directly. Also, with fewer T-cells in the blood there are fewer cells to be activated by pathogen antigens presented by phagocytes. This means that fewer B-cells are activated, so fewer antibodies are produced against the pathogens. With fewer antibodies, pathogens can survive longer in the body so opportunistic infections can cause problems.
Q2 Antibodies will be generated against antigens on the surface of *S. pyogenes*. These will then bind to antigens on the surface of heart cells because the antigens are so similar in shape. The immune system would then attack the heart cells and cause rheumatic fever.
The command word in this question is 'suggest', so you're not expected to know the exact answer. You're expected to use what you know about the immune system to come up with a possible explanation.

Page 15 — Application Questions
Q1 Mouse A had 10 units, Mouse B had 10 000 units.
Q2 Mouse B was already immune. You can tell this because the immune response was much quicker and stronger than the immune response of Mouse A.
Q3 a) Day 20
    b) The mouse's memory B-cells rapidly divided and produced the antibody needed to bind to the antigen. The mouse's memory T-cells rapidly divided into the correct type of T-cells to kill the cell carrying the antigen.

Page 15 — Fact Recall Questions
Q1 The molecules found on the surface of cells.
Q2 Phagocytosis is the engulfment of pathogens.
Q3 When activated by antigens presented by phagocytes, some T-cells release substances to activate B-cells and some attach to antigens on pathogens and kill the cell. The function of plasma cells is to produce antibodies.
Q4

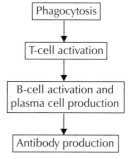

Q5 Coating the pathogen to make it easier for a phagocyte to engulf it. Coating the pathogen to prevent it from entering host cells. Binding to and neutralising toxins produced by the pathogen.

Q6 The cellular immune response involves the T-cells. The humoral response involves B-cells and the production of antibodies.

4. Vaccines
Page 17 — Application Questions
Q1 75% (accept answers in the range of 74-76%)
Q2 1000 cases
Q3 The number of cases decreased in a fluctuating pattern from a peak of around 6000 cases in the early 1960s to a peak of nearly 2000 cases around 1975. This is because more people were directly protected by the vaccine, and some people were protected by herd immunity.
Q4 a) Initially it increased slightly to about 80% of the population, and then decreased to around 50%.
        Don't just say it decreased — include data from the graph to back up your point.
    b) The number of cases increased from a peak of around 2000 cases in 1975 to a peak of around 4500 cases in 1983. This is because fewer people were directly protected by vaccination and fewer people were indirectly protected by herd immunity.
        The question asks you to explain, so you need to give reasons why the decreased uptake of the vaccine caused the change in the number of cases.

Page 17 — Fact Recall Questions
Q1 Vaccines contain antigens that cause your body to produce memory cells against a particular pathogen. This makes you immune.
Q2 Herd immunity is where unvaccinated people are protected because the occurrence of the disease is reduced by the number of people who are vaccinated.
Q3 Any two from, e.g. all vaccines are tested on animals and some people disagree with animal testing. / Testing vaccines on humans can be risky. / Some people don't want to take vaccines due to the risk of side effects, but they are still protected by herd immunity, which other people think is unfair. / If there was an epidemic of a new disease deciding who would receive a vaccine would be difficult.

5. Antigenic Variation
Page 18 — Fact Recall Questions
Q1 Antigenic variation is when the antigens on the surface of a pathogen change.
Q2 If the influenza virus undergoes antigenic variation the memory cells produced from the first infection will not recognise the different antigens. The immune system has to carry out a primary response to the new antigens. This takes time to get rid of the infection, which is why you get ill again.

6. Monoclonal Antibodies
Page 20 — Application Questions
Q1 a) A
    b) O

Person 1 had a positive result with anti-antigen A because it reacted with the antigen A in her blood, but a negative result with anti-antigen B because she doesn't have any B antigens for it to react with. That means Person 1 must be blood type A. Person 2 had two negative results because they don't have A or B antigens — so they must be blood type O.
Q2 a) No
    b) Yes

7. Validating New Knowledge About Vaccines and Antibodies
Page 22 — Application Questions
Q1 12 × 61 = **732**
Q2 Minor reactions are about five times more common than serious reactions. Serious reactions are about 120 times more common than Guillain-Barré syndrome.
    Rather than just saying it's more common, work out how much more common it is — manipulating data gets you higher marks in the exam.
Q3 No it does not support the idea that the influenza A vaccine increases the risk of Guillain-Barré syndrome. If the background rate is 1 per 100 000 people you would expect to see 10 cases per million people. The study only showed a rate of 0.1 cases per million people, which is far below the background rate.
Q4 The sample size of the study was enormous — 86.9 million. This makes the data very reliable.

Pages 24-25 — Exam-style Questions
1   a) By damaging host cells *(1 mark)*.
    b) (i) The blood clots at the area of damage to try and prevent pathogens from entering *(1 mark)*.
        (ii) Pathogens may enter via the gas-exchange system *(1 mark)* and the digestive system *(1 mark)*. In the lungs many pathogens are trapped by mucus and removed by cilia *(1 mark)*. In the stomach acidic conditions kill many pathogens *(1 mark)*.
    c) (i) The number of cases decreases from around 118 000 in 1980 to around 10 000 in 1995 *(1 mark)*. It then increases slightly to just above 20 000 in 2000 *(1 mark)*. Vaccine coverage increased from around 25% of people in 1980 to around 85% of people in 1990 *(1 mark)*. It then remained constant until 2000 *(1 mark)*.
        (ii) The evidence does not support the conclusion. The data is for the whole world, not for the UK, so the pattern may not be true for the UK *(1 mark)*. The data covers between 1980-2000, not up to 2011 so the pattern may not be true in 2011 *(1 mark)*.
        (iii) Any sensible answer, e.g. antigenic variation makes the vaccine ineffective *(1 mark)*.
    d) It prevents them from suffering from the disease because the antibodies bind to the toxin and prevent it from causing muscle spasms *(1 mark)*. The injection does not contain pathogen antigens, so does not stimulate the production of memory cells *(1 mark)*.

2   a) They're antibodies produced from a single group
        of genetically identical B-cells *(1 mark)*. They're
        specific because their binding sites have a unique
        structure *(1 mark)* that only one particular antigen
        with a complimentary shape will fit into *(1 mark)*.
     b) An antibody has variable regions where the antigen
        binds *(1 mark)*. Each antibody has a different shaped
        variable region *(1 mark)*. They also have a constant
        region that is the same in all antibodies *(1 mark)*.
        An antibody consists of light chains and heavy chains
        (1 mark) that are joined together by disulfide bridges
        (1 mark).

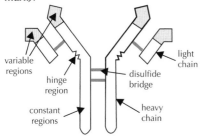

*If the question doesn't ask for a diagram (like here) you don't
need to draw one. But, if it helps you remember an antibody's
structure so you pick up an extra couple of marks then it's
worth adding one in if you've got time.*

     c) Bupropion has a similar structure to amphetamine
        (1 mark). So it may bind to the antibody specific to
        amphetamine, causing a positive result *(1 mark)*.
     d) E.g. monoclonal antibodies are made using animal
        cells, and some people disagree with using animals
        this way *(1 mark)*.
3   a) (i) When a phagocyte recognises the antigens on a
             pathogen, the cytoplasm of the phagocyte moves
             around the pathogen, engulfing it *(1 mark)*.
             The pathogen is now contained in a phagocytic
             vacuole inside the phagocyte *(1 mark)*.
             A lysosome fuses with the phagocytic vacuole
             (1 mark) and the lysosomal enzymes inside the
             lysosome break down the pathogen *(1 mark)*.
        (ii) Proteins on the surface of T-cells bind to the
             antigens presented by phagocytes, activating
             the T-cells *(1 mark)*. When B-cells, which are
             covered in antibodies, meet an antigen with a
             complementary shape they bind to it *(1 mark)*.
             This, along with substances released from T-cells,
             activate the B-cells *(1 mark)*. The B-cells then
             divide into plasma cells *(1 mark)*. The plasma
             cells then produce antibodies specific to the
             antigen *(1 mark)*.
        (iii) The humoral immune response *(1 mark)*.
     b) After the first infection their T-cells and B-cells
        produced memory cells *(1 mark)*. When they were
        exposed for a second time these memory cells
        divided into plasma cells and the correct type of
        T-cells to quickly destroy the virus *(1 mark)*.
     c) The neuraminidase and haemagglutinin antigens on
        the Asian flu strain were different from the antigens
        on the Spanish flu strain *(1 mark)*, so any memory
        cells created against H1N1 would not detect H2N2
        (1 mark). So the immune system would have to
        start from scratch and carry out a primary immune
        response if exposed to Asian flu *(1 mark)*.

*Make sure you use scientific terminology in your answer, e.g.
'antigens' and 'primary immune response'. Also, don't just write
a general answer about antigenic variation — make it specific
to the question by including details about the two strains of
flu.*

     d) To make people immune to more than one strain of
        flu *(1 mark)*.

Section 2: The Digestive System

1. Digestion

Page 28 — Application Questions
Q1 a) E.g. they may lose weight, as there's less ileum to
        absorb nutrients along.
     b) E.g. they may suffer from mineral deficiencies as
        there's less large intestine to absorb minerals along.
Q2   E.g. they may reduce the activity of pepsin. This may
     result in fewer amino acids being absorbed in the ileum.

Page 29 — Fact Recall Questions
Q1   A large, complex molecule composed of long chains of
     monomers.
Q2   monosaccharides
Q3   Carbon, hydrogen, oxygen and nitrogen.
Q4   The teeth and the movement of the stomach break down
     food into smaller pieces. This increases the surface area
     of the food for chemical digestion.
Q5   So the molecules can be absorbed into the blood.
Q6   Polymers are broken down into smaller, more soluble
     molecules by adding water.
Q7   1 — mouth, 2 — oesophagus, 3 — stomach, 4 —
     duodenum, 5 — ileum, 6 — colon, 7 — rectum,
     8 — anus.
Q8   It's moved down the oesophagus by peristalsis.
Q9   It is a small sac with lots of folds. The entrance and the
     exit have sphincter muscles.
Q10 The first part, the duodenum, receives bile and
     pancreatic juice, which break down chyme into smaller
     molecules. The second part, the ileum, absorbs soluble
     molecules. It's lined with villi, which increase the
     surface area for absorption.
Q11 Water, salts and minerals.
Q12 Carbohydrases
Q13 a) proteins / peptides
     b) lipases

2. Proteins

Page 31 — Application Questions
Q1   a) E.g.

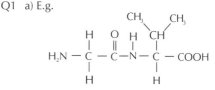

b) E.g.

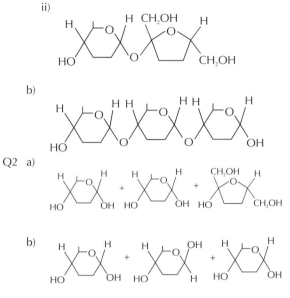

CH₃ structure...

H_2N — C — C — N — C — COOH (with CH₃, O, H, H groups)

c) E.g.

H_2N — C — C — N — C — C — N — C — COOH (with H, O, H, CH₃, O, H, CH groups and CH₃, CH₃)

Q2

H_2N — C — COOH and H_2N — C — COOH (with H and CH₂OH groups)

Page 33 — Application Questions
Q1 Orange juice and goat's milk.
Q2 As a control.
Q3 a) The liquid needs to be alkaline for the test to work.
   b) Not added any sodium hydroxide solution. / Not added a high enough concentration of sodium hydroxide solution.

Page 33 — Fact Recall Questions
Q1 Amino acids
Q2 A chain of more than two amino acids joined together.
Q3

H_2N—C—COOH (with R and H groups)

Q4 Condensation
Q5 Peptide
Q6 The α helix or β pleated sheet is coiled and folded further. More bonds form between different parts of the polypeptide chain.
Q7 Structural proteins are made of long polypeptide chains lying parallel to each other with cross links between them. This makes them physically strong.
Q8 a) sodium hydroxide solution
   b) copper(II) sulfate solution
   c) It would be purple.

3. Carbohydrates
Page 35 — Application Questions
Q1 a) i)

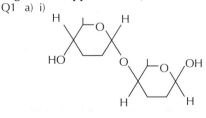

This diagram looks a bit different from other disaccharide diagrams. It's because the OH group needed to form the glycosidic bond is at the top of the galactose molecule rather than the bottom.

ii)

(structure with H, CH₂OH, H, O, HO, CH₂OH)

b)

(structure with H, H H, H H, H, O, HO, OH)

Q2 a)

(structure with H, O, H, +, H, O, H, +, CH₂OH, H, HO, OH, HO, OH, HO, CH₂OH)

b)

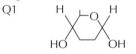

(structure with H, O, H, +, H, OH, +, H, O, H, HO, OH, HO, H, HO, OH)

Page 36 — Application Questions
Q1 Test 1 — no reducing sugars present, but non-reducing sugars might be present.
Test 2 — non-reducing sugars are present, but reducing sugars are not.
Test 3 — no sugars are present.
Test 4 — reducing sugars are present.
These tests are quite tricky. Think carefully about what sugars have been tested for and what the different colours of the results indicate. Remember that a negative result for a reducing sugar test doesn't rule out non-reducing sugars.

Page 37 — Fact Recall Questions
Q1

(structure with H, O, H, HO, OH)

Q2 water
Q3 glycosidic
Q4 a) glucose and glucose
   b) glucose and fructose
   c) glucose and galactose
Q5 Lactose intolerance is caused by insufficient lactase production. This means that lactose can't be broken down properly and instead is fermented by bacteria. This causes symptoms such as cramps, flatulence and diarrhoea.
Q6 Add Benedict's reagent to a test sample and heat it. Look at the colour of the sample for the result. A positive result would be brick red and a negative result would be blue.

Q7 α-glucose molecules

Q8 The salivary glands and the pancreas.

Q9 Use the iodine test — add iodine dissolved in potassium iodide solution to a test sample. Look at the colour of the sample for the result. A positive result would be dark blue-black and a negative result would be a browny-orange colour.

4. Enzymes
Page 40 — Fact Recall Questions

Q1 a) B

b) The activation energy needed for the reaction with the presence of an enzyme.

Q2 Activation energy is needed to start a chemical reaction. The activation energy is often provided as heat. With the presence of an enzyme, the activation energy required to start a reaction is lowered. Therefore not as much heat is needed, so the reaction can take place at lower temperatures than it could do without an enzyme.

Q3 The substrate has a complementary shape to the active site. This means they fit perfectly together the same way that a key fits into a lock. They form an enzyme-substrate complex and catalyse the reaction.

Q4 In the lock and key model the active site has a fixed shape that is complementary to the substrate, but in the induced fit model the active site has to change shape slightly to allow the substrate to bind tightly.

Q5 The enzyme's tertiary structure.

Q6 An enzyme can only bind with a substrate that has a complementary shape to its active site.

Q7 A gene mutation could alter the primary and tertiary structure of the enzyme. This could alter the shape of the active site meaning it would no longer be able bind to the substrate.

5. Factors Affecting Enzyme Activity
Page 43 — Application Questions

Q1 a) i) C — the enzyme is still active at 80 °C. This means the bacteria can live at very high temperatures and therefore is hyperthermophillic.

ii) A — the enzyme is active at temperatures between 0 and 17 °C. This means the bacteria can live at very cold temperatures, so is psychrotropic.

b) A — There would be no enzyme activity at all as the enzyme would be denatured at temperatures over 17 °C.

B — There would be some enzyme activity but the rate of reaction would gradually decrease until temperatures of around 70 °C were reached. At this point the enzyme would be denatured and there would be no further enzyme activity at higher temperatures.

C — There would be an increasing amount of enzyme activity. The rate of reaction would gradually increase as the temperature increased.

Q2 a) A — The rate of reaction is higher in relation to the hydrogen peroxide concentration. This is because there are more catalase molecules present, which means the hydrogen peroxide molecules will collide more frequently with the active sites.

b) The curves flatten out at the saturation point. All the active sites are full, so increasing the hydrogen peroxide concentration won't increase the rate of reaction any further.

Page 44 — Application Questions

Q1 Ethanol has a similar shape to methanol. This means it will act as a competitive inhibitor, binding to the active site of alcohol dehydrogenase and blocking methanol molecules. This means lower levels of methanol will be hydrolysed so the toxic products (formaldehyde and formic acid) won't build up to fatal levels.

Q2

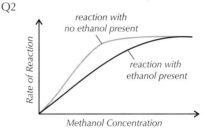

Your curve should be lower than the rate of reaction without any ethanol present. The reaction won't stop completely as some of the methanol molecules will still bind with the active sites. The plateau should be later as the reaction won't reach its maximum rate until the methanol concentration is much higher. The curve should start at zero.

Page 44 — Fact Recall Questions

Q1 At higher temperatures there is more kinetic energy, so molecules move faster. This makes the substrate molecules more likely to collide with the enzymes' active sites. The energy of these collisions also increases, which means each collision is more likely to result in a reaction.

Q2 The enzyme reaching a very high temperature in relation to its optimum temperature. The enzyme being in a very acidic or alkaline environment in relation to its optimum pH.

Q3 The bonds that hold the enzyme in shape are broken. This alters the shape of the active site meaning it is no longer a complementary shape to the substrate. The enzyme can't catalyse its usual reaction.

Q4 The point at which all active sites are occupied by substrate molecules.

Q5 The rate of reaction stays constant. All active sites are occupied so increasing the substrate concentration has no effect.

Q6 a) Away from the active site.
b) At the active site.

Q7 A non-competitive inhibitor molecule binds to the enzyme away from the active site. Its presence alters the shape of the active site meaning that substrate molecules can no longer bind here. This prevents enzyme activity.

Pages 46-47 — Exam-style Questions

1 a) They secrete saliva that consists of mucus, mineral salts and salivary amylase *(1 mark)*. Salivary amylase breaks down starch into maltose *(1 mark)*. Saliva also helps to lubricate food so it's easier to swallow *(1 mark)*.

b) The stomach has lots of folds *(1 mark)*, allowing it to expand so it can hold lots of food and liquid *(1 mark)*. Muscles in the stomach allow peristalsis *(1 mark)* which turns food into chyme *(1 mark)*. The stomach walls produce gastric juice *(1 mark)*, which helps in the chemical break down of food *(1 mark)*.

2 a) Sucrose is made from a fructose molecule *(1 mark)* and a glucose molecule *(1 mark)* which are joined by a glycosidic bond *(1 mark)* formed during a condensation reaction *(1 mark)*.

b)

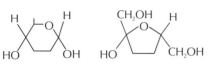

(1 mark for each correct diagram).
You don't need to learn the structure of fructose, but you do need to know that α-glucose and fructose are the monomers of sucrose.

c) Sucrose is hydrolysed into monosaccharides/ glucose and fructose by sucrase *(1 mark)* in the ileum *(1 mark)*.

d) Initially the sample is boiled with Benedict's reagent to rule out the presence of reducing sugars *(1 mark)*. A new test sample is then boiled with dilute hydrochloric acid *(1 mark)* and then neutralised with sodium hydrogencarbonate *(1 mark)*. Next the sample is heated with Benedict's reagent *(1 mark)*. The test sample would turn brick red if a non-reducing sugar was present *(1 mark)*.

3 a) Any two from, e.g. digestive enzymes / sodium hydrogencarbonate / specific enzymes, e.g. amylase, trypsin, cymotrypsin, lipase *(maximum of 2 marks available)*.

b) The duodenum is part of the small intestine *(1 mark)*. It receives chyme from the stomach and neutralises it with bile and sodium hydrogencarbonate from the pancreas *(1 mark)*. It receives digestive enzymes from the pancreas, which aid chemical digestion *(1 mark)*. It moves chyme into the ileum by peristalsis *(1 mark)*.

c) i) The pancreas secretes proteases *(1 mark)* which catalyse the breakdown of proteins into amino acids *(1 mark)*. The amino acids are then absorbed and assimilated by the body *(1 mark)*. In patients with cystic fibrosis this process can't happen because the blocked pancreatic duct means proteases don't reach the food in the duodenum *(1 mark)*.

ii)

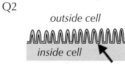

(1 mark)

4 a) i) *(1 mark for a value between pH 4 and pH 5)*
ii) pH 1 and pH 9 *(1 mark)*. There is no reaction at these pH levels *(1 mark)*.

iii) The shape of the active site has changed *(1 mark)* so it is no longer complementary in shape to the substrate, and will not bind to it to catalyse the reaction *(1 mark)*.

iv) E.g. temperature *(1 mark)* and substrate concentration *(1 mark)*.

b) i) A. The rate at which diglycerides and fatty acids are produced/the reaction rate is higher without the presence of orlistat *(1 mark)*.

ii) Molecules of orlistat have a similar shape to triglycerides *(1 mark)*. They bind to the active sites of gastric lipase and block the entry of triglycerides *(1 mark)*. This means the reaction that produces diglycerides and fatty acids can't take place as quickly *(1 mark)*.

Section 3: Cell Structure and Membranes

1. Cell Structure

Page 51 — Application Questions
Q1 Mitochondria, to provide lots of energy for muscle contraction.

Q2 E.g. they might have a lot of lysosomes to enable them to break down invading pathogens.

Q3 E.g. ribosomes, rough endoplasmic reticulum, Golgi apparatus.
You need to specify the rough endoplasmic reticulum in this answer (as the smooth endoplasmic reticulum is involved in lipid synthesis, not protein synthesis).

Q4 E.g. They might have microvilli on their surface to increase the surface area for reabsorbing molecules.

Page 51 — Fact Recall Questions
Q1 To regulate movement of substances into and out of the cell. To respond to chemicals like hormones.

Q2

outside cell

inside cell

plasma membrane

Q3 A — nuclear envelope, B — nucleolus, C — chromatin, D — nuclear pore.

Q4 Chromatin controls the cell's activities. The pores allow substances to move between the nucleus and the cytoplasm. The nucleolus makes ribosomes.

Q5 Any one from: To digest invading cells. / To break down worn out components of the cell.

Q6 The rough endoplasmic reticulum is covered in ribosomes, whereas the smooth endoplasmic reticulum is not.

Q7 It synthesises and processes lipids.

Q8 It is a group of fluid-filled sacs.

Q9

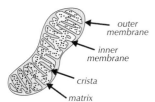

outer membrane
inner membrane
crista
matrix

2. Investigating Cell Structure
Page 53 — Application Questions
Q1 a) length of image ÷ magnification = length of specimen
      8 mm ÷ 3150 = **0.0025 mm**
    b) length of image ÷ magnification = length of specimen
      18 mm ÷ 3150 = **0.0057 mm**
Q2 length of specimen × magnification = length of image
    0.00002 mm × 40 = **0.0008 mm**
Q3 length of image ÷ magnification = length of specimen
    13 mm ÷ 7000 = 0.0019 mm
    Then times by 1000 to convert to μm
    0.0019 mm × 1000 = **1.9 μm**
Q4 length of specimen × magnification = length of image
    0.023 μm × 1500 = 34.5 μm
    Then divide by 1000 to convert to mm
    34.5 μm ÷ 1000 = **0.035 mm**
Q5 a) length of image ÷ length of specimen = magnification
      16 mm ÷ 2 mm = **× 8**
    b) length of specimen × magnification = length of image
      3 mm × 50 = **150 mm**
Q6 First you need to convert 10 μm to millimetres by
    dividing by 1000
    10 μm ÷ 1000 = 0.01 mm
    length of image ÷ length of specimen = magnification
    10 mm ÷ 0.01 mm = **× 1000**

Page 56 — Application Questions
Q1 a) Light microscope, as electron microscopes can only
      be used on dead specimens.
    b) SEM, as they can give 3-D images.
    c) Electron microscope (TEM/SEM) as the virus particles
      are smaller than the maximum resolution of light
      microscopes.
Q2 a) nuclei, mitochondria, lysosomes, ER, ribosomes
      *This is the filtered solution, so it should contain all the
      organelles.*
    b) Nuclei
      Nuclei are the heaviest, so will separate out first.
    c) ER, ribosomes.
      *The supernatant in this tube should contain everything except
      the nuclei (separated out in the first spin), mitochondria
      (separated out in the second spin) and the lysosomes (in the
      pellet in the bottom of Tube D)*

Page 56 — Fact Recall Questions
Q1 magnification = length of image ÷ length of specimen
Q2 How well a microscope can distinguish between two
    points that are close together.
Q3 a) 0.2 μm
    b) 0.0001 μm
Q4 Electron microscope

Q5 An electron microscope.
    *The maximum resolution of a light microscope is 0.2 μm, so you
    wouldn't be able to see something that was 0.001 μm with it.*
Q6 TEMs use electromagnets to focus a beam of electrons,
    which is then transmitted through the specimen. Denser
    parts of the specimen absorb more electrons, which
    makes them look darker on the image you end up with.
Q7 SEMs scan a beam of electrons across the specimen.
    This knocks off electrons from the specimen, which are
    gathered in a cathode ray tube to form an image.
Q8 Advantage: e.g. gives high resolution images, so can be
    used to look at small objects.
    Disadvantage: any one from, e.g. can only be used
    on thin specimens. / Can only be used on non-living
    specimens. / Produces black and white images. / Images
    may contain artefacts.
Q9 Any one from, e.g. can be used on thick specimens,
    whereas TEMs can't. / Can produce 3-D images, whereas
    TEMs can't.
Q10 By vibrating the cells, or by grinding the cells up in a
    blender.
Q11 To reduce the activity of enzymes that break down the
    organelles.
Q12 The homogenised cell solution is filtered through a
    gauze to separate any large cell debris or tissue debris,
    like connective tissue, from the organelles.
Q13 The cell fragments are poured into a tube. The tube is
    put into a centrifuge and is spun at a low speed. The
    heaviest organelles, like nuclei, get flung to the bottom
    of the tube by the centrifuge. They form a pellet at the
    bottom. The rest of the organelles stay suspended in
    supernatant. The supernatant is drained off, poured
    into another tube, and spun in the centrifuge at a higher
    speed. Again, the heaviest organelles form a pellet at the
    bottom of the tube. The supernatant containing the rest
    of the organelles is drained off and spun in the centrifuge
    at an even higher speed. This process is repeated at
    higher and higher speeds, until all the organelles are
    separated out.

3. Plasma Membranes
Page 58 — Fact Recall Questions
Q1 According to the fluid mosaic model, the plasma
    membrane consists of a continuous double layer of
    phospholipid molecules. The layer is fluid because
    the phospholipids are constantly moving. Proteins are
    scattered through the layer, like tiles in a mosaic.
Q2 Some proteins in the membrane allow the passage of
    large or charged water-soluble substances that would
    otherwise find it difficult to cross the membrane.
Q3 'Hydrophilic' means 'attracts water'. Hydrophobic
    means 'repels water'.
Q4 The centre of the phospholipid bilayer is hydrophobic,
    so the membrane doesn't allow water-soluble substances
    through it.
Q5 a) Detect chemicals released from other cells.
    b) Allow white blood cells to identify a body cell as
      'self', so they don't attack it.
    c) Helps make the membrane more rigid and stops it
      from breaking up.

4. Lipids in Membranes
Page 61 — Application Questions
Q1 a) Propanoic acid = CH_3CH_2, Palmitic acid = $CH_3(CH_2)_{14}$, Stearic acid = $CH_3(CH_2)_{16}$, Oleic acid = $CH_3(CH_2)_7CH=CH(CH_2)_7$

    b)

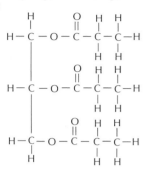

    c) oleic acid

Q2

Page 61 — Fact Recall Questions
Q1 A molecule of glycerol and three fatty acids.

Q2

Q3 A saturated fatty acid doesn't have any double bonds between its carbon atoms, an unsaturated fatty acid does.

Q4 water

Q5 One molecule of glycerol attached to a phosphate group and two fatty acids.

Q6 a) lipids / fats

    b) The student should shake the test substance with ethanol for about a minute, before pouring the solution into water. A milky emulsion will appear if the result is positive.

5. Exchange Across Plasma Membranes
Page 64 — Application Questions
Q1   The ink molecules are moving from an area of higher concentration (the original drop of ink) to an area of lower concentration (the surrounding water).

Q2 a) The distance the particles have to travel is further so the rate of diffusion will decrease.

    b) The surface area of the cell will increase, so the rate of diffusion will increase.

    c) The concentration gradient will increase, so the rate of diffusion will increase.

Q3 a) Water molecules will move from the cheek cells into the salt solution.

      A -300 kPa solution has a higher water potential (it's less negative) than a -325 kPa solution.

    b) Water molecules will move into the apple slices out of the beaker of water.

    c) There will be no movement of water molecules as the water potential in both solutions is the same/the solutions are isotonic.

Q4 a) The potato cells have a lower water potential than the sucrose solution, so they gain water by osmosis.

    b) The cells in both solutions will decrease in volume. This is because they have a higher water potential than the sucrose solutions, so will lose water by osmosis.

Page 67 — Application Questions
Q1 a) As the rate of sodium ion active transport increases, so does the rate of oxygen consumption.

    b) Sodium ion active transport requires energy from ATP. As the rate of active transport increases, the rate of aerobic respiration must also increase in order to produce more ATP, which means the rate of oxygen consumption must increase too.

Q2 None. Facilitated diffusion doesn't require energy from ATP, so there would be no need for the rate of oxygen consumption to increase.

Q3 E.g. the rate of glucose consumption.

Page 69 — Fact Recall Questions
Q1 The net/passive movement of particles from an area of higher concentration to an area of lower concentration.

Q2 It's a passive process.

Q3 In simple diffusion, small molecules pass freely through the plasma membrane. Facilitated diffusion uses carrier proteins and protein channels to aid the movement of large molecules through the plasma membrane.

Q4 E.g. concentration gradient, surface area, thickness of the exchange surface

Q5 Osmosis is the diffusion of water molecules across a partially permeable membrane, from an area of higher water potential to an area of lower water potential.

Q6 Water potential is the potential/likelihood of water molecules to diffuse out of or into a solution.

Q7 Small molecules (e.g. water) can diffuse through it easily, but larger molecules (e.g. solute molecules) can't.

Q8 Similarity: both facilitated diffusion and active transport use carrier proteins to transport molecules across plasma membranes.

    Differences: in facilitated diffusion, molecules move down a concentration gradient. In active transport, molecules are moved against a concentration gradient. Facilitated diffusion is a passive process, it doesn't require energy. Active transport is an active process that does require energy.

Q9 a) A molecule attaches to a carrier protein in the membrane. The protein then changes shape and releases the molecule on the opposite side of the membrane. The process requires energy.

    b) Protein channels form pores in the membrane for charged particles to diffuse through.

    c) Co-transporters bind two molecules at a time. The concentration gradient of one of the molecules is used to move the other molecule against its own concentration gradient.

Q10 a) The concentration of glucose in the small intestine becomes lower than the blood glucose concentration.

    b) active transport

Q11 Because sodium ions diffuse from the small intestine lumen into the intestinal epithelium cells down their concentration gradient, through a sodium-glucose co-transporter protein. At the same time, the co-transporter carries glucose into the epithelium cell against its concentration gradient. Glucose is then able to diffuse into blood from the epithelial cell.

Q12 Glucose diffuses out of the epithelial cells and into the blood through protein channels — this is facilitated diffusion.

6. Cholera

Page 72 — Fact Recall Questions

Q1 E.g. any three from: cell wall — supports the cell / capsule — helps protect bacteria from attack by immune system / plasmids — loops of DNA containing genes for things like antibiotic resistance / circular DNA — controls the cell / flagellum — rotates to make the bacterium move / plasma membrane — controls movement of substances into and out of the cell.

Q2 The toxin causes chloride ion protein channels in the plasma membranes of epithelial cells to open. Chloride ions move into the small intestine lumen. This lowers the water potential of the lumen. Water moves out of the blood across the epithelial cells and into the small intestine lumen by osmosis. The massive increase in water secretion causes diarrhoea.

Q3 An ORS is a drink that contains large amounts of salts and sugars dissolved in water. It's used to replace fluids in people suffering from a diarrhoeal disease.

Q4 E.g. trials are often carried out on children, who don't decide whether they take part in the trial or not. The trials are often blind, so patients don't know whether they are receiving the new treatment or an old one. When a new ORS is first trialled, there's no way of knowing whether it'll be better than the current ORS, which means the patient could die when a treatment that works was available.

Pages 73-74 — Exam-style Questions

1 a) i)   No. The microscope has a resolution of 200 nm/0.2μm *(1 mark)*. This means it can't distinguish between objects that are smaller than 200 nm/0.2μm — such as the ribosomes *(1 mark)*.

If you convert the diameter of the ribosomes and the resolution of the microscope into the same units, (e.g. both nm or both μm) it's easier to see that the ribosomes are too small for the microscope to pick up.

ii) length of specimen = length of image ÷ magnification

= 4 ÷ 100 = **0.04 mm/40 nm**

(2 marks for correct answer, 1 mark if only working is correct)

b) Any one from, e.g. ribosomes/rough endoplasmic reticulum as these are the site of protein synthesis. / Golgi apparatus because this processes and packages new proteins. *(1 mark for sensible choice of organelle, 1 mark for correct explanation)*

c) First the cell membranes are broken up by homogenisation to release the organelles into solution *(1 mark)*. The solution is kept ice cold and isotonic to prevent enzymes breaking down the organelles and the organelles from bursting or shrivelling *(1 mark)*. The homogenised cell solution is then filtered through a gauze to separate any large cell debris or tissue debris from the organelles *(1 mark)*. Ultracentrifugation is then carried out to separate each organelle from the others *(1 mark)*. The cell fragments are poured into a tube and spun in a centrifuge to separate out the heaviest organelle, which remains in the pellet at the bottom of the tube, leaving the others suspended in the supernatant *(1 mark)*. This process is then repeated at higher and higher speeds to separate out all the organelles *(1 mark)*.

2 a) i)   3.7 mmol dm^{-3} (accept 3.5 to 3.9) *(1 mark)*
ii) Glucose is being absorbed into the blood *(1 mark)*.
iii) E.g. it will decrease as the blood concentration increases *(1 mark)*. This is because glucose is diffusing out of the small intestine *(1 mark)*.

b) The glucose is transported using active transport *(1 mark)*. Sodium ions diffuse out of the small intestine *(1 mark)* and into the epithelial cells via a sodium-glucose co-transporter *(1 mark)*. This carries the glucose out of the lumen against its concentration gradient *(1 mark)*. The glucose then diffuses out of the epithelial cells into the blood by facilitated diffusion *(1 mark)*.

3 a) E.g. in case the cubes did not all start out at exactly the same mass *(1 mark)*.

b) 16% (accept 15-17%) *(1 mark)*

Don't forget that pure water is always 0 kPa.

c) i)   The water potential in these three solutions must have been lower than the water potential of the potato cells *(1 mark)* so water moved out of the cells by osmosis *(1 mark)*.
ii) 425 kPa (accept 400 - 450 kPa) *(1 mark)*

The cells won't lose or gain any mass in an isotonic solution, so all you need to do is read the water potential off the graph where the change in mass equals zero.

d) E.g. they could do repeats of the experiment for each concentration of sucrose solution and calculate the mean percentage change in mass *(1 mark)*. / They could repeat the experiment using smaller intervals between the sucrose concentrations *(1 mark)*.

e) Before 12 hours *(1 mark)* because the rate of osmosis will be faster due to the increase in surface area *(1 mark)*.

Section 4: The Respiratory System

1. Lung Function

Pages 77-78 — Application Questions

Q1 a) 1
b) A

c) Speed = distance ÷ time = 0.82 ÷ 2 = **0.41 mm s⁻¹**.
Always double-check the question to see if it tells you what units to use in your answer. If it doesn't say then make sure you pick a sensible unit.

Q2 The concentration gradient of oxygen between the alveoli and the capillaries will be lower than normal, so the rate of diffusion, and therefore gas exchange, will be slower.

Q3 Less air, and so less oxygen, would be inhaled in each breath. This means the concentration gradient of oxygen between the alveoli and the capillaries will be less steep, slowing the rate of diffusion.

Q4 a) The alveoli are enlarged/much larger in the diseased lungs than in the healthy lungs.
   b) Having enlarged alveoli means there's a smaller surface area for gas exchange, slowing the rate of diffusion of oxygen into the blood. So a patient with emphysema would have a low level of oxygen in the blood.

Page 78 — Fact Recall Questions

Q1 A — trachea
   B — ribcage
   C — lung
   D — diaphragm
   E — intercostal muscles
   F — bronchus
   G — bronchiole
   H — alveoli

Q2 The intercostal and diaphragm muscles contract, which causes the ribcage to move upwards and outwards and the diaphragm to flatten.

Q3 Expiration, because the diaphragm is curved.

Q4 An active process.

Q5 Oxygen diffuses out of the alveoli, across the alveolar epithelium and the capillary endothelium, and into haemoglobin in the blood.

Q6 Alveoli have a thin exchange surface, which means there's a short diffusion pathway. This speeds up the rate of diffusion into the blood. There is a large number of alveoli so there is a large surface area for gas exchange, which speeds up the rate of diffusion. There's also a steep concentration gradient of oxygen and carbon dioxide between the alveoli and the capillaries, which increases the rate of diffusion. This is constantly maintained by the flow of blood and ventilation.

2. Measuring Lung Function
Page 80 — Application Questions

Q1 a) tidal volume = 0.5 dm³
      ventilation rate = (60 ÷ 90) × 24 = 16 min⁻¹
      PV = tidal volume × ventilation rate = 0.5 × 16
      = **8 dm³ min⁻¹**
   b) ventilation rate = (60 ÷ 300) × 70 = 14 min⁻¹
      tidal volume = PV ÷ ventilation rate
      = 7.84 ÷ 14 = **0.56 dm³**
   c) ventilation rate = PV ÷ tidal volume = 8.2 ÷ 0.41
      = **20 min⁻¹**
   Take your time with calculation questions and always show your working — you can pick up marks for using the correct calculation in the exam, even if you don't get the right answer.

Q2 a) The person took a deep breath in and then a deep breath out.
   b) 1.3 dm³ = 1.3 litres
   c) tidal volume = 2.6 − 2.1 = 0.5 dm³
      ventilation rate = 9.5 peaks in the first minute = 9.5 min⁻¹
      PV = tidal volume × ventilation rate = 0.5 × 9.5
      = **4.75 dm³ min⁻¹**

Q3 a) The peaks are closer together after the first 30 seconds. This shows that the person's breathing rate/ventilation rate increased to take in more oxygen. The distance between the top and the bottom of the peaks increased after 30 seconds, showing that tidal volume/depth of breath increased to take in more oxygen.
   b) tidal volume at rest = 2.6 − 2.2 = 0.4 dm³
      tidal volume when breathing most deeply
      = 3.15 − 1.75 = 1.4 dm³
      1 − 1.4 = 0.4
      % increase = (1 ÷ 0.4) × 100 = **250%**
   c) Ventilation rate increases and tidal volume increases, so pulmonary ventilation also increases.

Page 80 — Fact Recall Questions

Q1 a) The volume of air taken into the lungs in one minute.
   b) The volume of air in each breath.
   c) The number of breaths per minute.

Q2 dm³ min⁻¹ (or litres min⁻¹)

Q3 pulmonary ventilation = tidal volume × ventilation rate

3. Lung Diseases
Page 81 — Application Questions

Q1 Graph A, because the tidal volume is much lower.

Q2 E.g. in general, there's poorer hygiene and more crowded living conditions in Africa than in Europe, so TB bacteria spread more easily. Cases of asymptomatic TB in Africa may be more likely to become activated because of malnutrition and infection with other diseases, allowing the sufferer to pass TB on to others. TB can be prevented with the BCG vaccine and can be treated with antibiotics, which may be more widely available in richer European countries than in African countries.

Page 83 — Application Questions

Q1 10 mm²

Q2 The data shows that before inhaling salbutamol, the median area of a bronchial cross-section in healthy volunteers was bigger than in the asthmatics — 29 mm² compared to 10 mm². Inhaling salbutamol reduced the area of the cross-section in healthy volunteers by 2 mm², but in asthmatics the area of the cross-section almost doubled to 18 mm².

Q3 Salbutamol could be used in inhalers to relax the smooth muscles lining the bronchioles in asthmatics. During an asthma attack, the smooth muscle contracts, causing constriction of the airways. The graph shows that after inhaling salbutamol the bronchioles aren't as constricted, so the salbutamol must relax the muscles.
You need to use your knowledge of the symptoms of asthma here as well as the results shown in the graph to work out the answer.

Page 83 — Fact Recall Questions

Q1 *Mycobacterium tuberculosis*

Q2 By droplet infection. When an infected person coughs or sneezes, tiny droplets of saliva and mucus containing the bacteria are released from their mouth and nose. If an uninfected person breathes in these droplets, the bacteria are passed on.

Q3 E.g. with the BCG vaccine

Q4 Scar tissue is thicker and less elastic than normal lung tissue. This means that the lungs are less able to expand and so can't hold as much air as normal, so the tidal volume is reduced.

Q5 Fibrosis is the formation of scar tissue in the lungs, which is thicker than normal lung tissue, so diffusion of gases is slower.

Q6 A respiratory condition where the airways become inflamed and irritated.

Q7 By drugs (often in inhalers) which cause the muscle in the bronchioles to relax, opening up the airways.

Q8 E.g. smoking / long-term exposure to air pollution.

Q9 E.g. shortness of breath, wheezing.

4. Interpreting Lung Disease Data

Page 87 — Application Questions

Q1 Male deaths due to COPD increased from just over 10 per 100 000 people in 1946 to almost 80 per 100 000 in 1972. It then slowly decreased to about 40 per 100 000 by 1998.

Q2 E.g. between about 1948 and 1969 there doesn't seem to be any correlation between female deaths from COPD and tobacco consumption. After this year the number of female deaths from COPD increases as tobacco consumption decreases (there's a negative correlation). This isn't enough to say that COPD in women is not caused by smoking though. Tobacco consumption in women might have risen while tobacco consumption in the overall population was decreasing, but you can't tell from this data. Also, female deaths from COPD could be increasing for other reasons, e.g. industrial causes, even if tobacco consumption is still a cause of the disease.

Pages 88-89 — Exam-style Questions

Q1 a) (i) ratio = 21:17
   21 ÷ 17 = 1.24
   so ratio = **1.24:1 *(1 mark)***

   (ii) Inhaled air has a higher percentage composition of oxygen and a lower percentage composition of carbon dioxide than exhaled air *(1 mark)*. This is because some of the oxygen in inhaled air diffuses from the alveoli into the blood, so there's a lower percentage of oxygen in exhaled air *(1 mark)*. Carbon dioxide diffuses from the blood into the alveoli to be breathed out, so there's a higher percentage of carbon dioxide in exhaled air *(1 mark)*.

b) In inspiration the intercostal and diaphragm muscles contract *(1 mark)*. This causes the ribcage to move upwards and outwards and the diaphragm to flatten, increasing the volume of thorax *(1 mark)*. As the volume of the thorax increases the lung pressure decreases, causing air to flow into the lungs *(1 mark)*. In expiration the intercostal and diaphragm muscles relax *(1 mark)*. The ribcage moves downwards and inwards and the diaphragm becomes curved again *(1 mark)*. The thorax volume decreases, causing the air pressure to increase (to above atmospheric pressure), forcing air out of the lungs *(1 mark)*.

c) (i) The formation of scar tissue in the lungs *(1 mark)*.

   (ii) Diffusion of gases is slower across a thicker scarred membrane *(1 mark)*, so the rate of gaseous exchange is reduced *(1 mark)*.

   (iii) There would be a steeper concentration gradient of oxygen between the alveoli and the capillaries *(1 mark)*. This would increase the rate of diffusion of oxygen into the blood *(1 mark)*.

Q2 a) width of alveolus = width of image ÷ magnification = 9 mm ÷ 60
   = 0.15 mm × 1000 (to convert to micrometres)
   = **150 μm *(1 mark for correct calculation, 2 marks for correct answer)***

   The question tells you to give your answer in μm, so you need to remember to convert your answer from mm to μm. If you're a bit rusty on this, check out p. 52.

b) E.g. the walls of the alveoli have been destroyed in the diseased alveoli *(1 mark)*. Destruction of the alveolar walls reduces the surface area of the alveoli *(1 mark)*, so the rate of gaseous exchange would decrease *(1 mark)*.

c) (i) E.g. smoking / long-term exposure to air pollution *(1 mark)*.

   (ii) E.g. an increased breathing rate *(1 mark)*. Their breathing rate will increase as they try to increase the amount of air/oxygen reaching their lungs *(1 mark)*.

Q3 a) The person breathed out/expired *(1 mark)*.

b) tidal volume = 2.6 – 2.15 = **0.45 dm³ *(1 mark)***

c) Their tidal volume would increase, to get more air into the lungs *(1 mark)*. Their ventilation rate would also increase, to get more air into the lungs *(1 mark)*. Pulmonary ventilation = tidal volume × ventilation rate, so pulmonary ventilation would increase *(1 mark)*.

   Exercise makes you breathe faster and deeper, so it's going to affect your tidal volume and ventilation rate (and so your pulmonary ventilation).

d) (i) The smooth muscle lining the bronchioles contracts *(1 mark)* and a large amount of mucus is produced *(1 mark)*. This causes the airways to constrict *(1 mark)*.

   (ii) The tidal volume would decrease *(1 mark)* because the airways are constricted and so less air is flowing in and out of the lungs *(1 mark)*.

   (iii) They would relax the muscles in the bronchioles and so open up the airways *(1 mark)*.

Q4 a) (i) The number of reported TB cases in the UK increased overall, from about 6750 cases in 2000 to about 9000 cases in 2009 *(1 mark)*.

(ii) 9000 − 7250 = 1750

(1750 ÷ 7250) × 100 *(1 mark)* = **24.1% *(1 mark)***

(iii) E.g. although the number of TB cases has risen by about 33% between 2000 and 2009, it doesn't necessarily mean this trend will continue *(1 mark)*. The graph shows the number of reported cases of TB but the newspaper refers to the number of cases of TB, so it may be that the reason for the increasing trend is just because more cases of TB are being reported (i.e. there's not an increase in overall number of cases) *(1 mark)*. The graph shows the number of reported cases of TB in the UK but the newspaper refers to the number of cases of TB in England, so this prediction doesn't fit the data shown in the graph *(1 mark)*.

Always read questions carefully — the introduction mentions that the graph shows the number of reported cases of TB in the UK. You'll miss this if you skim over the introduction and look at the graph first.

c) The UK has high standards of hygiene *(1 mark)* and living conditions which are relatively uncrowded *(1 mark)*. This means people are less likely to contract TB through droplet infection/via infected people coughing or sneezing *(1 mark)*. The UK has a (BCG) vaccine available to prevent people contracting TB *(1 mark)* and antibiotics to treat people with the disease *(1 mark)*.

Section 5: The Circulatory System

1. The Heart

Page 92 — Application Questions

Q1 There would be back-flow of blood into the ventricles after the ventricles have contracted.

Q2 stroke volume × heart rate = cardiac output
61 × 79 = **4819 cm³ per minute**

Q3 cardiac output ÷ stroke volume = heart rate
5075 ÷ 72.5 = **70 beats per minute**

Q4 cardiac output ÷ heart rate = stroke volume
5175 ÷ 75 = **69 cm³**

Q5 0.067 L × 1000 = **67 cm³**
Remember, you need to multiply by 1000 to convert litres to cm³.
stroke volume × heart rate = cardiac output
67 × 76 = **5092 cm³ per minute**

Q6 0.071 L × 1000 = 71 cm³
cardiac output ÷ stroke volume = heart rate
5538 ÷ 71 = **78 beats per minute**

Q7 cardiac output ÷ heart rate = stroke volume
5402 ÷ 74 = 73 cm³
73 ÷ 1000 = **0.073 L**
Remember, you need to divide by 1000 to convert cm³ to litres.

Page 95 — Application Questions

Q1 The left atrium is contracting.

Q2 Open. The left ventricle is contracting, so the pressure is higher in the ventricle than in the aorta, forcing the semi-lunar valve open.

Q3 The left ventricle is relaxing.

Q4 The left atrium is filling up.
At point D, the increase in atrial pressure can't be due to the left atrium contracting because the diagram shows that the left ventricle is relaxing — i.e. the left ventricle doesn't contract next. So you need to think about what happens in the left atrium as the left ventricle is relaxing — it's filling up with blood to prepare for the next atrial contraction.

Q5 Open. The ventricle is relaxing, increasing the volume and reducing the pressure in the chamber. The atrium has been filling, increasing the pressure in the chamber. So as the pressure in the atrium becomes higher than that in the ventricle, the atrioventricular valve will open.

Page 95 — Fact Recall Questions

Q1 right side

Q2 A — pulmonary artery
B — aorta
C — inferior vena cava
D — pulmonary vein
E — right atrium
F — semi-lunar valve
G — right atrioventricular valve
H — left ventricle

Q3 Because it needs to contract powerfully to pump blood all the way round the body, whereas the right ventricle only pumps blood to the lungs.

Q4 a) semi-lunar valves
b) They stop blood flowing back into the heart after the ventricles contract.

Q5 It can contract and relax without receiving signals from nerves.

Q6 It sets the rhythm of the heartbeat by sending out regular waves of electrical activity to the atrial walls. This causes the right and left atria to contract at the same time.

Q7 non-conducting collagen tissue

Q8 It conducts waves of electrical activity from the AVN to the Purkyne fibres.

Q9 cardiac output = stroke volume × heart rate

Q10 An ongoing sequence of contraction and relaxation of the atria and ventricles that keeps blood continuously circulating round the body.

Q11 The volume of the atria decreases and the pressure increases.

2. Cardiovascular Disease

Page 98 — Application Questions

Q1 aneurysm

Q2 Thrombocytosis would be likely to increase a person's risk of thrombosis. This is because there would be a greater amount of platelets in the blood to accumulate at damaged sites on the artery walls and, together with fibrin, form blood clots.

Q3 a) Damage can occur to the endothelium of a coronary artery causing white blood cells and lipids from the blood to clump together under the lining, forming fatty streaks. Over time, more white blood cells, lipids and connective tissue build up and harden to form an atheroma.
b) E.g. a heart attack/myocardial infarction.

Q4 Aspirin stops platelets from aggregating at the site of damage on an artery wall. This means it stops the formation of a blood clot, which is caused by platelets and fibrin accumulating at the site of damage on an artery. In turn, this decreases the risk of a heart attack which is caused by a blockage such as a blood clot.

Page 98 — Fact Recall Questions

Q1 An atheroma is a fibrous plaque formed from the build up and hardening of white blood cells, lipids and connective tissue.

Q2 Under the endothelium.

Q3 An atheroma partially blocks the lumen of an artery and restricts blood flow.

Q4 A — atheroma
B — lumen
C — endothelium

Q5 a) A balloon-like swelling of an artery.
b) Atheroma plaques damage and weaken arteries. They also narrow arteries, increasing blood pressure. When blood travels through a weakened artery at high pressure, it may push the inner layers of the artery through the outer elastic layer to form an aneurysm.

Q6 thrombosis

Q7 coronary arteries

Q8 a heart attack

3. Risk Factors and Coronary Heart Disease (CHD)

Page 101 — Application Questions

Q1 It could decrease the number of new cases of CHD by 37 000 per year (accept 36 000 to 38 000).
Look carefully at the values on the y-axis — the projected annual change in the number of new cases of CHD is negative, which means there are fewer new cases of CHD.

Q2 There'd be 59 000 fewer new cases of CHD by reducing BMI, but only 41 000 fewer new cases by reducing tobacco use/exposure — so between the two there'd be 18 000 fewer new cases by reducing BMI.

Q3 Intervention 3 / reducing salt intake by 3 g per day. This is because this intervention is predicted to reduce the number of new cases of CHD per year by 110 000 — which is greater than any other intervention shown on the graph.

Q4 a) The more salt intake is reduced by, the fewer new cases of CHD there are per year.
b) A diet low in salt will decrease the risk of high blood pressure, which in turn will decrease the risk of damage to the coronary artery walls.
This means it's less likely that atheromas form in the coronary arteries, so the risk of CHD is reduced and it's likely that there'll be fewer new cases of CHD.
This question is asking you to explain why a low salt diet could lead to a lower risk of CHD — that's the opposite way round to how you've learnt it.

Page 102 — Fact Recall Questions

Q1 It's when the coronary arteries have lots of atheromas in them, which restricts blood flow to the heart.

Q2 Cholesterol is one of the main constituents of the fatty deposits that form atheromas. Atheromas can lead to increased blood pressure and blood clots. A blood clot could block the flow of blood to coronary arteries and lead to a heart attack.

Q3 a) Smoking decreases the amount of antioxidants in the blood. Fewer antioxidants increases the risk of cell damage in the walls of the coronary arteries, which can lead to atheroma formation.
b) Carbon monoxide combines with haemoglobin and reduces the amount of oxygen transported in the blood, and so reduces the amount of oxygen available to tissues. If heart muscle doesn't receive enough oxygen it can lead to a heart attack.

Q4 a) High blood pressure increases the risk of damage to the coronary artery walls. Damaged walls have an increased risk of atheroma formation.
b) E.g. any three from: atheroma formation / being overweight / not exercising / excessive alcohol consumption.

Pages 103-104 — Exam-style Questions

1 a) Stage one — the atria contract, decreasing their volume *(1 mark)* and so increasing the pressure in the atria *(1 mark)*.
Stage two — the atria relax, increasing their volume *(1 mark)* and so decreasing the pressure in the atria *(1 mark)*.
To get full marks you need to fully explain the pressure change in the atria at each stage. It's not enough to say that the atria contract or relax, you need to say how this affects the volume, which then causes the change in pressure.
b) i) Atrioventricular valves / AV valves *(1 mark)*. They prevent the back-flow of blood into the atria when the ventricles contract *(1 mark)*.
ii) During stage one, the atrioventricular valves are open because the pressure in the atria is greater than that in the ventricles *(1 mark)*. During stage two, the atrioventricular valves are closed because the pressure in the ventricles is greater than that in the atria *(1 mark)*.
c) Because the atria are filling up with blood *(1 mark)*.
d) Cardiac output = 5.244 × 1000
= 5244 cm^3 per minute
stroke volume = cardiac output ÷ heart rate
5244 ÷ 76 = 69 cm^3
(1 mark for correct working only, 2 marks for correct answer)

2 a) control group
b) E.g. by taking a larger sample size *(1 mark)*. By making sure the men in the test group followed the dietary information *(1 mark)*.
c) A diet high in saturated fat is associated with high blood cholesterol levels *(1 mark)*. Cholesterol is one of the main constituents of the fatty deposits that form atheromas *(1 mark)*.
A diet high in salt increases the risk of high blood pressure *(1 mark)*. High blood pressure increases the risk of damage to the artery walls *(1 mark)*. Damaged walls have an increased risk of atheroma formation *(1 mark)*.
d) E.g. any two from: high blood pressure / high blood cholesterol / cigarette smoking.

3 a)

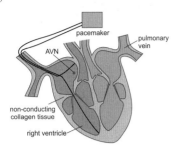

pacemaker
pulmonary vein
AVN
non-conducting collagen tissue
right ventricle

(1 mark for each correct label)

b) It prevents the waves of electrical activity from being passed directly from the atria to the ventricles *(1 mark)*.

c) There must be a delay so that the atria empty *(1 mark)* before the ventricles contract *(1 mark)*.

To get both marks you need to make two points. It's not enough just to say that there's a delay for the atria to empty, you need to give a full answer.

d) The AVN passes the waves of electrical activity onto the Bundle of His *(1 mark)*. The Bundle of His conducts the waves of electrical activity to the Purkyne fibres *(1 mark)*. The Purkyne fibres carry the waves of electrical activity into the muscular walls of the right and left ventricles *(1 mark)*.

4 a) Because the coronary arteries are narrowed in coronary heart disease *(1 mark)*.

b) An atheroma plaque can rupture the endothelium of an artery *(1 mark)*, damaging the artery wall and leaving a rough surface *(1 mark)*. Platelets and fibrin then accumulate at the site of damage and form a blood clot *(1 mark)*.

c) A myocardial infarction is caused by a coronary artery becoming completely blocked *(1 mark)*, so an area of the heart muscle will be totally cut off from its blood supply *(1 mark)*, receiving no oxygen *(1 mark)*.

Unit 2

Section 1: Variation

1. Causes of Variation
Page 107 — Application Question
Q1 a) The mean difference in head circumference is approximately 0.5 cm for identical twins, 3 cm for non-identical siblings and 8.5 cm for unrelated individuals. So the mean difference in head circumference is much larger for unrelated individuals than for either identical twins or non-identical siblings.

b) The data suggests that genetic factors have a larger effect on head circumference, because the mean difference in head circumference is much larger for unrelated individuals than for either identical twins or non-identical siblings. However, the mean difference for identical twins wasn't zero, so environmental factors appear to play some role.

c) The mean difference in the number of steps taken is between 800 and 900 for all three sample groups. Identical twins and non-identical siblings show the lowest difference and unrelated individuals the highest but the margins are very small. This suggests that environmental factors play a more important role than genetic factors in determining activity level when measured by the number of steps taken per day.

Page 107 — Fact Recall Questions
Q1 Variation that exists between different species.
Q2 The differences that occur within a species.
Q3 E.g. eye colour / blood type
Q4 E.g. a person's height / a person's skin colour / overeating / antioxidant levels in berries.

2. Investigating Variation
Page 111 — Application Questions
Q1 a) The mean wing span is approximately 27 cm for species A and 31 cm for species B. Both curves follow a normal distribution. Species A has a higher standard deviation than species B.

b) Species A, because it has a higher standard deviation.

c) Genetics, because species A and species B live in the same environment, so the difference in wing span is probably a result of genetic factors.

Q2 $(31 - 27) \div 27 \times 100 = $ **14.8%**

Make sure you're confident at calculating percentages — they're a common mathsy-type question that examiners like to ask.

Page 112 — Fact Recall Questions
Q1 Because looking at the whole population would either be too time consuming or impossible to do.
Q2 E.g. by using random sampling.
Q3 B
Q4 C

Pages 113-114 — Exam-style Questions

1 a) The method used was good because it used random samples which increases the reliability of the results *(1 mark)*. The plants were grown in the same environment to control the variables, which also increases the reliability of the results *(1 mark)*. However, there was no control used which decreases the reliability of the results *(1 mark)* and they didn't repeat the experiment which also decreases the reliability of the results *(1 mark)*.

   b) Both sets of values show a normal distribution *(1 mark)*. The largest number of plants survived 120 hours without water for species A, whereas this was 168 hours for species B *(1 mark)*. The range in hours survived is 12-204 for species A whereas it was 12-324 for species B *(1 mark)*.

   c) The variation is likely to be down to genetics because the plants were grown in the same environment *(1 mark)*.

   d) The mean number of hours survived without water was higher for species B than species A, so species B would survive better in the area of Africa with low rainfall *(1 mark)*. However, the standard deviation is higher for species B than species A, so there is more variation in the results *(1 mark)*.

   e) The standard deviation shows the spread/variation about the mean *(1 mark)*.

   f) Gene Y, because the mean number of days survived without water is highest *(1 mark)* and the standard deviation is lowest *(1 mark)*.

2 a) 21% *(1 mark)*
   Make sure you read the correct value off the graph here, and read the key carefully.

   b) The incidence of breast cancer is higher with alcohol consumption, at about 9 cases per 100 women *(1 mark)* compared to 6 cases per 100 women with no alcohol consumption *(1 mark)*.

   c) The first graph suggests that age and genetics affect a woman's risk of developing breast cancer *(1 mark)*. A young woman is more likely to develop breast cancer if members of her family have had breast cancer *(1 mark)*. The second graph suggests that age and the environment (drinking alcohol) affect a woman's risk of developing breast cancer *(1 mark)*. A woman is more likely to develop breast cancer as she gets older, and this risk increases further the more alcohol she drinks *(1 mark)*. So both graphs together suggest that there is a link between breast cancer and both genetic and environmental factors *(1 mark)*.

Section 2: Genetics

1. DNA

Page 117 — Application Questions

Q1 a) TGACAGCATCAGCTACGAT
    b) ACGTGGTACACCATTTAGC

Q2 a) 22
    b) 12
    c) 12
    If there are 34 base pairs in total and 22 of them contain adenine, then the other 12 must contain both cytosine and guanine — it's all to do with specific base pairing.

Page 117 — Fact Recall Questions

Q1 A = phosphate group, B = deoxyribose (sugar), C = (nitrogenous) base

Q2 deoxyribose

Q3 The phosphate group of one nucleotide bonds with the sugar of another.

Q4 The double helix structure is very stable so that important genetic information doesn't get lost. DNA is long and tightly coiled so lots of genetic information can be stored in a small space. DNA molecules are paired so they can be easily replicated.

Q5 In eukaryotes DNA is linear and wound around histone proteins to form chromosomes.
    In prokaryotes DNA is circular and not wound around proteins. It condenses to fit in the cell by supercoiling.

2. Genes

Pages 118-119 — Application Questions

Q1 a) (i) CATAGACATGGCTGCAGATACTACGGCAGA
       (ii) TACTGCAGAAGAGGCTGCGGCTACCATGGC
    b) (i) Gly-Tyr-Gly-His-Arg-Arg-Cys-Tyr-His
       (ii) His-Tyr-Tyr-Arg-Gly-Cys-His-Arg-Gly

Q2 Valine = GTC, Threonine = ACT, Leucine = TTG

Page 119 — Application Questions

Q1 ACTGTATTGATCGAATGTCTA

Q2 a) 10
    b) GC

Page 121 — Application Questions

Q1
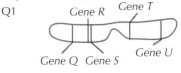
Gene R   Gene T
Gene Q Gene S   Gene U

Homologous chromosomes are the same so all of the genes should be in the same place.

Q2 a) i)   White
       ii) Pink
       iii) Red
    b) The gene coding for the protein substrate has mutated.

Page 121 — Fact Recall Questions

Q1 A gene is a section of DNA that codes for a protein.

Q2 Three

Q3 Introns and multiple repeats.

Q4 The DNA sequence determines the amino acid sequence of an enzyme. Enzymes control metabolic pathways. Metabolic pathways help determine nature and development.

Q5 An allele is a different form of a gene.

Q6 locus

Q7 through mutation

Answers   229

Q8 Mutations may prevent an enzyme from folding properly. This may produce an active site that's the wrong shape, stopping the enzyme from working properly.

3. Meiosis and Genetic Variation
Page 125 — Application Questions
Q1 a) The DNA is being replicated to produce two copies of each chromosome.
   b) The DNA is condensing and the chromosomes are arranging themselves into homologous pairs.
   c) Meiosis I occurs — the homologous pairs are separated halving the chromosome number.
   d) Meiosis II occurs — the pairs of sister chromatids are separated generating haploid cells.
Q2 A, C, D and F could all be produced by meiosis from this cell. Gametes B and E could not.
   Gametes contain one chromosome from each homologous pair. If a gamete contains two chromosomes from the same homologous pair it couldn't have been produced by meiosis.
Q3

Q4 a) After meiosis II, because there is only one chromatid of each chromosome.
   b) Between meiosis I and meiosis II, because there are no homologous pairs, but each chromosome has two sister chromatids.
   c) Before meiosis I, because there are homologous pairs of chromosomes.

Page 125 — Fact Recall Questions
Q1 a) diploid
   b) haploid
   c) diploid
Q2 a) The homologous pairs separate.
   b) The sister chromatids separate.
Q3 a) Crossing over and independent segregation of chromosomes.
   b) Crossing over is when chromatids twist around each other and bits of chromatid swap over. The resulting chromosomes contain the same genes but now have a different combination of alleles. This means that when the chromatids separate at meiosis II, each of the four daughter cells will contain chromatids with different alleles.
   Independent segregation is when different combinations of maternal and paternal chromosomes go into each cell. This produces genetic variation in the gametes.

4. Genetic Diversity
Page 127 — Application Questions
Q1 The differences between the longest and the smallest tail lengths decreased dramatically. There was a reduction in the diversity of tail lengths.
Q2 a genetic bottleneck

Q3 Any one from, e.g. a natural disaster/volcanic eruption/flood/earthquake may have reduced the population size of the lemurs. / The lemurs may have been hunted, leading to a reduction in their population size.

Page 129 — Application Questions
Q1 Select the chickens that produce the most eggs. Breed the chickens together. From the offspring produced select the ones that produce the most eggs. Continue until a population of chickens is generated that produces lots of eggs.
Q2 Selective breeding reduces genetic diversity because only similar organisms with similar traits are bred. As a result the allele for the inherited disease in the chicken population could increase, increasing the incidence of disease.

Page 129 — Fact Recall Questions
Q1 Genetic bottlenecks are events that cause a big reduction in a population. They decrease genetic diversity because they reduce the number of different alleles in the gene pool.
Q2 The founder effect describes what happens when just a few organisms from a population start a new colony. It can lead to an increased incidence of genetic diseases because only a small number of organisms have contributed to the gene pool. There's more inbreeding in the new population, which can lead to a higher incidence of genetic disease.
Q3 Selective breeding is when humans select which domesticated animals or strains of plants reproduce together to produce useful characteristics, e.g. high-yields.
Q4 Selective breeding decreases genetic diversity because only similar organisms with similar traits and therefore similar alleles are bred together.
Q5 It can produce high-yielding animals and plants.
   It can produce animals and plants with increased resistance to diseases.
   It can produce animals and plants with increased tolerance of bad conditions (e.g. drought or cold).
Q6 It can cause health problems.
   It reduces genetic diversity / increases incidence of genetic disease/susceptibility to new diseases.

Pages 130-131 — Exam-style Questions
1 a) Breed together a cow and a bull that both have higher than normal muscle mass *(1 mark)*. Continually select the offspring with the highest muscle mass and breed them together until a breed of cow with a very high muscle mass is created *(1 mark)*.
   b) Advantages: It can produce high yielding animals *(1 mark)*. It can increase resistance to disease *(1 mark)*. It can increase tolerance of bad conditions *(1 mark)*.
   Disadvantages: It can cause health problems *(1 mark)*. It reduces genetic diversity *(1 mark)*. It increases the incidence of genetic disease/ susceptibility to new diseases *(1 mark)*.
   c) i) Mean muscle mass increases with each generation *(1 mark)*.

ii) 50% of 1 = 0.5, 1 + 0.5 = 1.5 *(1 mark)*
The mean muscle mass is 1.5 in generation 3, so it took 3 generations of cows to increase the mean muscle mass by 50% *(1 mark)*.

iii) 1.6 relative units (accept 1.5 to 1.7) *(1 mark)*

iv) Generation 10, because it has the smallest standard deviation *(1 mark)*.

d) In both selective breeding and the founder effect, only a small number of organisms contribute their alleles to the gene pool of the breeding population *(1 mark)*. This reduces genetic diversity *(1 mark)*.

2 a) i) CGTGAACATACGGATACC *(1 mark)*

ii) 6 *(1 mark)* because three bases/a triplet of bases code for one amino acid *(1 mark)*.

Remember, each amino acid is coded for by a sequence of three bases. So all you need to do for this one is count up the total number of bases (18) and divide by 3.

b) Deoxyribose sugar *(1 mark)*, a phosphate group *(1 mark)* and a (nitrogenous) base *(1 mark)*.

c) The DNA will lose its double helix structure/the two DNA strands will unravel *(1 mark)*. This is because the double helix/two DNA strands are held together by hydrogen bonding between the base pairs *(1 mark)*.

d) The DNA molecule is long and tightly coiled so lots of genetic information can be stored in a small space *(1 mark)*.
The DNA molecule has a paired structure so it can be easily replicated *(1 mark)*.
The double helix structure is very stable so that important genetic information doesn't get lost *(1 mark)*.

3 a) i) Because all genes are found at fixed positions (loci) on chromosomes *(1 mark)*.

ii) Genes code for proteins (such as enzymes) *(1 mark)*. Without the gene associated with brain development, the protein it codes for won't be made *(1 mark)*. This could affect metabolic pathways in the body which affect brain development, resulting in a lower intellectual ability *(1 mark)*.

b) i) E.g any six from: the DNA unravels and replicates to produce two copies of each chromosome/two chromatids *(1 mark)*. The DNA then condenses to form double-armed chromosomes, made from two sister chromatids *(1 mark)*. The chromosomes arrange themselves into homologous pairs *(1 mark)* which are separated during meiosis I *(1 mark)*. This halves the chromosome number *(1 mark)*. The pairs of sister chromatids are separated during meiosis II *(1 mark)*. This produces four genetically different haploid gametes *(1 mark)*.

ii) Crossing over is where pairs of chromatids twist around each other and bits of chromatid swap over *(1 mark)*. This increases genetic variation in the gametes *(1 mark)*.

Section 3: Variation in Biochemistry & Cell Structure

1. Variation in Haemoglobin
Page 135 — Application Questions
Q1 a) B. The dissociation curve would be further to the right after a bike ride than whilst watching television, because during the bike ride the man's respiration rate would have increased, raising the pCO_2. This increases the rate of oxygen unloading so the dissociation curve shifts right.

b) The Bohr effect.

Q2 Badger — A. In an underground sett the oxygen concentration will be low, so the badger's haemoglobin will have the highest affinity for oxygen compared to the other animals, so the dissociation curve is furthest to the left.

The badger needs to be able to get any available oxygen at a low pO_2. Its dissociation curve is furthest to the left meaning it loads oxygen more readily at a lower oxygen concentration.

Bush dog — C. Above ground there will be more oxygen than underground, so the bush dog's haemoglobin will have a lower affinity for oxygen than the badger's haemoglobin. The bush dog is more active than the brown-throated sloth, so it has a greater oxygen demand. This means its haemoglobin will also have a lower affinity for oxygen than the brown-throated sloth's, so its dissociation curve is furthest to the right.
Brown-throated sloth — B. Above ground there will be more oxygen than underground, so the brown-throated sloth's haemoglobin will have a lower affinity for oxygen than the badger's haemoglobin. However, the brown-throated sloth's oxygen demand won't be as high as the bush dog's, as the brown-throated sloth is less active. This means the brown-throated sloth's haemoglobin will have an affinity for oxygen (and therefore dissociation curve) that is between the badger's and the bush dog's.

Page 135 — Fact Recall Questions
Q1 in red blood cells
Q2 Loading describes oxygen binding with/joining to haemoglobin, and unloading describes oxygen being released from/leaving haemoglobin.
Q3 oxyhaemoglobin
Q4 In the alveoli / lungs. This is the site where oxygen first enters the blood so it has the highest concentration of oxygen.
Q5 How saturated haemoglobin is with oxygen at any given partial pressure.

2. Variation in Plant and Animal Cells
Page 137 — Application Question
Q1 E.g. companion cells have lots of mitochondria because they need to provide energy for their own needs as well as for the sieve cells. More mitochondria mean they can release more energy from respiration. Similarly, they have lot of ribosomes as they need to synthesise proteins to meet both their own needs and the needs of the sieve cells.

Page 137 — Fact Recall Questions

Q1 A — cell wall, B — cytoplasm, C — mitochondria/mitochondrion, D — nucleus, E — chloroplast, F — vacuole, G — cell membrane, H — ribosome

Q2 cytoplasm

Q3 Plant cells have a rigid cell wall, a permanent vacuole and chloroplasts.

Q4 a) It is surrounded by a double membrane. It has membranes inside called thylakoid membranes. These are stacked up to form grana. Grana are linked together by lamellae. Chloroplasts contain a thick fluid called stroma.
    b) grana, stroma

Q5 ribosomes

3. Variation in Carbohydrates

Pages 139-140 — Fact Recall Questions

Q1 a) starch
    b) glycogen

Q2
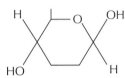

Q3 glycosidic

Q4 a) cellulose
    b) Cellulose is made from long, unbranched chains of β-glucose. These are joined by hydrogen bonds to form microfibrils. Microfibrils are very strong, which means they provide support/strength/rigidity in a cell wall.

Q5
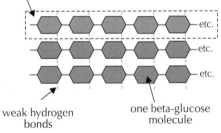
one cellulose molecule

etc.
etc.
etc.

weak hydrogen bonds

one beta-glucose molecule

Q6 a) insoluble
    b) It doesn't cause water to enter cells by osmosis, which would make them swell.

Q7 a) A — amylopectin, B — amylose
    b) It has lots of side branches, which means the enzymes that break amylopectin down can get to the glycosidic bonds easily. This means glucose can be released quickly when it is needed.

Q8 Glycogen is made from long, branched chains of α-glucose. It has lots of side branches which means that stored glucose can be released quickly. It's a very compact molecule which makes it good for storage.

Pages 141-142 — Exam-style Questions

1   a) It is a protein with a quaternary structure *(1 mark)*. Each polypeptide chain has a haem group containing iron *(1 mark)*.

    b) Each animal's haemoglobin was 50% saturated at a lower pO_2 at high altitude than at sea level *(1 mark)*. This means that haemoglobin has a higher affinity for oxygen / unloads oxygen less readily at high altitudes than at sea level *(1 mark)*. This suggests that the animals living at high altitudes live in environments with a lower oxygen concentration than those living at sea level *(1 mark)*.

    c) Cat — B, Puma — C, Fox — A
       (1 mark for all three answers correct)
       To help you work this answer out, draw a line across the graph at 50%. Then for each curve, draw another line down to the x-axis from the point where the first line crosses the curve. This gives you the pO_2 value at which the haemoglobin is 50% saturated. You can then compare the values you get to the information given in the table.

    d) The gradient of the curve decreases / The curve becomes flatter as the saturation level approaches 100% *(1 mark)*. At high saturation levels it becomes harder for haemoglobin to load more oxygen molecules *(1 mark)*. This means even as the pO_2 increases, the % saturation of haemoglobin with oxygen only increases slightly *(1 mark)*.

    e) C / The puma. Animals with a higher respiration rate have a higher oxygen demand *(1 mark)*. This means their haemoglobin must have a low affinity for oxygen / unload oxygen readily to meet these high oxygen demands *(1 mark)*. The puma's haemoglobin becomes saturated at a higher pO_2 compared to the other animals *(1 mark)*, so its haemoglobin must have a low affinity for oxygen *(1 mark)*.

    f) Haemoglobin gives up its oxygen more readily at a higher pCO_2 / the rate of oxygen unloading is increased *(1 mark)*, so the saturation of haemoglobin with oxygen will be lower for a given pO_2 *(1 mark)*. This means the fox's haemoglobin dissociation curve would have shifted to the right *(1 mark)*.

2   a) Chloroplasts *(1 mark)* have membranes inside called thylakoid membranes *(1 mark)* which are stacked up to form grana *(1 mark)*. Grana are linked together by lamellae *(1 mark)*. Chloroplasts contain a thick fluid called stroma *(1 mark)*.

    b) i) amylopectin *(1 mark)*
       ii) Amylose is a long, unbranched chain of α-glucose *(1 mark)*. It has a coiled structure /cylindrical shape *(1 mark)*. These features make it compact meaning it's good for storage *(1 mark)*.

3   a) i) X — hydrogen bond *(1 mark)*, Y — β-glucose *(1 mark)*, Z — glycosidic bond *(1 mark)*
       ii) The strong fibres *(1 mark)* mean cellulose provides strong structural support for cells *(1 mark)*.
       Remember to make sure you say β-glucose and not just glucose here.

    b) Any three from: e.g. starch is used to store energy whereas cellulose is used to strengthen cell walls. / Starch is made from α-glucose whereas cellulose is made from β-glucose. / Starch has a compact shape whereas cellulose is a long, straight molecule. / The bonds between the glucose molecules in starch (amylose) are angled whereas the bonds between glucose molecules in cellulose are straight. *(3 marks for 3 correct answers)*.

c) i) See below.

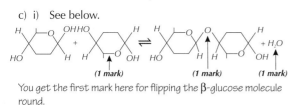

(1 mark)   **(1 mark)**   **(1 mark)**

You get the first mark here for flipping the β-glucose molecule round.

    ii) condensation reaction **(1 mark)**

Section 4: The Cell Cycle & Differentiation

1. DNA Replication
Page 144 — Application Question
Q1

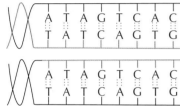

In semi-conservative replication of DNA, each of the new pieces of DNA contains a strand from the original molecule (shown in black in the diagram) and a new strand (green in the diagram).

Page 145 — Application Question
Q1   Radioactive phosphate (^{32}P) was found inside the bacteria, which means DNA was transferred to the bacterial cells. Viruses inject their genetic material into bacterial cells so DNA must be the genetic material.

Page 145 — Fact Recall Questions
Q1   DNA helicase, DNA polymerase
Q2   DNA helicase breaks the hydrogen bonds between the two polynucleotide DNA strands. The helix unzips to form two single strands.
Q3   Free-floating DNA nucleotides join to the exposed bases on the original template strand by specific base pairing — A with T and C with G.
Q4   It's where half of the new molecules of DNA are from the original piece of DNA.

2. The Cell Cycle and Mitosis
Page 148 — Application Questions
Q1   a) i)   B
       ii)   C
To answer this you need to quickly go through each stage of mitosis in your head and think about the main thing that's happening, e.g. in metaphase all the chromosomes are in middle of the cell. Then ask yourself if you can see that in the photo.
     b) The centromeres are dividing, separating each pair of sister chromatids. The spindles are contracting, pulling chromatids to opposite poles of the cell, centromere first.

Q2   a) 12-16 hours and 36-40 hours, because the mass of DNA doubles.
     b) 24 hours and 48 hours, because the mass of DNA halves.
     c) The cell is growing and new organelles and proteins are made. The cell replicates it's DNA, and then continues growing and making proteins needed for cell division.
     d) i)   Two (at 24 and 48 hours) because the mass of the cell and its DNA doubles and halves twice.
       ii)   At 72 hours.

Page 148 — Fact Recall Questions
Q1   The process that all body cells from multicellular organisms use to grow and divide.
Q2   two
Q3   false
     Mitosis produces two genetically identical daughter cells.
Q4   For growth and for repairing damaged tissues.
Q5   During prophase the chromosomes condense, getting shorter and fatter. The centrioles start moving to opposite ends of the cell, forming the spindle. The nuclear envelope breaks down and chromosomes lie free in the cytoplasm.
Q6   metaphase
Q7   anaphase
Q8   During telophase the chromatids reach the opposite poles on the spindle. They uncoil and become long and thin again. They're now called chromosomes again. A nuclear envelope forms around each group of chromosomes, so there are now two nuclei. The cytoplasm divides and there are now two daughter cells that are genetically identical to the original cell and to each other.

3. Cancer
Page 150 — Application Questions
Q1   a)   synthesis / interphase
     b)   mitosis
     Methotrexate stops A and G nucleotides from forming — these nucleotides are needed to make new strands of DNA during DNA synthesis. Spindle fibres separate chromosomes during mitosis.
Q2   a)   four
     This is the same as the number of times on the graph where both types of cells decrease.
     b) Cancer cells divide much more frequently than healthy cells, so they are more likely to be killed by chemotherapy because it targets the cell cycle.
     c) i)   three weeks
       ii)   So the body can recover but the cancer can't grow back to the same size as before.
     d) A large dose could kill so many normal cells that the patient could die.
Q3   The ATM protein won't be made/a faulty version of the ATM protein will be made. This means the cell with damaged DNA will go through the cell cycle and divide. The cell will continue to divide, which can lead to the formation of a tumour.

Page 150 — Fact Recall Questions

Q1 When normal body cells have divided enough times to make enough new cells, they stop. Cancer cells keep on dividing to make more and more cells.

Q2 It's a tumour that invades surrounding tissues.

Q3 E.g. chemotherapy prevents the synthesis of enzymes needed for DNA replication. If these aren't produced, the cell is unable to enter the synthesis phase (S), disrupting the cell cycle and forcing the cell to kill itself. / Radiation damages DNA. When the cell gets to S phase it checks for damaged DNA and if any is detected it kills itself, preventing further tumour growth.

Q4 It removes a lot of tumour cells and increases the access of any left to nutrients and oxygen, which triggers them to enter the cell cycle, making them more susceptible to treatment.

4. Cell Differentiation and Organisation
Page 151 — Application Question

Q1 a) E.g. the biconcave shape gives a large surface areas for absorbing oxygen. / There is no nucleus so there's more room for carrying haemoglobin.

b) E.g. it has a large surface area for efficient diffusion of water into the cells. / It has a thin cell wall for efficient diffusion of water into the cell.

Page 154 — Fact Recall Questions

Q1 A cell that is adapted to carry out a specific function.

Q2 differentiation

Q3 E.g. squamous epithelial cell / palisade mesophyll cell.

Q4 A tissue is where similar cells are grouped together, whereas an organ is where different tissues are grouped together to perform a particular function.

Q5 An organ system is where different organs work together to carry out a particular function.

Q6 E.g. the circulatory system. It is an organ system because it is made up of different organs such as the heart and blood vessels that work together to transport gases and other substances around the body. / The respiratory system. It is an organ system because it is made up of different organs such as the lungs, trachea and bronchi that work together to bring oxygen into the body and remove carbon dioxide.

Pages 155-156 — Exam-style Questions

Q1 a) i) synthesis/S-phase *(1 mark)*

ii) It doubles *(1 mark)* so that each new daughter cell produced by mitosis has an exact copy of the DNA of the parent cell *(1 mark)*.

iii) DNA helicase *(1 mark)* breaks the hydrogen bonds between the two polynucleotide DNA strands *(1 mark)*. Free-floating DNA nucleotides join to the exposed bases on each original template strand by specific base pairing (A with T and C with G) *(1 mark)*. The nucleotides on the new strand are joined together *(1 mark)* by DNA polymerase *(1 mark)*. Hydrogen bonds form between the bases on the original and the new strand *(1 mark)*.

b) A is gap phase 1 because it contains 1 arbitrary unit of DNA *(1 mark)*. B is synthesis because the mass of DNA is increasing *(1 mark)*. C is gap phase 2 because it contains 2 arbitrary units of DNA *(1 mark)*.
The key to this question is to look at the amount of DNA at each stage on the graph and link that back to how the amount of DNA in a cell changes during the stages of interphase.

c) E.g. because Phase A lasts longer *(1 mark)*.
If each phase lasted the same length of time, then each phase would have broadly the same number of cells.

Q2 a) In G_1 the cell grows and new organelles and proteins are made *(1 mark)*. In G_2 the cell keeps growing and proteins needed for cell division are made *(1 mark)*.

b) The cell is unable to enter the synthesis phase / the cell cycle is disrupted *(1 mark)* forcing the cell to kill itself *(1 mark)*.

c) Cancer cells divide much more frequently than normal cells *(1 mark)*.

Q3 a) Shortly after the activity of protein X reaches its highest level, the % of dividing cells reaches its highest level *(1 mark)*.

b) No, you can't tell from the data that the activity of protein X is causing the cells to divide — it might just be a coincidence / there might be other factors involved *(1 mark)*. Also the graph only shows data for one species of yeast so you can't apply any trend to other species of yeast *(1 mark)*.

c) E.g. cell division could be measured in yeast cells that do not produce this protein *(1 mark)*. The purpose of this would be to make sure that the change in the percentage of cells diving is due to the activity of protein X and nothing else *(1 mark)*.

d) Advantage — e.g. the microscope is quick/easy to use *(1 mark)*.
Disadvantage — e.g. it is difficult to accurately measure the percentage of dividing cells *(1 mark)*.

Q4 a) It is an organ because it is made up of lots of different tissues, such as the cornea and the retina *(1 mark)*, which work together to allow us to see *(1 mark)*.

b) A mutation in the gene for Rb means the Rb protein is not made / a faulty version of the Rb protein is made *(1 mark)*. This means the damaged cell goes through the cell cycle and divides *(1 mark)*. The cells continue to divide which can lead to the formation of a tumour *(1 mark)*.

Section 5: Exchange and Transport Systems

1. Size and Surface Area
Page 158 — Application Question

Q1 a) i) A — surface area = $6 \times 2 \times 2$ = **24 cm²**
B — surface area = $(4 \times 4 \times 2) + (2 \times 2 \times 2)$
$= 32 + 8 =$ **40 cm²**
C — surface area = $(4 \times 10 \times 5) + (2 \times 5 \times 5)$
$= 200 + 50 =$ **250 mm²**

ii) A — volume = 2 × 2 × 2 = **8 cm³**
    B — volume = 2 × 4 × 2 = **16 cm³**
    C — volume = 10 × 5 × 5 = **250 mm³**
iii) A — SA : V = 24 : 8 (or 3 : 1)
    B — SA : V = 40 : 16 (or 5 : 2 or 2.5 : 1)
    C — SA : V = 250 : 250 (or 1 : 1)
b) A
Simplify all of the ratios to 1 in order to compare them, e.g. A = 3 : 1, B = 2.5 : 1 and C = 1 : 1 — it's then obvious that A is the largest ratio.

Page 159 — Application Questions
Q1 a) Adélie penguin
The Adélie penguin would have the larger surface area : volume ratio because it's smaller than the Emperor penguin.
b) The Emperor penguin because its large size means it has a lower surface area to volume ratio than the Adélie penguin. This means it's harder for it to lose heat from its body / easier for it to retain heat in its body, so it'll be better suited to living in colder regions than the Adélie penguin.
Q2 The Adélie penguin because it has a more compact shape, and so has a lower surface area : volume ratio than the Rockhopper penguin. Therefore it won't lose heat as easily so it'll be better suited to living in colder regions than the Rockhopper penguin.

Page 160 — Application Questions
Q1 Small animals have a high surface area : volume ratio meaning they will lose heat easily in cold temperatures. Underground temperatures will be warmer than on the surface, so they go underground to keep warm.
Q2 Small birds. Smaller birds have a higher surface area : volume ratio so they will lose heat more quickly than larger birds. Therefore they are more likely to have adaptations to keep warm.
Q3 Large animals have a low surface area : volume ratio so they find it hard to lose heat. They are active at night because it is cooler.

Page 160 — Fact Recall Questions
Q1 a) Any two from: e.g. oxygen / nutrients / water.
b) E.g. carbon dioxide, urea.
Q2 Lower surface area : volume ratio.
Q3 Some cells are deep within the body so the distance between them and the outside environment is too great for diffusion to take place quickly. Larger animals have a low surface area : volume ratio. This means they don't have a large enough area exposed to the environment to be able to exchange all the substances they need quickly enough using diffusion.
Q4 A system in a multicellular organism that carries substances to and from individual cells.
Q5 High surface area : volume ratio.
Q6 An animal with a compact shape has a low surface area : volume ratio. This means they lose less heat. An animal with a less compact shape has a higher surface area : volume ratio. This means they lose heat more easily.

Q7 Any two from: e.g. they might have a higher metabolic rate. / They might hibernate. / They might have thick layers of fur.
Q8 Any two from: e.g. they might spend a lot of time in water. / They might have features that increase their surface area, e.g. large ears.

2. Gas Exchange
Page 164 — Application Questions
Q1 B. E.g. the leaf is curled with the stomata inside, protecting them from the wind so less water is lost. / There are lots of hairs on the epidermis to trap water vapour, reducing the diffusion gradient. / The stomata are sunken in pits to trap water vapour, reducing evaporation by lowering the diffusion gradient.
Q2 A concentration gradient would still be maintained between the water and the blood, but it would be less steep. This means the fish wouldn't be able to take in as much oxygen as they would in clean water.
Q3 a) It increases steadily.
To answer this question you need to look at the arrow head of the red line — it's pointing upwards so the oxygen concentration of the blood is increasing.
b) It decreases steadily.
c) 80%
d) Because at point X the oxygen concentration of the water is higher than in the blood (about 92 %) — so oxygen has diffused into the blood down its concentration gradient.

Page 164 — Fact Recall Questions
Q1 Any two from: they have a large surface area. / They're thin. / They maintain a steep concentration gradient.
Q2 Single-celled organisms can exchange gases directly through their outer surface. This has a large surface area, is thin and has a short diffusion pathway, so there's no need for a gas exchange system.
Q3 Each gill is made of lots of thin plates called gill filaments. These are covered in lots of tiny structures called lamellae. Lamellae have a thin surface layer of cells and a good blood supply.
Q4 The counter-current system works by maintaining a steep concentration gradient between the water and the blood. Blood flows through the lamellae in one direction and water flows over the lamellae in the opposite direction. This means that water with a relatively high oxygen concentration always flows next to blood with a lower oxygen concentration. Oxygen then diffuses into the blood from the water down the concentration gradient.
Q5 The surface of the mesophyll cells in the leaf.
Q6 Through the stomata in the epidermis.
Q7 Through the spiracles on the surface of the insect's body.
Q8 Carbon dioxide from the cells moves down its concentration gradient towards the spiracles to be released into the atmosphere.
Q9 A plant specially adapted for life in a warm, dry or windy habitat.
Q10 Any three from: stomata sunk in pits / curled leaves with stomata inside / a layer of hairs on the epidermis / a reduced number of stomata / waxy, waterproof cuticles on leaves and stems.

3. The Circulatory System
Page 166 — Application Question
Q1 A — Vena cava
B — Renal vein
C — An arteriole
D — Renal artery
E — Aorta
Relative blood pressure is highest in the aorta as it has just left the heart. Relative blood pressure in the other blood vessels decreases as they get further away from the heart. The vessel with the lowest relative blood pressure is the vena cava as it is the last blood vessel before blood returns to the heart.

Page 168 — Application Questions
Q1 a) i) From the blood into the tissue fluid.
ii) E.g. water, oxygen and nutrients (like glucose and amino acids)
b) i) Vein end of the capillary bed.
ii) Artery end of the capillary bed.
Q2 The water potential of the capillary is higher because there is less albumin in the blood. This means less water is absorbed by osmosis back into the capillary at the vein end of the capillary bed, which leads to an increase in tissue fluid.

Page 168 — Fact Recall Questions
Q1 Mammals have a low surface area : volume ratio so they can't rely on diffusion to exchange substances with their environment — the distance is too large.
Q2 pulmonary vein, vena cava
Q3 pulmonary artery
Q4 To carry blood from the gut to the liver.
Q5 renal artery
Q6 The (left and right) coronary arteries.
Q7 A — vein, B — capillary, C — artery, D — arteriole
Q8 An artery has a thick muscular wall with elastic tissue, and a folded endothelium.
Q9 A blood vessel that branches off from an artery.
Q10 a) veins
b) To stop the backflow of blood.
Q11 Any two from: the walls are only one cell thick / they're always very near the cells in exchange tissues / there's a large number of them in exchange tissues.
Q12 The fluid that surrounds cells in tissues.
Q13 a) At the artery end the pressure inside the capillaries is higher than the pressure in the tissue fluid. This means fluid is forced out of the capillaries and into the spaces around the cells, forming tissue fluid.
b) At the vein end of the capillary bed, the water potential is lower in the capillary than it is in the tissue fluid. This means that some water re-enters the capillaries from the tissue fluid by osmosis.

4. Water Transport in Plants
Page 172 — Application Questions
Q1 a) 10 °C — (15 + 12 + 14) ÷ 3 =**13.7 mm**
20 °C — (19 + 16 + 19) ÷ 3 = **18 mm**
30 °C — (25 + 22 + 23) ÷ 3 = **23.3 mm**

b) See graph below. The bubble would move approximately 21 mm in 10 minutes at 25 °C.

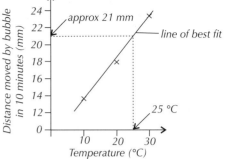

Q2 As the temperature increased, the distance moved by the bubble in 10 minutes increased too. This means the rate of transpiration increased with increasing temperatures. At higher temperatures water molecules have more energy so they evaporate from the cells inside the leaf faster. This increases the water potential between the inside and outside of the leaf, making water diffuse out of the leaf faster.

Page 172 — Fact Recall Questions
Q1 Water is absorbed from the soil into the root hair cells. It then passes through the cortex, including the endodermis, before it reaches the xylem.
Q2 In the symplast pathway, water moves through the cytoplasm in the root to the xylem. Plasmodesmata connect the cytoplasm of neighbouring cells. In the apoplast pathway water moves through the cell walls of the root. Water diffuses through the cell walls and passes through the spaces between them. However, the apoplast pathway is blocked at the endodermis cell layer by a waxy strip in the cell walls called the Casparian strip. The water then has to take the symplast pathway until it reaches the xylem.
Q3 Water can move up a plant by cohesion and tension. Water evaporates from leaves at the top of the xylem. This creates tension which pulls more water into the leaf. As water molecules are cohesive, the whole column of water in the xylem moves upwards. More water then enters the stem through the roots.
Root pressure can move water up a plant. When water is transported into the xylem in the roots, it creates a pressure and moves water already in the xylem further upwards.
Q4 An increase in wind increases transpiration rate. Lots of air movement blows away water molecules from around the stomata. This increases the water potential gradient, which increases the rate of transpiration.

Pages 173-174 — Exam-style Questions
1 a) (i) E.g. there are lots of lamellae on each gill filament which increases the surface area *(1 mark)*. Lamellae are thin which reduces the diffusion distance between the water and the blood *(1 mark)*.
(ii) It maintains a large concentration gradient between the water and the blood *(1 mark)*, so as much oxygen as possible can be diffused into the blood *(1 mark)*.

b) (i) Air enters through an insect's spiracles *(1 mark)*. Air then passes to an insect's trachea / tracheoles *(1 mark)*. Oxygen then diffuses down a concentration gradient directly into respiring cells *(1 mark)*.

(ii) Any two from: they can close their spiracles. / They have a waxy, waterproof cuticle all over their body. / They have hairs around their spiracles. *(1 mark each)*

(iii) Because single-celled organisms have a short diffusion pathway *(1 mark)* and a large surface area : volume ratio *(1 mark)*. This means they can exchange substances quickly across their outer surface *(1 mark)*.

To help you answer this question, think about why multicellular organisms do have a gas exchange system — it's because the diffusion pathway is too big and they have a small surface area:volume ratio, which makes diffusion too slow.

2   a) (i) As the animals get bigger in size, the surface area : volume ratio gets smaller *(1 mark)*.

(ii) The rat because it has the highest surface area : volume ratio *(1 mark)*.

(iii) Rhinos have a low surface area : volume ratio *(1 mark)* which makes it hard for them to lose heat *(1 mark)*. Bathing in mud will help them to keep cool *(1 mark)*.

b) Wolf A because it has larger ears and a longer nose *(1 mark)*. This increases its surface area : volume ratio *(1 mark)* which means it will lose heat more easily *(1 mark)*.

3   a) (i) X — xylem *(1 mark)*
Y — endodermis *(1 mark)*

(ii) The water moves through the apoplast pathway *(1 mark)* until it is blocked by the Casparian strip in the endodermis layer/layer Y *(1 mark)*. Then the water moves through the symplast pathway to the xylem *(1 mark)*.

Make sure you look carefully at the diagram to work out which part of the cell water is moving through, i.e. is the water moving through the cell wall or the cytoplasm?

b) Water evaporates from the leaves at the top of the xylem *(1 mark)*. This creates tension which pulls more water into the leaves *(1 mark)*. Water molecules are cohesive so then a whole column of water moves up the xylem *(1 mark)*. Water then enters the stem through the roots *(1 mark)*.

c) Slower. With more water in the air the water potential gradient between the air and the leaf would be lower *(1 mark)* which would decrease transpiration *(1 mark)*.

d) The transpiration rate increases during the summer because there are more hours of daylight *(1 mark)* so the stomata are open for longer periods *(1 mark)*. Also, temperatures are higher during the summer *(1 mark)* which means water molecules have more energy *(1 mark)* so they evaporate from the cells inside the leaf faster *(1 mark)*. This increases the water potential gradient between the inside and outside of the leaf, making water diffuse out of the leaf faster *(1 mark)*.

4   a) X — hepatic artery
Y — hepatic vein
Z — hepatic portal vein
(1 mark for each correct answer)

b) X / hepatic artery *(1 mark)* because arteries carry blood away from the heart at high pressure *(1 mark)*.

As the blood travels round the circulatory system the pressure of the blood gradually decreases and it is returned to the heart at low pressure via the veins.

c) At the start of the capillary bed the pressure inside the capillaries is higher than the pressure in the tissue fluid *(1 mark)*. The difference in pressure forces fluid out of the capillaries into the tissue fluid *(1 mark)*. The liver cells then take in the substances they need from the tissue fluid across their membranes by processes such as diffusion or active transport *(1 mark)*.

Section 6: Classification

1. Classification Basics
Page 177 — Application Questions
Q1 sharks
Q2 salamanders
Q3 a) crocodiles
     b) lizards

Page 177 — Fact Recall Questions
Q1 The science of classification.
Q2 Phylum, Family, Genus (in this order).
Q3 A species is a group of similar organisms able to reproduce to give fertile offspring.
Q4 The major problem scientists face when classifying species is that they can't always test the reproductive behaviour of different organisms. To overcome this, scientists now use a variety of other techniques to classify species including comparing their DNA.

2. Classification Using DNA or Proteins
Page 180 — Application Questions
Q1 a) Species A: TCGACGTGGGTAATCGAGC
        Species B: TCCACGTGTGTAATCGAGT
        Species C: ACGCCGAGTGTTATGGAGT
     b) 3
     c) 7

Take your time with questions like this. Once you've got your answer, recount it to make sure it's right.

     d) Species B. There are fewer base differences in the DNA when comparing A and B than A and C.
     e) Species B. There are only 6 base differences between species C and B. This is fewer than for species C and A so species C and B are more closely related.

Q2 a) DNA from the two different species has been collected, separated into single strands and then mixed together. The DNA from the two different species was then allowed to hybridise. The temperature required to melt the hybridised DNA was then recorded.

b) Orangutans. The melting temperature was highest for human:orangutan hybrid DNA. This suggests the orangutan DNA is most similar to human DNA and that orangutans are most closely related to humans.

c) Lower. Humans are less closely related to dandelions than to guinea pigs. This means human and dandelion DNA is likely to be more different and so their hybrid DNA will have a lower melting temperature.

Remember, the lower the melting temperature of hybrid DNA, the less closely related are the two species the DNA came from.

Page 181 — Application Questions

Q1 That horses are more closely related to humans than chickens.

Q2 Species B. The higher relative fluorescence indicates that more anti-X antibody bound to cells from species B than to cells from A or C. This suggests that proteins from species B are most similar to those from species X, so B is most closely related to X.

3. Classification Using Courtship Behaviour
Page 183 — Application Questions

Q1 Fireflies 4 and 9 belong to the same species.

Q2 6

Different species will have different patterns of light pulses.

Q3 Distantly. The patterns of light pulses produced by fireflies 1 and 3 are very different.

Q4 Yes. Fireflies 4 and 9 also start their display with three light pulses so probably belong to the same family.

Pages 184-185 — Exam-style Questions

1 a) A species is a group of similar organisms able to reproduce and give fertile offspring *(1 mark)*.

b) E.g. it will be difficult to observe the reproductive behaviour of the mice. / It will be hard to capture and study because they're rare and nocturnal *(1 mark)*.

c) *Mus (1 mark)*

d) i) phylum, class, order, family, genus, species *(1 mark for all six names correct, 1 mark for the correct order)*

ii) Organisms are classified into a system where small groups are contained within larger groups *(1 mark)* and there is no overlap between groups *(1 mark)*.

2 a) DNA from the two different species is separated into single strands and mixed together *(1 mark)*. Where the base sequences are the same on both strands, hydrogen bonds will form by specific base pairing/ the DNA bases will hybridise *(1 mark)*. The DNA is then heated to separate the strands again *(1 mark)*. The more similar the DNA, the more bonds there will be holding the two strands together *(1 mark)*, so the melting temperature/the temperature needed to separate the strands will be higher *(1 mark)*.

b) By sequencing the DNA and directly comparing the base order *(1 mark)*.

c) It is present in all plants so any two species of plant can be compared by looking at RuBisCo *(1 mark)*.

d) Any one from, e.g by comparing the amino acid sequence *(1 mark)*. The more similar the amino acid sequences the more closely related the species are *(1 mark)*. / By using immunological comparison *(1 mark)*. If two proteins are bound by the same antibody they must be similar and the two species must be closely related *(1 mark)*.

3 a) E.g. courtship behaviour is species specific *(1 mark)*. This reduces the probability of animals mating with different species and producing an infertile hybrid *(1 mark)*.

b) i) 8 *(1 mark)*

ii) Length of phrase = 4 seconds
$60 \div 4 = $ **15 phrases/minute**
(1 mark for correct calculation, 2 marks for correct answer)

iii) 4 *(1 mark)*

c) Songbirds A and C produce the same song *(1 mark)*. This suggests that they may be the same species *(1 mark)*.

d) Courtship behaviour can be used to classify organisms because it is species specific *(1 mark)*. Only members of the same species will do and respond to that courtship behaviour *(1 mark)*. The more closely related the species, the more similar their courtship behaviour *(1 mark)*.

Section 7: Evolving Antibiotic Resistance

1. Antibiotics
Page 186 — Fact Recall Questions

Q1 Antibiotics are chemicals that either kill or inhibit the growth of bacteria.

Q2 Antibiotics are used to treat bacterial diseases.

Q3 The antibiotics inhibit enzymes that are needed to make the chemical bonds in the cell wall. This prevents the cell from growing properly and weakens the cell wall. Water moves into the cell by osmosis, causing the cell contents to expand. This increases the pressure against the cell wall. The weakened cell wall can't withstand the increase in pressure and bursts (lyses).

You need to make sure you include all the steps when you're asked to describe a process. Break it down into individual steps and try to remember how many there are to aid your memory in the exam.

2. Antibiotic Resistance
Page 189 — Application Questions

Q1 a) The *vanA* gene was passed from the vancomycin-resistant *E. faecalis* to the *S. aureus* via horizontal gene transmission. The two strains came together in a process called conjugation and a copy of the *vanA* gene was passed over.

b) Subsequent generations would receive a copy of the gene via vertical gene transmission. Asexual reproduction of the *S. aureus* carrying the *vanA* gene would result in a copy of the gene being passed on to the daughter cells, and so on down the generations.

Remember, in gene transmission (and in life in general) horizontal is across and vertical is down.

Q2 a) Strain A increases in number fairly steadily until the antibiotic is added. The number of bacteria then reduces until barely any are left. Strain B increases in number fairly steadily throughout the experiment, even after the addition of the antibiotic.

b) Strain B.

c) DNA analysis of gene X shows a difference in the third base between Strain A (T) and Strain B (A). This data, along with the graph, suggests that the mutation in the third base of gene X has resulted in antibiotic resistance in Strain B.

Page 189 — Fact Recall Questions

Q1 DNA

Q2 A change in the base sequence of an organism's DNA.

Q3 A mutation in the DNA of a gene could change a protein that the antibiotic usually acts on, so the antibiotic no longer has its usual effect on the bacteria. This would result in a new characteristic in the bacteria — antibiotic resistance.

Q4 Vertical gene transmission.

Q5 a) It's the process in which two bacteria join together and a copy of a plasmid is passed from one cell to the other.

b) Horizontal gene transmission.

3. Evolution of Antibiotic Resistance

Page 191 — Application Questions

Q1 Some individuals in the population have a darker colouring that helps them to blend into their environment (wooded areas) better. This is beneficial because it helps them to avoid predators and sneak up on prey. So these individuals are more likely to survive, reproduce and pass on the allele for darker colouring. After some time most organisms in the population will carry the allele for darker colouring.

Q2 Some individuals in the population have an allele that gives them resistance to DDT. The population is exposed to DDT, killing the mosquitoes without the resistance allele. Individuals with the resistance allele survive, reproduce and pass on the allele. After some time most organisms in the population will carry the allele for DDT resistance.

See, I told you. It's the same answer whatever the adaptation — it helps them to survive, reproduce and pass on the allele for that adaptation.

Page 191 — Fact Recall Questions

Q1 An adaptation is a characteristic that increases an organism's chances of survival.

Q2 Some individuals in a population have alleles that give them resistance to an antibiotic. The population is exposed to that antibiotic, killing bacteria without the antibiotic resistance allele. The resistant bacteria survive and reproduce without competition, passing on the allele that gives antibiotic resistance to their offspring. After some time most organisms in the population will carry the antibiotic resistance allele.

4. Treating Antibiotic-Resistant Infections

Page 192 — Fact Recall Questions

Q1 a) methicillin-resistant *Staphylococcus aureus*

b) A range of illnesses from minor skin infections to life-threatening diseases such as meningitis and septicaemia.

Q2 The main problem is that some strains are resistant to nearly all antibiotics. Also, it can take a long time to determine if any antibiotics will kill the strain. During this time the patient may become very ill or even die.

Q3 TB is tuberculosis, a lung disease caused by bacteria.

Q4 The number of patients dying from TB decreased due to specific antibiotics that killed the bacterium, and a vaccine that reduced the number of people catching TB.

Q5 More recently some strains of TB have become resistant to antibiotics, so treatment has become more difficult, often involving a combination of antibiotics taken for about 6 months. Also, multidrug-resistant strains are evolving quicker than drug companies can develop new antibiotics.

5. Evaluating Antibiotic Resistance Data

Page 195 — Application Questions

Q1 a) Accept any answer between 5-8%.

b) No, the results do not agree with his conclusion. The percentage resistant to ampicillin and amoxicillin have both gone up between 2009 and 2010. For example, amoxcillin resistance has doubled from about 5-8% to about 15%. Also, the results only show the data for two consecutive years, this is not long enough to determine that resistance has stabilised, resistance could continue increasing in following years.

Don't jump to conclusions like the doctor did — look back at the data and check what it actually shows.

Q2 a) E.g. sterilised water without antibiotic. It's used to make sure that the water the antibiotic is diluted in is not the reason for any change in turbidity, and hence bacterial growth changes.

b) From 0 to 4 hours, the turbidity of the sample was increasing as the bacteria reproduced and the number in the sample increased. After the addition of the antibiotic at 4 hours, the turbidity remained the same. The antibiotic killed any bacteria present, stopping them reproducing any more and so turbidity stayed at the same level as before the addition of the antibiotic.

6. Making Decisions About Antibiotic Resistance

Page 197 — Application Questions

Q1 a) The study only looked at one hospital and 40 ties so the sample was quite small. It only looked at two strains of bacteria. The study makes no mention of how often the doctors washed their ties, and so if washing them at all or frequently decreases the chance of them carrying bacteria.

b) E.g. doctors should stop wearing ties as they can carry bacteria around the hospital.

Q2 E.g. For: compulsory screening would enable immigrants to be offered treatment for TB infections sooner rather than later. It would also mean that anyone diagnosed with antibiotic-resistant TB could be isolated and treated before being able to spread the disease further. Against: compulsory screening could mean some immigrants are refused entry on the basis of health. It could also mean immigrants found to be carrying the disease face stigma or discrimination.

With ethical issues you need to make sure you can present both sides of the argument.

Pages 198-199 — Exam-style Questions

1. a) E.g. by inhibiting cell wall synthesis leading to osmotic lysis *(1 mark)*.
   b) Some individuals in a population have genes that make them able to produce tetracycline-based antibiotics. This means they can kill other bacteria in the area, reducing competition for nutrients *(1 mark)*. So these bacteria are more likely to survive, reproduce and pass on their genes *(1 mark)*. After some time most bacteria in the population will have the genes to produce tetracycline-based antibiotics *(1 mark)*.
   c) The genes have been passed on from *Streptomyces* to other species by horizontal gene transmission *(1 mark)*. Two bacteria joined together by a process called conjugation and a copy of the resistance genes was passed from one cell to the other *(1 mark)*.
   d) i) E.g. any two from: they should all be the same breed of cattle. / The cattle should all be the same age. / The cattle should all be kept in the same type of environment. / None of the cattle should have been given any other antibiotics before the experiment started. *(2 marks for two correct answers)*
      ii) To see what percentage of the *E. coli* present in the cows' stomachs were already resistant to tetracycline *(1 mark)*.
      iii) Tetracycline resistance is present in some of the cattle who do not receive any antibiotics in their feed *(1 mark)*. The percentage of samples that were resistant to tetracycline was lowest in the cattle who did not have antibiotics in their feed, at about 38% *(1 mark)*. Catttle in group B showed the highest percentage of resistance to tetracycline, at about 57% more than the control group *(1 mark)*. This was followed by group A at 37% higher than the control group *(1 mark)* and then group C at 17% higher than the control group *(1 mark)*.

2. a) It is resistant to a number of commonly used antibiotics, making it difficult to treat *(1 mark)*.
   b) If the mutation occurred in a gene *(1 mark)*, it could have changed the protein produced *(1 mark)*, which could have enabled MRSA to become resistant to a particular antibiotic *(1 mark)*.

c) E.g. some people believe that antibiotics should only be used in life-threatening situations to reduce the increase of resistance *(1 mark)*. Others argue against this because people would take more time off work for illness, it could reduce people's standard of living, it could increase the incidence of disease and it could cause unnecessary suffering *(1 mark)*. A few people believe doctors shouldn't prescribe antibiotics to those suffering from dementia. They argue that they may forget to take them, increasing the chance of resistance developing *(1 mark)*. However, some people argue that all patients have the right to medication *(1 mark)*. Some also argue that terminally ill patients shouldn't receive antibiotics because they're going to die *(1 mark)*. But withholding antibiotics from these patients could reduce their length of survival and quality of life *(1 mark)*.

The question says discuss — this means that you need to give both sides of the argument.

d) i) Ward B. Compared to Ward A, Ward B showed a greater overall reduction in the total aerobic colony count *(1 mark)*. Fluctuations in the aerobic colony count were also smaller *(1 mark)*.
   ii) 42 − 9 = 33 CFU's/cm^2 (accept 32-34) *(1 mark)* (33 ÷ 42) × 100 = 79% (accept 78-81%) *(1 mark)*
   iii) E.g. it may encourage hospitals to increase the number of cleaning staff on their wards *(1 mark)*.
   iv) E.g. encouraging the use of antiseptic hand gels on the wards *(1 mark)*.

Section 8: Species Diversity

1. Investigating Species Diversity

Pages 201-202 — Application Questions

Q1 a) i) Pond A
$$d = \frac{18 \times (18 - 1)}{6 + 20 + 2 + 6 + 0 + 12} = \frac{306}{46} = \mathbf{6.65}$$
   ii) Pond B
$$d = \frac{54 \times (54 - 1)}{156 + 20 + 42 + 2 + 306 + 72} = \frac{2862}{598}$$
$$= \mathbf{4.79}$$

If you have to calculate species diversity in the exam, always show your full working out. You can pick up a mark for showing you understand the equation if nothing else.

b) Pond A. It has a higher diversity of insects, so it will be able to support a higher diversity of birds and amphibians.

Q2 a) i) Wood
$$d = \frac{101 \times (101 - 1)}{210 + 306 + 272 + 342 + 72 + 56 + 42 + 56 + 0}$$
$$= \frac{10\,100}{1356} = \mathbf{7.45}$$

ii) Town

$$d = \frac{41 \times (41 - 1)}{0 + 6 + 2 + 0 + 0 + 2 + 380 + 30 + 20}$$

$$= \frac{1640}{440} = \textbf{3.73}$$

b) Comparing the number of species present in a community doesn't take into account the population size of each species. Species that are in a community in very small numbers shouldn't be treated the same as those with bigger populations. For example, the graph shows nine species of tree in the town and eight in the wood. However, eight of the nine tree species in the town are present only in small numbers. The tree species in the wood are all present in higher numbers. Calculating the index of diversity for the wood gives a much higher estimate of species diversity than simply counting the number of species present.

2. Human Impacts on Biodiversity and Species Diversity

Page 204 — Fact Recall Questions

Q1 Deforestation directly reduces the number of trees and sometimes the number of different tree species. It also destroys habitats, so some species could lose their shelter and food source. This means that these species will die or be forced to migrate to another suitable area, further reducing diversity.

Q2 a) It increases the area of land available for farming.
 b) Woodland clearance and hedgerow removal reduce diversity by directly removing trees and hedgerow plants. This destroys habitats. Some species also lose their shelter and food source. This means that these species will die or be forced to migrate to another suitable area.

Q3 a) i) Chemicals that kill organisms (pests) that feed on crops.
  ii) Chemicals that kill unwanted plants (weeds).
 b) Pesticides reduce species diversity by directly killing pests. Also, any species that feed on the pests will lose a food source, so their numbers could decrease too.
 Herbicides reduce plant diversity by killing weeds and could reduce the number of organisms that feed on the weeds.

Q4 It's when farmers grow fields containing only one type of plant.

Q5 Some crops may be better at competing for certain resources than other plants. The other plants can't get the resources they need to survive and die — so species diversity is reduced.

Q6 Benefits — e.g. it produces wood and land for homes to be built. / Local areas become more developed by attracting businesses.
 Risks — any two from, e.g. diversity is reduced — species could become extinct. / Less carbon dioxide is stored because there are fewer plants and trees, which contributes to climate change. / Many medicines come from organisms found in rainforests — possible future discoveries may be lost. / Natural beauty is lost.

3. Species Diversity Data

Pages 206-207 — Application Questions

Q1 a) At Site A the index of diversity of bees was 5.25 in 1986. It fell slowly until 1989 and then rapidly between 1990 and 1992. The index of diversity then remained at around 1.8 until 2006. Between 2006 and 2010 the index rose to 2.5.
 b) Site A, because it shows the greatest fall in the index of diversity of bees (from 5.25 to 1.8), which could have been caused by the removal of the trees.
 c) Between 2004 and 2006. The diversity index of bees begins to increase in 2004, suggesting that the diversity of trees has already been increasing.

Q2 a) The plant diversity index rose from around 4.25 in 1965 to 6 in 1976. It then remained roughly constant until around 1987 when it dropped dramatically, reaching 4 by 1992. It gradually rose again, reaching 5 in 2010.
 b) i) 1987 (accept answers in the range of 1986-1988). Plant diversity fell sharply from this date on the plantations growing native trees but not on the plantations growing exotic trees.
  ii) Advantage — e.g. there was a higher species diversity on plantations growing native trees than on plantations growing exotic trees.
  Disadvantage — the native trees were vulnerable to a fungal blight but the exotic trees were not.
 c) No. The data on the graph shows the average coffee bean yield across both types of plantation. So it's not possible to conclude anything from this data about coffee bean yield in plantations that grew native trees only.
 You need to have read the question and studied the graph carefully here — if you missed the 'average yield' stuff, you won't have got the answer.

Pages 208-209 — Exam-style Questions

1 a) The number of different species and abundance of each species within a community *(1 mark)*.
 b) i) Farm A
  $$d = \frac{47 \times (47 - 1)}{6 + 30 + 72 + 42 + 110 + 110}$$
  $$= \frac{2162}{370} = \textbf{5.8}$$
  (2 marks for correct answer, otherwise 1 mark for correct working)
  Farm B
  $$d = \frac{27 \times (27 - 1)}{132 + 2 + 12 + 30 + 6 + 0}$$
  $$= \frac{702}{182} = \textbf{3.9}$$
  (2 marks for correct answer, otherwise 1 mark for correct working)
  ii) Farm A. It has a higher species diversity *(1 mark)* and using chemical herbicides tends to reduce species diversity *(1 mark)*.
 c) i) E.g. they could include a sample of hedgerows on farms that do not use biological pesticides *(1 mark)*.

ii) Any two from, e.g. they could make sure variables (such as the crops grown/the length of the hedgerow sampled) are kept the same on all farms. / They could sample several of the hedgerows on each farm and take an average of the number of each insect species recorded in order to calculate the indices of diversity. / They could sample a large number of farms *(2 marks for two correct answers)*.

When it comes to suggesting ways to make results reliable, you always need to think about the same things. The main ones are controlling the variables (or using controls/control groups), having a big enough sample size and carrying out repeats.

d) i) E.g it increases the area of farmland by turning lots of small fields into fewer large fields, which can increase crop production *(1 mark)*.

ii) Hedgerow removal could reduce insect species diversity *(1 mark)*. It destroys habitats, so insect species could lose their shelter and food sources *(1 mark)*. This could kill insects or force them migrate to other areas *(1 mark)*.

e) Benefits — e.g. more food could be produced *(1 mark)*. Food would be cheaper to produce, so food prices would be lowered *(1 mark)*. Local areas might become more developed through attracting business *(1 mark)*.

Risks — e.g. species diversity would be reduced *(1 mark)*. The natural beauty of the woodland would be lost *(1 mark)*. Less carbon dioxide would be stored because there would be fewer plants and trees, which would contribute to climate change *(1 mark)*.

2 a) 12.2 + 4.6 + 6.1 + 8.2 = 31.1
31.1 ÷ 4 = **7.8** *(1 mark)*

b) Calculating the index of diversity because it takes both the number of species present and the abundance of each species into account *(1 mark)*. This makes it a closer to the true value of species diversity than simply counting the number of species present *(1 mark)*.

c) No. The study included data on tree diversity from only two cities *(1 mark)* so the sample size is too small to draw conclusions for the whole of the UK *(1 mark)*.

3 a) Between 0 and 600 m in altitude, the area of land under cultivation was high, but fell to 0 between 600 m and 900 m *(1 mark)*. Flower diversity fluctuated but increased gradually with altitude up to 800 m, before falling to its lowest point at 1200 m *(1 mark)*.

b) Altitude. Up to an altitude of 800 m there's a roughly positive correlation between altitude and flower diversity *(1 mark)* and after 800 m, there's a negative correlation *(1 mark)*. There's no evidence of any sort of correlation between flower diversity and the area of land under cultivation *(1 mark)*. For example, flower diversity increases between 0 and 500 m while the area of land under cultivation remains roughly constant *(1 mark)*.

Glossary

A

Accurate result
A result that is really close to the true answer.

Activation energy
The energy that needs to be supplied before a chemical reaction will start.

Active site
The part of an enzyme where a substrate molecule binds.

Active transport
Movement of molecules and ions across plasma membranes, against a concentration gradient. Requires energy.

Adaptation
A characteristic that increases an organism's chances of survival, e.g. antibiotic-resistance.

Affinity for oxygen
The tendency a molecule has to bind with oxygen.

Allele
An alternative form of a gene.

Alveolus
A microscopic air sac in the lungs where gas exchange occurs.

Amino acid
A monomer of proteins.

Aneurysm
A balloon-like swelling of an artery.

Anomalous data
Measurements that fall outside the range of values you'd expect or any pattern you already have.

Antibiotic
A chemical used to treat bacterial diseases.

Antibiotic resistance
When bacteria are able to survive in the presence of antibiotics.

Antibody
A protein produced by B-cells in response to the presence of a pathogen.

Antigen
A molecule found on the surface of a cell. A foreign antigen triggers an immune response.

Antigenic variation
Where pathogens change their antigens.

Apoplast pathway
A route that water takes through a plant root to the xylem, through cell walls.

Arteriole
A blood vessel that branches off an artery.

Asthma
A respiratory condition where the airways become inflamed and irritated, usually because of an allergic reaction to substances such as pollen and dust.

Atheroma
A fibrous plaque caused by the build up and hardening of white blood cells, lipids and connective tissue.

Atrioventricular node (AVN)
A group of cells in the heart wall that are responsible for passing waves of electrical activity from the SAN on to the bundle of His.

Atrioventricular valve (AV)
A valve in the heart linking the atria to the ventricles.

B

B-cell
A type of white blood cell involved in the immune response. It produces antibodies.

Base
A nitrogen-containing molecule that forms part of a DNA nucleotide.

Benedict's test
A biochemical test for the presence of sugars.

Biodiversity
The variety of living organisms and ecosystems on Earth.

Biuret test
A biochemical test for the presence of polypeptides and proteins.

Bohr effect
An effect by which an increase of carbon dioxide in the blood results in a reduction of haemoglobin's affinity for oxygen.

Bundle of His
A group of muscle fibres in the heart, responsible for conducting waves of electrical activity from the AVN to the Purkyne fibres.

C

Cancer
A tumour that invades surrounding tissue.

Capillary bed
A network of capillaries.

Carbohydrase
An enzyme that catalyses the hydrolysis of carbohydrates.

Cardiac cycle
An ongoing sequence of contraction and relaxation of the atria and ventricles that keeps blood continuously circulating round the body.

Cardiac output
The volume of blood pumped by the heart per minute (measured in cm^3 per minute).

Cardiovascular disease
Any disease associated with the heart and blood vessels.

Casparian strip
A waxy strip in the cell wall of an endodermis cell.

Catalyst
A chemical that speeds up a chemical reaction without being used up itself.

Causal relationship
Where a change in one variable causes a change in the other.

Cell cycle
The process that all body cells from multicellular organisms use to grow and divide.

Cell fractionation
A method that separates the organelles in a cell.

Cell-surface membrane
See plasma membrane.

Cell wall
The outermost cell layer found in plant cells.

Cellular immune response
The immune response that involves T-cells.

Cellulose
A polysaccharide made of long, unbranched chains of β-glucose.

Centromere
The point at which two strands of a chromosome are joined together.

Chlorophyll
A green substance found in chloroplasts.

Chloroplast
An organelle present in plant cells where photosynthesis occurs.

Chromatid
One 'arm' of a double stranded chromosome.

Chromosome
A thread like structure made up of one long DNA molecule.

Classification
The act of arranging organisms into groups based on their similarities and differences.

Common ancestor
An organism from which all other organisms in a particular taxonomic group have evolved.

Competitive inhibitor
A molecule that has a similar shape to a substrate and blocks an enzyme's active site.

Condensation reaction
A reaction that releases a small molecule (e.g. water) when it links molecules together.

Confounding variable
See control variable.

Conjugation
When two bacteria come together and exchange genetic material.

Control experiment
An extra experiment set up to eliminate the effect of some variables that can't be controlled.

Control group
A group in a study that is treated in exactly the same way as the experimental group, apart from the factor you're investigating.

Control variable
A variable you keep constant throughout an experiment.

Coronary artery
An artery supplying the heart muscle with blood.

Coronary heart disease
When the coronary arteries have lots of atheromas in them, which restricts blood flow to the heart.

Correlation
A relationship between two variables.

Cortex (plants)
The outer layer of cells in a plant root.

Counter-current system
The system in which blood flows in one direction and water flows in the opposite direction across the gills of a fish.

Courtship behaviour
Behaviour carried out by organisms to attract a mate of the right species.

Crossing over
When chromatids twist around each other and bits of them swap over during meiosis.

Cytoplasm
A gel-like substance where most of the chemical reactions in a cell happen.

D

Denatured
The point at which an enzyme no longer functions as a catalyst

Deoxyribose
The pentose sugar in DNA.

Dependent variable
The variable you measure in an experiment.

Dicotyledonous plant
A type of flowering plant, e.g. non-woody plants, bushes and trees.

Differentiation
The process of a cell becoming specialised.

Diffusion (simple)
Net movement of particles from an area of higher concentration to an area of lower concentration.

Digestion
The process of breaking down food into substances that can be used by the body.

Dipeptide
A molecule formed from two amino acids.

Diploid
When a cell contains two copies of each chromosome.

Disaccharide
A molecule formed from two monosaccharides.

DNA (deoxyribonucleic acid)
The molecule in cells that stores genetic information.

DNA helicase
An enzyme that breaks the hydrogen bonds between two polynucleotide DNA strands during DNA replication.

DNA hybridisation
A technique that combines single-stranded DNA sequences from two species to determine how similar they are.

DNA polymerase
An enzyme that joins together the nucleotides on a new strand of DNA during DNA replication.

DNA sequencing
The process of determining the base order of a section of DNA.

Double-blind trial
A study involving a control group and an experimental group where neither the scientists involved nor the participants know which group the participants are in.

Double helix
The structure of a DNA molecule — two separate strands wound together in a spiral.

E

Emphysema
A lung disease caused by smoking or long-term exposure to air pollution, where foreign particles in the smoke or air become trapped in the alveoli.

Endodermis
A single layer of cells between the cortex and the xylem.

Endoplasmic reticulum
A system of membranes enclosing a fluid-filled space. Involved with lipid and protein processing.

Endothelium
The inner lining of a blood vessel.

Enzyme
A protein that speeds up the rate of chemical reactions.

Enzyme-substrate complex
The intermediate formed when a substrate molecule binds to the active site of an enzyme.

Epidermis (plants)
The outer most layer of cells on a leaf.

Eukaryote
Organism made up of a cell (or cells) containing a nucleus, e.g. animals and plants.

Exchange organ
An organ (e.g. the lungs) specialised to exchange substances.

Exon
A section of DNA within a gene that codes for amino acids.

F

Facilitated diffusion
The diffusion of particles through carrier proteins or channel proteins in the plasma membrane.

Fair test
A test in which only the independent variable has been allowed to affect the dependent variable.

Fertilisation
When a haploid sperm fuses with a haploid egg to generate a diploid zygote.

Fibrosis
The formation of scar tissue in the lungs, which can be the result of an infection or exposure to substances like asbestos or dust.

Fluid mosaic model
Model describing the arrangement of molecules in a cell membrane.

Founder effect
The reduction in genetic diversity that occurs when just a few organisms from a population start a new colony.

G

Gamete
A sex cell — e.g. the sperm cell in males or the egg cell in females.

Gas exchange
The process of taking in gases that are needed for life processes and getting rid of waste gases.

Gas exchange surface
A boundary between the outside environment and the internal environment of an organism, over which gas exchange occurs.

Gene
A section of DNA which codes for a protein.

Gene flow
Different alleles being moved between populations when individuals migrate from one population into another.

Gene pool
The complete range of alleles in a population.

Genetic bottleneck
An event that causes a big reduction in a population and reduces genetic diversity.

Genetic diversity
Differences in DNA.

Genotype
The alleles an organism has.

Gill
The respiratory organ of a fish.

Gill filament
A thin plate in a fish's gill.

Glycogen
A polysaccharide made from a long, very branched chain of α-glucose.

Glycosidic bond
A bond formed between monosaccharides.

Golgi apparatus
A group of fluid-filled flattened sacs. Involved with processing and packaging lipids and proteins, and making lysosomes.

Granum
A structure in chloroplasts formed from the stacking of thylakoid membranes

Guard cell
A cell that controls the opening and closing of stomata.

H

Haemoglobin
An oxygen-carrying protein found in red blood cells.

Haploid
When a cell contains one copy of each chromosome.

Heart rate
The number of heartbeats per minute.

Herd immunity
Where unvaccinated people are protected because the occurrence of the disease is reduced by the number of people who are vaccinated.

Histone
Protein that DNA is wound around in order to fit into the nucleus.

Homologous pair
A pair of matching chromosomes — each chromosome contains the same genes but could have different alleles.

Horizontal gene transmission
When genes are passed on horizontally to other members of the same or different species, without reproduction occurring.

Humoral immune response
The immune response that involves B-cells and the production of antibodies.

Hydrolysis
A chemical reaction that uses a water molecule when it breaks bonds between molecules.

Hydrophilic
Attracts water.

Hydrophobic
Repels water.

Hypothesis
A specific testable statement, based on a theory, about what will happen in a test situation.

I

Immunity
The ability to respond quickly to an infection.

Immunological comparison
Using antibodies to determine how similar proteins are.

Incidence of disease
How many people suffer from a disease.

Independent segregation
The random division of maternal and paternal chromosomes into gametes during meiosis.

Independent variable
The variable you change in an experiment.

Index of diversity
A measure of species diversity that takes into account the number of species present and the number of individuals of each species.

Infectious disease
A disease caused by infection with a pathogen, e.g. a virus.

Intraspecific variation
Variation between members of the same species.

Interphase
A period of the cell cycle in which the cell grows and DNA is replicated.

Interspecific variation
Variation between different species.

Intron
A section of DNA within a gene that does not code for amino acids.

Iodine test
A biochemical test for the presence of starch.

Isotonic solution
A solution with the same water potential as another solution or cell.

Lactose-intolerance
The inability to digest lactose due to an insufficient amount of the enzyme lactase.

Lamella (in chloroplasts)
A thin, flat piece of thylakoid membrane found in chloroplasts.

Lamella (in fish)
A tiny structure found on the gill filament in a fish.

Lipase
An enzyme that catalyses the hydrolysis of lipids.

Loading of oxygen (onto haemoglobin)
The action of an oxygen molecule binding with a haemoglobin molecule.

Locus
The position on a chromosome where a particular allele is found.

Lymphatic system
A network of tubes which transports excess tissue fluid back into the circulatory system.

Lysosome
A round organelle that contains digestive enzymes.

M

Magnification
How much bigger an image from a microscope is compared to the specimen.

Mass transport system
A system (e.g. the circulatory system) that carries substances to and from individual cells.

Mean
The average of the values collected in a sample.

Meiosis
A type of cell division where a parent cell divides to create four genetically different haploid cells.

Memory cell
A white blood cell that remains in the body and remembers how to respond to infections.

Mesophyll cell
A type of plant cell present in a leaf and the main gas exchange surface in a plant.

Metabolic rate
The rate at which energy is used by an organism.

Microfibril
A strong fibre formed by chains of cellulose linked together by hydrogen bonds.

Microvillus
A fold in the plasma membrane that increases the surface area.

Mitochondrion
An oval-shaped organelle with a double membrane. The site of anaerobic respiration.

Mitosis
A type of cell division where a parent cell divides to produce two genetically identical daughter cells.

Monoclonal antibody
An antibody produced from a single group of genetically identical B-cells.

Monomer
A small, basic molecular unit, e.g. amino acids and monosaccharides.

Monosaccharide
A monomer of carbohydrates.

MRSA (methicillin-resistant *Staphylococcus aureus*)
Staphylococcus aureus bacteria that are resistant to the antibiotic methicillin.

Multicellular organism
An organism that has more than one cell, e.g. a human.

Multiple repeat
A section of repetitive DNA found outside of genes — does not code for amino acids.

Mutation
A change in the base sequence of an organism's DNA.

Myocardial infarction
A heart attack.

N

Natural selection
The process whereby a characteristic (adaptation) becomes common in a population because it makes an organism more likely to survive, reproduce and pass on the gene for that characteristic to its offspring.

Non-competitive inhibitor
A molecule that binds away from an enzyme's active site and alters the shape of the active site, so the substrate can no longer bind.

Non-infectious disease
A disease caused by the body malfunctioning (e.g. cancer, genetic disorders) or by lifestyle or the environment.

Non-reducing sugars
A class of monosaccharides and disaccharides.

Normal distribution
A bell-shaped curve symmetrical about the mean.

Nucleotide
The monomer that makes up polynucleotides — consists of a pentose sugar, a phosphate group and a nitrogenous base.

O

Oral Rehydration Solution (ORS)
A drink that contains large amounts of salts and sugars dissolved in water. It's used to replace fluids in people suffering from a diarrhoeal disease.

Organ
A group of different tissues that work together to perform a particular function.

Organ system
A group of organs that work together to carry out a particular function.

Organelle
A part of a cell, e.g. the nucleus.

Osmosis
Diffusion of water molecules across a partially permeable membrane, from an area of higher water potential to an area of lower water potential.

Osmotic lysis
When so much water moves into a cell by osmosis that the cell bursts. (Some antibiotics kill bacteria by causing osmotic lysis.)

Oxygen dissociation curve
A curve on a graph that shows how saturated with oxygen haemoglobin is at any given partial pressure.

Oxyhaemoglobin
The molecule formed when oxygen binds to haemoglobin.

P

pCO$_2$
Partial pressure of carbon dioxide — a measure of carbon dioxide concentration.

pO$_2$
Partial pressure of oxygen — a measure of oxygen concentration.

Palisade cell
A plant cell found just below the epidermis (the outer layer of cells) in leaves.

Partially permeable membrane
A membrane that lets some molecules through it, but not others.

Pathogen
An organism that causes disease.

Peptide bond
A bond formed between amino acids.

Phagocyte
A type of white blood cell that carries out phagocytosis, e.g. a macrophage.

Phagocytosis
The engulfment of pathogens.

Phenotype
The characteristics displayed by an organism.

Phospholipid
A lipid containing one molecule of glycerol attached to two fatty acids and a phosphate group. Main component of the plasma membrane.

Phylogenetics
The study of the evolutionary history of groups of organisms.

Placebo
A dummy pill or injection that looks exactly like the real drug, but doesn't contain the drug.

Plasma cell
A type of B-cell that produces antibodies.

Plasma membrane
The membrane found on the surface of animal cells (and just inside the cell wall of plant and prokarykotic cells). Regulates the movement of substances into and out of the cell.

Plasmodesmata
Small channels in plant cell walls that connect neighbouring plant cells.

Polymer
A large, complex molecule composed of long chains of monomers, e.g. proteins and carbohydrates.

Polynucleotide
A long strand of nucleotides — two polynucleotide strands coil together to make the DNA double helix.

Polypeptide
A molecule formed from more than two amino acids.

Polysaccharide
A molecule formed from more than two monosaccharides.

Population sample
A small group of organisms used as a model for the whole population.

Potometer
A special piece of apparatus used to estimate transpiration rates.

Precise result
A result taken using sensitive instruments that measure in small increments.

Prediction
See hypothesis.

Primary immune response
The immune response triggered when a foreign antigen enters the body for the first time.

Prokaryote
Single-celled organism without a nucleus or membrane-bound organelles, e.g. bacteria.

Protease
An enzyme that catalyses the hydrolysis of proteins.

Pulmonary tuberculosis (TB)
A lung disease caused by the bacterium *Mycobacterium tuberculosis*.

Pulmonary ventilation
The volume of air taken into the lungs in one minute.

Purkyne fibres
Fine muscle fibres in the heart that carry waves of electrical activity into the muscular walls of the right and left ventricles.

Q

Qualitative test
A qualitative test tells you what's present, e.g. an acid or an alkali.

Quantitative test
A quantitative test tells you how much of something is present, e.g. an acid that's pH 2.46.

R

Reducing sugars
A class of monosaccharides and disaccharides.

Reliable evidence
Evidence that can be consistently reproduced in independent experiments.

Resolution
How well a microscope distinguishes between two points close together.

Ribosome
A small organelle that makes proteins.

Risk factor
Anything that increases the chance of getting a disease.

Root hair/root hair cell
A cell found on the surface of a plant root that has a thin, hair-like extension.

Root pressure
The pressure that pushes water from the roots up through the xylem of a plant.

S

Sample size
The number of samples in the investigation, e.g. the number of people in a drug trial.

Saturated fatty acid
A fatty acid with no double bonds between its carbon atoms.

Secondary immune response
The immune response triggered when a foreign antigen enters the body for the second time.

Selective breeding
When humans select which domesticated animals or strains of plants reproduce for useful characteristics, e.g. high yields.

Semi-conservative replication of DNA
Replication of DNA in which half of the new molecules of DNA are from the original piece of DNA.

Semi-lunar (SL) valve
A valve in the heart linking the ventricles to the aorta and pulmonary artery.

Single-celled organism
An organism that only has one cell.

Sino-atrial node (SAN)
A group of cells in the wall of the right atrium that set the rhythm of the heartbeat by sending out regular waves of electrical activity to the atrial walls.

Sister chromatids
Two identical copies of a chromosome joined together in the middle.

Specialised cell
A cell adapted to carry out specific functions.

Species
A group of similar organisms able to reproduce to give fertile offspring.

Species diversity
The number of different species and the abundance of each species within a community.

Specific base pairing
Hydrogen bonds between specific pairs of bases on opposing polynucleotide strands.

Spiracle
A pore on the surface of an insect.

Standard deviation
A measure of the spread of values about the mean.

Starch
A carbohydrate molecule made up of two polysaccharides — amylose and amylopectin.

Stoma
A pore in the epidermis of a plant leaf.

Stroke volume
The volume of blood pumped during each heartbeat (measured in cm³).

Stroma
A thick fluid found in chloroplasts.

Substrate
A substance that interacts with an enzyme.

Sugar-phosphate backbone
Alternating sugar and phosphate groups joined together in a polynucleotide chain.

Supercoiling
The way that DNA is condensed to fit in the cell in prokaryotes.

Surface area : volume ratio
An organism or structure's surface area in relation to its volume.

Symplast pathway
A route that water takes through a plant root to the xylem, through the cytoplasm of cells.

T-cell
A type of white blood cell involved in the immune response. Some types activate B-cells and some kill pathogens directly.

Taxonomy
The science of classification.

Theory
A possible explanation for something.

Thrombosis
The formation of a blood clot.

Thylakoid membrane
A membrane found inside chloroplasts, stacked up to form grana.

Tidal volume
The volume of air in each breath.

Tissue
A group of similar cells.

Tissue fluid
The fluid that surrounds cells in tissues.

Toxin
A harmful molecule released by some pathogens.

Trachea (insects)
A pipe that carries air between the external environment and the inside of an insect's body.

Tracheole
A small pipe that branches off the trachea in an insect and is used for gas exchange.

Transpiration
The evaporation of water from a plant's surface.

Triglyceride
A lipid containing one molecule of glycerol attached to three fatty acids.

Triplet
A series of three bases which codes for one amino acid in a protein.

Ultracentrifugation
A method where cell components are separated out using a centrifuge.

Unloading of oxygen (from haemoglobin)
The action of an oxygen molecule being released from a haemoglobin molecule.

Unsaturated fatty acid
A fatty acid with at least one double bond between its carbon atoms.

Vaccination
The administering of a vaccine containing antigens to give immunity.

Vacuole
An organelle that contains cell sap (a weak solution of sugar and salts).

Valid conclusion
A conclusion that answers the original question and uses reliable data.

Variable
A quantity that has the potential to change, e.g. weight, temperature, concentration.

Variation
The differences that exist between individuals.

Ventilation
Breathing in and breathing out.

Ventilation rate
The number of breaths per minute.

Vertical gene transmission
When genes are passed on during reproduction to subsequent generations.

Water potential
The likelihood of water molecules to diffuse into or out of solution.

Xerophyte
A plant specially adapted for life in a warm, dry or windy habitat.

Xylem
A system of vessels that transports water and minerals from the roots to the rest of the plant.

Z

Zygote
The diploid cell formed when two gametes fuse during fertilisation.

Acknowledgements

AQA Specification reference points are reproduced by permission of Assessment and Qualifications Alliance.

Data acknowledgements

Data used to construct the graph of BMI and cancer on page 8 reproduced from the British Medical Journal, Gillian K Reeves, Kristin Pirie, Valerie Beral et al. 335: 1134. Copyright © 2007, with permission from BMJ Publishing Group Ltd.

Graph of average alcohol consumption and the relative risk of CHD on page 9 reprinted from Preventative Medicine, Vol number 38, Issue 5, G. Corrao, V. Bagnardi, A. Zambon, C. LaVecchia. A meta-analysis of alcohol consumption and the risk of 15 diseases, 613-619, Copyright 2004, with permission from Elsevier.

Graph of whooping cough and vaccine uptake on page 17 from Health in Scotland 2000, CMO Annual Report, September 2001. This information is licensed under the terms of the Open Government Licence http://www.nationalarchives.gov.uk/doc/open-government-licence (www.department.gov.uk/document, accessed November 2011).

MMR graph on page 21 adapted from H. Honda, Y. Shimizu, M. Rutter, No effect of MMR withdrawal on the incidence of autism: a total population study. Journal of Child Psychology and Psychiatry 2005; 46(6):572-579.

Data used to construct Herceptin graph on page 22 from M.J. Piccart-Gebhart, et al., Trastuzumab after Adjuvant Chemotherapy in HER2_positive Breast Cancer: NEJM 2005; 353: 1659-72.

Data used to construct Influenza A vaccine graph on page 22 from Xiao-Feng Liang et al., Safety of Influenza A (H1N1) Vaccine in Postmarketing Surveillance in China: N Engl J Med 2011; 364:638-647.

Data used to construct tetanus graph on page 24 from http://www.who.int/immunization_monitoring/diseases/tetanus/en/index.html accessed November 2011.

Data used to construct graph of bronchial cross-sectional areas on page 83, Beigelman-Aubry et al., Radiology, 2002, 223, 181-187, © 2011 by Radiological Society of North America.

With thanks to Cancer Research UK for permission to reproduce the graphs on pages 84-85.
Cancer Research UK, http://info.cancerresearchuk.org/cancerstats/types/lung/mortality/, January 2008.
Cancer Research UK, http://info.cancerresearchuk.org/cancerstats/types/lung/smoking/, January 2008.

Data used to construct asthma and sulfur dioxide graphs on page 86. Source: National Statistics website: www.statistics.gov.uk. Crown copyright material is reproduced with the permission of the Controller Office of Public Sector Information (OPSI).

Graph of tobacco consumption and death rates for COPD on page 87 © Australian Institute of Health and Welfare 2011, Source: AIHW: de Looper M & Bhatia K 2001: Australian Health Trends 2001. AIHW Cat. No. PHE 24. Canberra: AIHW; the National Mortality Database.

With thanks to the HPA for permission to use the graph on page 89, adapted from Tuberculosis in the UK: Annual report on tuberculosis surveillance in the UK, 2010. London: Health Protection Agency Centre for Infections, October 2010.

Data used to construct the graph on page 100 from R. Doll, R. Peto, J. Boreham, I. Sutherland, Mortality in relation to smoking: 50 years observations on male British doctors. BMJ 2004; 328: 1519

Data used to construct projected annual number of new CHD cases against interventions graph on page 101 from K. Bibbins-Domingo et al., Reductions in Cardiovascular Disease Projected from Modest Reductions in Dietary Salt: N Engl J Med. 2010 February 18; 362(7): 590–599.

Graph of breast cancer and family history on page 114 reprinted from the Lancet, Vol number 358, Collaborative Group on Hormonal Factors in Breast Cancer, Familial breast cancer: collaborative reanalysis of individual data from 52 epidemiological studies including 58209 women with breast cancer and 101986 women without the disease, 1389 -1399, Copyright 2001, with permission from Elsevier.

Graph of breast cancer and alcohol consumption on page 114 © Cancer Research UK, http://info.cancerresearchuk.org/cancerstats/types/breast/riskfactors/?a=5441#alcohol, January 2008.

Graph of haemoglobin dissociation curves on page 141 reprinted from Comparative Biochemistry and Physiology Part A Physiology, Vol number 113, Issue 4, F León-Velarde, C De Muizon, J A Palacios, D Clark, C Monge, Hemoglobin affinity and structure in high-altitude and sea-level carnivores from Peru, 407-411, Copyright 1996, with permission from Elsevier.

Graph of activity of protein X on mitosis on page 156 reprinted from Cell, 58 (2), Moreno S, Hayles J, Nurse P, 361-72, Copyright 1989, with permission from Elsevier.

Data used to construct the graphs on page 194 from National Statistics online. Reproduced under the terms of the Click-Use licence.

Data used to construct graph on *E. coli* and tetracycline resistance on page 198 from P. Mirzaagha et al., Distribution and characterization of ampicillin- and tetracycline-resistant Escherichia coli from feedlot cattle fed subtherapeutic antimicrobials: BMC Microbiol. 2011; 11: 78.

Data used to construct graph of bacterial colonies on hospital wards on page 199 from Dancer et al., Measuring the effect of enhanced cleaning in a UK hospital: a prospective cross-over study: BMC Med. 2009; 7: 28

Graph of rainforest diversity on page 205 from Schulze et al., Biodiversity Indicator Groups of Tropical Land-Use Systems: Comparing Plants, Birds and Insects. Ecological Applications 2004: 14(5) Ecological Society of America.

Photograph acknowledgements

Cover photo **Laguna Design**/Science Photo Library, p 1 **Dr Jeremy Burgess**/Science Photo Library, p 3 **Monty Rakusen**/Science Photo Library, p 4 **Cordelia Molloy**/Science Photo Library, p 10 **Steve Gschmeissner**/Science Photo Library, p 11 **Thomas Deerinck, NCMIR**/Science Photo Library, p 12 Science Photo Library, p 14 **Phantatomix**/Science Photo Library, p 18 **CNRI**/Science Photo Library, p 19 **Life In View**/Science Photo Library, p 27 (middle) **David Musher**/Science Photo Library, p 27 (bottom) **Eye Of Science**/Science Photo Library, p 32 (top) **animate4.com**/Science Photo Library, p 32 (middle) **Laguna Design**/Science Photo Library, p 32 (bottom) **Andrew Lambert Photography**/Science Photo Library, p 36-37 all **Andrew Lambert Photography**/Science Photo Library, p 39 **Clive Freeman, The Royal Institution**/Science Photo Library, p 49 (top) **Steve Gschmeissner**/Science Photo Library, p 49 (middle) **Biophoto Associates**/Science Photo Library, p 50 (top) Science Photo Library, p 50 (middle) **Don W. Fawcett**/Science Photo Library, p 53 (top) **Steve Gschmeissner**/Science Photo Library, p 53 (middle) **NIAID/CDC**/Science Photo Library, p 53 (bottom) **CNRI**/Science Photo Library, p 54 (Fig. 2 top) **Herve Conge, ISM**/Science Photo Library, p 54 (Fig. 2 bottom) **Dr. Fred Hossler/Visuals Unlimited, Inc.** /Science Photo Library, p 54 (Fig. 4 top) Science Photo Library, p 54 (Fig. 4 bottom) **Pasieka**/Science Photo Library, p 55 **TEK Image**/Science Photo Library, p 57 **Russell Kightley**/Science Photo Library, p 60 **Andrew Lambert Photography**/Science Photo Library, p 64 **Andrew Lambert Photography**/Science Photo Library, image on p 65 © The Science Picture Company, p 71 (top) **Eye Of Science**/Science Photo Library, p 71 (bottom) **Mauro Fermariello**/Science Photo Library, p 75 **Innerspace Imaging**/Science Photo Library, p 76 **Science VU, Visuals Unlimited**/Science Photo Library, p 78 (top) **Dr Keith Wheeler**/Science Photo Library, p 78 (bottom) **Manfred Kage**/Science Photo Library, p 79 **John Thys/Reporters**/Science Photo Library, p 81 (middle) **Du Cane Medical Imaging Ltd**/Science Photo Library, p 81 (bottom) **Dr. John Brackenbury**/Science Photo Library, p 82 (top) **PHT**/Science Photo Library, p 82 (middle) **CNRI**/Science Photo Library, p 82 (bottom) **Biodisc, Visuals Unlimited**/Science Photo Library, p 83 **Biophoto Associates**/Science Photo Library, p 88 (left) **Eye Of Science**/Science Photo Library, p 88 (right) **Dr. Fred Hossler, Visuals Unlimited**/Science Photo Library, image on p 91 © The Science Picture Company, p 96 **BSIP VEM**/Science Photo Library, p 97 (top) Science Photo Library, p 97 (middle) **Professor P.M. Motta, G. Macchiarelli, S.A Nottola**/Science Photo Library, p 97 (bottom) NCE Photo Library, p 105 **Linn Currie**/Shutterstock, p 106 (top) **Zero Creatives**/Science Photo Library, p 106 (bottom) **National Cancer Institute**/Science Photo Library, p 116 (top) Science Photo Library, p 116 (middle) **A. Barrington Brown**/Science Photo Library, p 120 (bottom) **CNRI**/Science Photo Library, p 122 **Eye Of Science**/Science Photo Library, p 123 (middle) **Power And Syred**/Science Photo Library, p 123 (bottom) **Pr. G Gimenez-Martin**/Science Photo Library, p 124 **Adrian T Sumner**/Science Photo Library, p 127 **John Beatty**/Science Photo Library, p 128 **Michael P. Gadomski**/Science Photo Library, p 136 (middle) **Claude Nuridsany & Marie Perennou**/Science Photo Library, p 136 (bottom) **Biology Pics**/Science Photo Library, p 137 **Professors P. Motta & T. Naguro**/Science Photo Library, p 138 **Biophoto Associates**/Science Photo Library, p 144 **Andrew Brookes, National Physical Laboratory**/Science Photo Library, p 145 **Eye Of Science**/Science Photo Library, p 146 **Pr. G Gimenez-Martin**/Science Photo Library, p 147 all **Pr. G Gimenez-Martin**/Science Photo Library, p 148 **Steve Gschmeissner**/Science Photo Library, p 149 **Medical Photo NHS Lothian**/Science Photo Library, p 151 (middle) **Dr. Gladden Willis/Visuals Unlimited, Inc.** /Science Photo Library, p 151 (bottom) **Dr Keith Wheeler**/Science Photo Library, p 152 (middle) **Dr Keith Wheeler**/Science Photo Library, p 152 (bottom) **Steve Gschmeissner**/Science Photo Library, p 153 (top) **Eye Of Science**/Science Photo Library, p 157 (bottom) **William Weber**/Science Photo Library, p 158 **AMI Images**/Science Photo Library, p 160 (middle) **John Serrao**/Science Photo Library, p 161 **Power And Syred**/Science Photo Library, p 163 (top) **Microfield Scientific Ltd**/Science Photo Library, p 163 (bottom) **Power And Syred**/Science Photo Library, p 164 (left) **Eye Of Science**/Science Photo Library, p 164 (right) **Power And Syred**/Science Photo Library, p 167 **Biophoto Associates**/Science Photo Library, p 169 **Microfield Scientific Ltd**/Science Photo Library, p 173 (left) **Art Wolfe**/Science Photo Library, p 173 (right) **Jeff Lepore**/Science Photo Library, p 179 **Patrick Dumas/Eurelios**/Science Photo Library, p 182 (top) **XuRa**/Shutterstock, p 182 (middle) **B. G Thomson**/Science Photo Library, p 186 **CNRI**/Science Photo Library, p 189 **Dr L. Caro**/Science Photo Library, p 191 **John Serrao**/Science Photo Library, p 192 **Scott Camazine**/Science Photo Library, p 193 **Sotiris Zafeiris**/Science Photo Library, p 196 **Gabrielle Voinot/Look At Sciences**/Science Photo Library, p 203 both **Planet Observer**/Science Photo Library, p 205 **Patrick Landmann**/Science Photo Library, p 206 **Kaj R. Svensson**/Science Photo Library.

Index

A

α-glucose 34, 37
absorption of glucose 68
accuracy 3
activation energy 38
active site 38-40
active transport 66
adaptations 190
   for heat exchange 159, 160
   in xerophytes 163
adenine 116
affinity for oxygen 132
agriculture 203, 204
alleles 105, 120, 121, 126, 127
alveoli 76, 77
amino acids 30
   sequence comparison 181
amylase 28, 37
amylopectin 37, 139
amylose 37, 139
analysing data 213
anaphase 147
aneurysm 97
animal cells 48, 136
anomalous data 5
answering data questions 211
antibiotic resistance 187, 188,
   190, 192-196
antibiotics 186, 187, 192-197
antibodies 12-15, 19-23,
   32, 181
anti-cancer drugs 20
antigenic variation 18
antigens 12
apoplast pathway 170
arteries 165, 166
arterioles 166
asthma 82
atheromas 96, 97, 99
ATP 50, 66
atria 90, 91, 93, 94
atrioventricular (AV) valves
   90, 93
atrioventricular node (AVN) 91

B

β-glucose 138
bacteria 10, 71, 186, 190, 192,
   193
base triplets 118
bases (DNA) 115, 116, 118
B-cells 12
Benedict's test 36
bias 4
biodiversity 203
   human impact on 203, 204
biuret test 32
blood cholesterol 99
blood clots 97
blood pressure 99
blood vessels 165, 166
Bohr effect 134
breathing 75, 76
bundle of His 91

C

cancer 49
cancer treatments 20, 149
capillaries 167
carbohydrases 28
carbohydrates 26, 34
   variation in 138, 139
cardiac cycle 93, 94
cardiac output 92
cardiovascular disease 96
carrier proteins 65, 66
Casparian strip 170
causal relationships 5
cell cycle 146, 147, 149
cell fractionation 55
cell function 50, 51
cell structure 48-52
cell-surface membrane 48
cell walls 136, 138
cellular immune responses 14
cellulose 138
centrifuges 55
centromere 147
chemical digestion 26
chemotherapy 149
chloroplasts 136
cholera 70, 71

chromatids 123, 124, 147
chromosomes 117, 120,
   123, 147
chyme 27
cilia 10
circulatory system 90, 165-167
class (taxonomic group) 175
classification 175
   problems with 176
cohesion and tension 170
collecting data 4, 213
command words 210
competitive inhibitors 43
concentration gradients 62, 65,
   66, 162, 163
conclusions 5, 212
condensation reactions 30,
   34, 60, 138
confounding variables 3
conjugation 188, 189
control experiments 3, 4
control groups 3, 4
control variables 3
controls 4, 213
coronary arteries 97, 165
coronary heart disease (CHD)
   99-101
correlations 5
cortex 169
co-transporters 66
counter-current system 162
courtship behaviour 182
crossing over of chromatids 124
cytoplasm 48
cytosine 116

D

data interpretation 8
decision making 6, 196, 206
deforestation 203, 204
denatured enzymes 41
deoxyribose sugar 115
dependent variables 3
dicotyledonous plants 162
differentiation 151
diffusion 62, 158, 161

risk factors 7, 8
    for lung disease 84
    of coronary heart disease
        99, 100
root hair 169
root pressure 170

S

S phase 146, 149
salivary glands 28
sample size 4, 212
scanning electron microscopes
    (SEMs) 54
scientific journals 2
secondary immune responses
    14, 15
secondary structure of proteins
    31
selective breeding 128
semi-conservative replication
    143, 144
semi-lunar (SL) valves 90, 93
similarity 178, 181
sino-atrial node (SAN) 91
sister chromatids 123
small intestine 27
smoking 99, 100
society and science 6
specialised cells 151
species 175, 177
species diversity 200, 201,
    203
    data interpretation 205, 206
    human impact on 203, 204
specific base pairing 116
spiracles 163
spirometers 79
standard deviation 110, 111,
    214
starch 37, 139
stomach 27
stomata 162, 163, 171
stroke volume 92
stroma 136
structural proteins 32
substrate concentration (effect
    on enzyme activity) 42
sucrose 34, 35
sugar-phosphate backbone 115
supercoiling 117
surface area : volume ratio
    135, 157, 159, 160
symplast pathway 169

T

taxonomic hierarchies 175
taxonomy 175
T-cells 12
telophase 147
tertiary structure of proteins 31
theories 1
thrombosis 97
thylakoid membrane 136
thymine 116
tidal volume 79
tissue fluid 167
tissues 152
toxins 11
tracheae 163
tracheoles 163
transmission electron microscopes
    (TEMs) 54
transpiration 171
transport proteins 32
triglycerides 59, 60
triplets (of bases) 118
tuberculosis (TB) 81, 192
tumour 149
twin studies 107

U

ultracentrifugation 55
unloading (of oxygen) 132

V

vaccines 16, 21
validity 5
valves 91, 166
variables 3, 212
variation 105
    investigating variation 108
veins 165, 166
ventilation 75, 76
ventilation rate 79
ventricles 90, 91, 93, 94
vertical gene transmission 188
villi 27
viruses 10

W

water loss (control of) 163
water potential 63, 167, 169

water transport (in plants)
    169-171
white blood cells 12

X

xerophytes 163
xylem 152, 169, 170

Z

zygotes 122